Biodiversity
in the New I

Edited by
Adrian C. Newton

Centre for Conservation Ecology and Environmental Change,
School of Conservation Sciences,
Bournemouth University,
Poole,
Dorset,
United Kingdom

piscespublications

Newbury, Berkshire

Dedicated to the memory of
Muriel Eliza Newton (1929–2009),
who loved the New Forest,
especially the donkeys.

First published 2010.

British-Library-in-Publication Data
A catalogue record for this book is available from the British Library.

ISBN 978-1-874357-42-1

Designed and published for Bournemouth University by Pisces Publications

Pisces Publications is the imprint of NatureBureau, 36 Kingfisher Court, Hambridge Road, Newbury, Berkshire RG14 5SJ
www.naturebureau.co.uk

Printed by Information Press, Oxford

Cover photographs
Front cover: Red deer *Cervus elaphus* (Isobel Cameron / Forest Life picture library, Forestry Commission); noble chafer *Gnorimus nobilis* (Matt Smith); Dartford warbler *Sylvia undata* (David Kjaer); wild gladiolus *Gladiolus illyricus* (Adrian Newton)
Back cover: Wood Crates (Adrian Newton)

The maps in this book are for illustrative purposes only, and do not represent the legal definition of National Park boundaries or any other feature

Contents

Contributors

Keith Alexander, 59 Sweetbrier Lane, Heavitree, Exeter, Devon EX1 3AQ.

Patrick D. Armitage, Freshwater Biological Association, Moor House, Field Station, Garrigill, Alston, Cumberland DL12 0HQ.

Andrew J. Barker, 13 Ashdown Close, Chandler's Ford, Eastleigh, Hampshire SO53 5QF.

Ian Barker, New Forest National Park Authority, South Efford House, Milford Road, Everton, Lymington, Hampshire SO41 0JD.

Samantha Broadmeadow, Forest Research, Alice Holt Lodge, Farnham, Surrey GU10 4LH.

Libby Burke, Forestry Commission, The Queen's House, Lyndhurst, Hampshire SO43 7NH.

Elena Cantarello, Centre for Conservation Ecology and Environmental Change, School of Conservation Sciences, Bournemouth University, Poole, Dorset BH12 5BB.

Clive Chatters, c/o Hampshire and Isle of Wight Wildlife Trust, Beechcroft, Vicarage Lane, Curdridge, Hampshire SO32 2DP.

Greg Conway, British Trust for Ornithology, The Nunnery, Thetford, Norfolk IP24 2PU.

John Davy-Bowker, Centre for Ecology and Hydrology, c/o Freshwater Biological Association, East Stoke, Wareham, Dorset BH20 6BB.

Sarah Douglas, Centre for Conservation Ecology and Environmental Change, School of Conservation Sciences, Bournemouth University, Poole, Dorset BH12 5BB.

Maxine Elliott, Environment Agency, Solent and South Downs Office, Colvedene Court, Colden Common, Hampshire SO21 1WP.

Naomi C. Ewald, Department of Biology and Environmental Science, School of Life Sciences, University of Sussex, Falmer, Brighton, Sussex BN1 9QG.

David Green, Butterfly Conservation, The Cottage, West Blagdon, Cranborne, Dorset BH21 5RY.

Rachel Green, Natural England, 1 Southampton Road, Lyndhurst, Hampshire SO43 7BU.

Sue E. Hartley, Department of Biology and Environmental Science, School of Life Sciences, University of Sussex, Falmer, Brighton, Sussex BN1 9QG.

Timothy Holzer, Environment Agency, Solent and South Downs Office, Colvedene Court, Colden Common, Hampshire SO21 1WP.

John G. Jones, Centre for Environmental Sciences, School of Civil Engineering and the Environment, University of Southampton, Highfield, Southampton, Hampshire SO17 1BJ.

Terry Langford, Centre for Environmental Sciences, School of Civil Engineering and the Environment, University of Southampton, Highfield, Southampton, Hampshire SO17 1BJ.

Colleen Mainstone, Hampshire Bat Group, 42 Saxon Way, Halterworth, Romsey, Hampshire SO51 5QY.

Gillian Myers, Centre for Conservation Ecology and Environmental Change, School of Conservation Sciences, Bournemouth University, Poole, Dorset BH12 5BB.

Adrian C. Newton, Centre for Conservation Ecology and Environmental Change, School of Conservation Sciences, Bournemouth University, Poole, Dorset BH12 5BB.

Martin Noble, New Forest Ecological Consultants, Keepers Cottage, Holmsley, Burley, Ringwood, Hampshire BH24 4HY.

Andrew Page, Forestry Commission, The Queen's House, Lyndhurst, Hampshire SO43 7NH.

Bryan J. Pinchen, 7 Brookland Close, Pennington, Lymington, Hampshire SO41 8JE.

Rory Putman, Keil House, Ardgour by Fort William, Inverness-shire PH33 7AH.

Martin Rand, South Hampshire Vice-county Recorder, Botanical Society of the British Isles, email: vc11recorder@hantsplants.org.uk.

Neil A. Sanderson, Botanical Survey and Assessment, 3 Green Close, Woodlands, Southampton, Hampshire SO40 7HU.

Peter Shaw, Centre for Environmental Sciences, School of Civil Engineering and the Environment, University of Southampton, Highfield, Southampton, Hampshire SO17 1BJ.

Jane Smith, Forestry Commission, The Queen's House, Lyndhurst, Hampshire SO43 7NH.

Rod Stern, British Bryological Society, 15 Selham Close, Chichester, West Sussex PO19 5BZ.

Alan J. A. Stewart, Department of Biology & Environmental Science, School of Life Sciences, University of Sussex, Falmer, Brighton, Sussex BN1 9QG.

Natalia Tejedor, Centre for Conservation Ecology and Environmental Change, School of Conservation Sciences, Bournemouth University, Poole, Dorset BH12 5BB.

David J. Thompson, School of Biological Sciences, University of Liverpool, Crown Street, Liverpool, Lancashire L69 7ZB.

Stephen Trotter, New Forest National Park Authority, South Efford House, Milford Road, Everton, Lymington, Hampshire SO41 0JD.

Lena K. Ward, 53 Miles Avenue, Sandford, Wareham, Dorset BH20 7AS.

Phillip C. Watts, School of Biological Sciences, University of Liverpool, Crown Street, Liverpool, Lancashire L69 7ZB.

Diana Westerhoff, Natural England, 1 Southampton Road, Lyndhurst, Hampshire SO43 7BU.

Simon Wotton, Royal Society for the Protection of Birds, The Lodge, Sandy, Bedfordshire SG19 2DL

Preface

The New Forest is widely recognised to be one of the most important areas for wildlife in the UK, being home to large numbers of species of flowering plants, bryophytes, lichens, fungi, bats, birds, mammals, reptiles and invertebrates, among many others. Its extensive areas of semi-natural habitats, occurring in a complex mosaic, justify its inclusion among the most valuable areas for biodiversity conservation in lowland western Europe (Chatters 2006). Despite this, the current status and distribution of many species occurring within the New Forest remains very poorly understood.

The aim of this book is to provide an overview of biodiversity in the New Forest, by summarising what is currently known and identifying where the knowledge gaps lie. The book emerged from a conference held during 25– 26 September 2007 at the Balmer Lawn Hotel in Brockenhurst, organised by staff at Bournemouth University in association with the British Ecological Society, the New Forest National Park Authority and the Forestry Commission. At the meeting, specialists on different groups of organisms presented current information regarding the status and distribution of species occurring within the New Forest, focusing on those of particular conservation interest or concern, and with the aim of identifying current trends in abundance. Information on the status and trends in the condition of different habitats was also presented, with the aim of informing future management decisions and identifying particular issues of concern.

Much of the information on species and habitats in the New Forest is widely dispersed and difficult to access. The principal aim of this book is to bring this information together for the first time, and to make it available to a wider audience. Based on the presentations made at the conference, the book comprises a series of chapters on individual groups of species, which are then followed by an overview of selected habitats and communities. The final chapters provide a brief consideration of current management approaches and future challenges.

Despite the large number of specialists that have generously contributed to this volume, it cannot be considered a comprehensive account of biodiversity in the New Forest. An attempt was made to include as many different groups of species as possible, but inevitably there are significant gaps. The coverage of different groups of organisms is uneven, reflecting variation in the current state of knowledge, their taxonomic size and complexity, and the availability of appropriate expertise. If the end result is somewhat heterogeneous and idiosyncratic, then perhaps this is appropriate, given that these are attributes of the New Forest itself! At the very least, the chapters in this book highlight how much still remains to be discovered, and emphasise the urgent need for further research and survey work.

It should be remembered that this is not the first book to be devoted to the New Forest. As befits an area of such outstanding importance, it has generated a substantial literature, dating back almost 150 years to the classic account by John Wise (Wise 1863). The closest antecedent to the current volume is perhaps that of Berlin et al. (1960), which provided a general account of different elements of the natural history of the New Forest, including mammals, birds and herbaceous plants. However, in terms of recent work on ecology and conservation, it is the two books by Colin Tubbs (Tubbs 1968, 2001) that are widely acknowledged to be the most significant. Both provide clear evidence of the deep understanding of the ecology of the New Forest that Tubbs acquired from many years' close involvement with the area. Coincidentally, the conference on which this book is based was held within a few weeks of the tenth anniversary of Colin Tubbs' untimely death, and it therefore provided a welcome opportunity to pay tribute to his outstanding contribution to our understanding of the area. This volume will hopefully be viewed as building on Tubbs' substantial legacy. The information presented here is designed to be complementary to that presented in Tubbs' books (Tubbs 1968, 2001), which the reader is strongly encouraged to consult.

A brief description of the New Forest is provided here as context for the chapters that follow, based on the information provided in Tubbs (2001) and Chatters (2006). The Forest is situated on the south coast of England in the counties of Hampshire and Wiltshire, immediately north of the River Solent, and between the conurbations of Bournemouth and Southampton (Figure 1). The Forest lies on a series of gravel terraces overlaying sedimentary sands and clays of Tertiary age, located within the Hampshire Basin. As noted by Tubbs (2001), the New Forest as an ecological system has developed under the influence of large, free-ranging herbivores, including deer as well as livestock. The present character of the New Forest is therefore strongly dependent on its history as a medieval hunting forest, and the survival of a traditional commoning system, which became formalised in late medieval times.

The 'perambulation' of the Forest, encompassing some 37,907 ha, refers to the area within which forest bye-laws apply, relating to the pasturage of livestock on common land. Almost a quarter of this area consists of farmland and settlements, whereas around three-quarters are referred to as the 'Crown lands', reflecting their status as Royal Forest. The Crown lands include the Silvicultural Inclosures, designated for silviculture; unenclosed land, over which common rights prevail; and a number of farm holdings. The unenclosed Forest is referred to by Tubbs (2001) as the largest area of semi-natural vegetation in lowland Britain, and includes large tracts of heathland, valley mire and

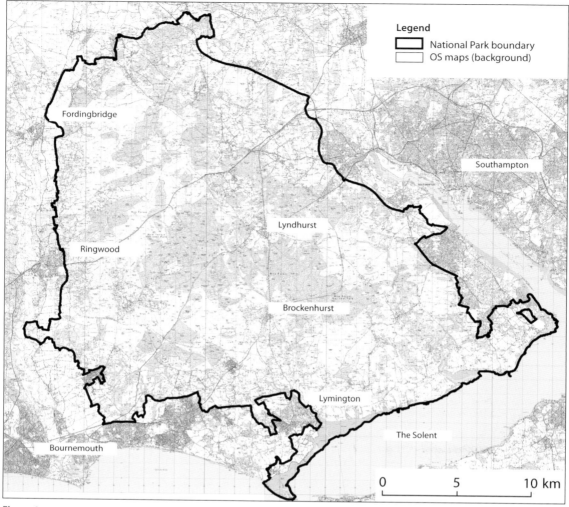

Legend
National Park boundary
OS maps (background)

Fordingbridge

Southampton

Lyndhurst

Ringwood

Brockenhurst

Lymington

The Solent

Bournemouth

0   5   10 km

Figure 1
Map of the New Forest National Park, with the Park boundary overlaid on an Ordnance Survey (OS) map (©Crown Copyright/ database right 2008. An Ordnance Survey/EDINA supplied service).

ancient pasture woodland, three habitats that are now fragmented and rare throughout lowland western Europe. With a total area of almost 20,000 ha, the unenclosed Forest includes around 3700 ha of oak, beech and holly woodland, 12,500 ha of heathland and acid grassland, and 2900 ha of valley mires and wet heath.

The New Forest National Park was designated in 2005 and extends over 57,100 ha (Chatters 2006), a substantially larger area than that included within the perambulation (Figure 2). The conservation importance of the National Park is reflected in a variety of designations, with some 20 SSSIs, six Natura 2000 sites and two Ramsar Convention sites included at least partly within the Park boundaries. The National Park includes extensive areas of common land that border the Crown lands but lie outside the perambulation. In total, about 50% of the land area of the Park is covered by unenclosed vegetation, which is collectively referred to by Chatters (2006) as the 'Open Forest'. In recent years, some 6000–7400 ponies, cattle, donkeys, pigs and sheep have been depastured on the Open Forest, by about 550 commoners (NPA 2008).

This brief summary highlights the difficulty in answering the deceptively simple question: what is the New Forest? With respect to the scope of this book, different authors have considered a variety of different entities, such as the Crown lands, the perambulation or the National Park. However, unless otherwise stated, the focus of this text is primarily on the area designated as being of particular conservation importance, namely the New Forest Special Area of

Conservation (SAC). This is a Natura 2000 site, which essentially forms the core of the National Park. Over 90% of the SAC is Crown land, managed by the Forest Commission. Most, but not all, of the SAC falls within the National Park boundaries (Chatters 2006).

The New Forest is a very special place, unique in very many ways. The chapters of this book provide an indication of just why it is so special. Tubbs (2001) considers the New Forest to be a highly dynamic ecosystem, which has proved remarkably resilient to trauma and catastrophe in the past. Yet the environmental and socio-economic changes currently underway are likely to be unprecedented in the long history of the Forest, and are likely to test its resilience as never before. Maintenance of what makes the New Forest so important and valuable therefore represents a significant challenge. It is hoped that the information presented here will support future management and conservation efforts, but will also, in the memorable words of Derek Ratcliffe, 'inspire others – both strangers and those who already know the Forest – to cherish this marvellous place, with its stately woods, wide heaths and bogs, and to absorb its peace and beauty' (Tubbs 2001).

The production of this book would have been entirely impossible without the great efforts made by the contributing authors. I am very grateful to all contributors for devoting their precious time to providing texts for inclusion, despite the often intense pressures from competing professional commitments. The financial contributions from the British Ecological Society, the Forestry Commission, the New Forest National Park Authority and the New Forest Trust in support of publication costs are gratefully acknowledged. Many thanks also to the administrative staff and students of Bournemouth University who helped organise the conference, in particular Marie Dunning, Rebecca Dolling, Elena Cantarello, Gillian Myers, Sarah North, Niels Brouwers and Natalia Tejedor. Simon Weymouth of the Forestry Commission provided valuable support at the planning stage. In addition I would particularly like to thank Palmer Newbould for his generous provision of literature relating to the New Forest, which was very deeply appreciated. Thanks also to Lynn Davy for checking the manuscript.

Adrian C. Newton
Dorset, April 2009

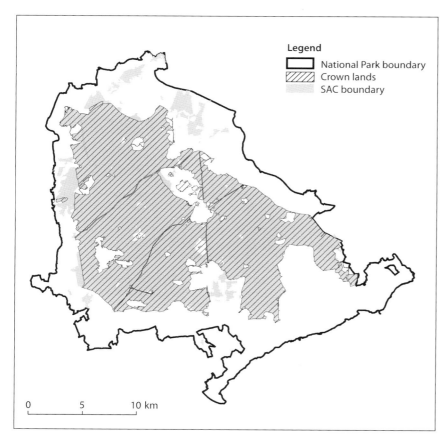

Figure 2
Crown lands, SAC and National Park boundaries of the New Forest.

Legend
- National Park boundary
- Crown lands
- SAC boundary

0   5   10 km

References

Berlin, J., Cohen, E., Copley, G. J., Edlin, H. L., Hook, O., De Bairacli Levy, J., Venning, F. E. W., Widnell, H., Myers, W. R. and Pigott, B. (1960). *The New Forest*. Galley Press, London.

Chatters, C. (2006). The New Forest – National Park status for a medieval survivor. *British Wildlife* (December 2006), 110–119.

New Forest National Park Authority (NPA) (2008). *New Forest National Park Plan. Consultation Draft. August 2008*. New Forest National Park Authority, Lymington, Hampshire.

Tubbs, C. R. (1968). *The New Forest: an ecological history*. David and Charles, Newton Abbot.

Tubbs, C. R. (2001). *The New Forest. History, ecology and conservation*. New Forest Ninth Centenary Trust, Lyndhurst.

Wise, J. (1863). *The New Forest, its history and scenery*. Henry Southeran, London.

1 Birds

Introduction

It is widely recognised that the New Forest supports a rich bird fauna with a wide variety of species, at least 36 of which are considered to be particularly notable in conservation terms (Table 1). The international importance of the New Forest as a habitat for birds was recognised by the designation of the Crown lands and surrounding common land as a Special Protection Area (SPA) in 1993, in accordance with the EC Directive on the Conservation of Wild Birds 1979, and as a Wetland of International Importance under the Ramsar Convention (Tubbs 2001). The SPA designation reflects the occurrence of breeding populations of species considered threatened at the European scale, including honey buzzard, nightjar, kingfisher, woodlark, Dartford warbler and wintering hen harrier, and requires that the Forest be managed in ways that maintain and enhance its ornithological importance (Tubbs 2001).

Within the New Forest, important bird communities are associated with woodland and heathland vegetation, and wetland habitats such as valley mires and wet heath (Table 1). The abundance of large, old trees in wood pasture provides extensive habitat for species associated with crevices and rot holes, including woodpeckers (great spotted, lesser spotted and green), treecreeper, nuthatch, tits (blue, coal and marsh), spotted flycatcher, tawny owl and redstart (Wright and Westerhoff 2001). Species associated with the woodland understorey include woodcock, willow warbler and wood warbler. In situations where the shrub layer is sufficiently well developed, large numbers of relatively common species occur, including chaffinch, wren, robin, blackbird, song thrush, bullfinch, dunnock, chiffchaff, blackcap, garden warbler, greenfinch, goldfinch and linnet (Wright and Westerhoff 2001).

Tubbs (2001) noted that the bird communities of broadleaved plantations have been relatively little studied, but available evidence suggests that the species composition of the avifauna is similar to that of the pasture woods, although the number of bird territories is significantly smaller. The establishment of conifer plantations since the early 19th century has encouraged the development of a bird community with boreal affinities, including crossbill, siskin, redpoll, coal tit and goldcrest, as well as firecrest. Conifers are also important in providing nesting sites for birds of prey (Tubbs 2001). Raptors breeding in woodland include buzzard, honey buzzard, kestrel, sparrowhawk, and occasionally goshawk (see Section B, below). According to Tubbs (2001), raptor population densities appear to be limited by the relative scarcity of prey items such as small mammals and heathland birds.

Heathland habitats support species for which the New Forest is designated as an SPA, namely Dartford warbler, nightjar and woodlark. However, the abundance and diversity of birds associated with heathland is relatively low, partly as a result of the relatively uniform vegetation structure and the lack of a year-round food supply (Wright and Westerhoff 2001). Those species that overwinter on heathland (such as wren, stonechat, meadow pipit and Dartford warbler) are highly dependent upon gorse to provide an invertebrate food supply. Skylark are common and wheatear breed very occasionally on grassland sites, whereas other passerines (such as linnet, willow warbler, chiffchaff, dunnock, robin, blackbird and green woodpecker) tend to be more reliant on woodland edge/ scrub habitats than directly upon heathland (Wright and Westerhoff 2001). It should be noted that yellowhammer, grasshopper warbler, whitethroat and whinchat have all but been lost as breeding heathland species in the last 15 years and that redpoll is now a very scarce breeding bird. Raptors associated with heathland include hen harrier and merlin, which overwinter, and hobby and Montagu's harrier, which are summer visitors (see Section B below).

Wetland sites (mires, bogs, pools, wet heathland and wet grassland) provide valuable habitat for inland breeding waders, including redshank, snipe, curlew and lapwing, breeding mallard and teal, and occasionally shelduck (Wright and Westerhoff 2001). Kingfisher and grey wagtail are associated with the rivers and larger streams. Tubbs (2001) notes that there were 7–10 breeding pairs of kingfisher within the Forest in the 1980s and 1990s, with 48–65 pairs of grey wagtail recorded in the early 1980s.

At least three bird species are known to have been lost from the New Forest during the past century. The red-backed shrike had a population of around 100 pairs in the New Forest in the late 1950s, but was last known to have bred in the Forest in 1978 (Tubbs 2001). The wryneck, which is now nearly extinct as a breeding species in Britain, was known from New Forest woods in the early 20th century, but is thought to have been extirpated by 1940 (Tubbs 2001). Black grouse is believed to have been absent from the New Forest since the 1930s (Table 1). The factors responsible for the loss of these species are not known with precision; red-backed shrike and wryneck are members of a group of insectivorous migratory birds that have declined throughout north-west Europe during the 20th century. Both are now nearly extinct as breeding species in the UK. Habitat loss and possibly also climate change (e.g. cooler, wetter springs) reducing insect prey are thought to have been influential in their decline (Tubbs 2001, Wright and Westerhoff 2001).

This chapter provides an overview of recent monitoring activities, which provide insights into the current status and trends of bird species in the New Forest, focusing on those species of particular conservation importance. The chapter is divided into two sections: the first (Section A) focuses on a range of species that are currently the focus of monitoring efforts, and the second (Section B) focuses explicitly on raptors.

Table 1
Selected bird species of conservation concern (BoCC; Gregory *et al*. 2002), known from the New Forest, and their current status in the New Forest. Updated from Wright and Westerhoff (2001) by Page and Westerhoff (2010). Status follows Eaton *et al*. (2009).

Species	Habitat	Distribution / breeding status	Protection status
Shelduck *Tadorna tadorna*	Valley mires / permanent ponds	Uncommon, occasional breeder	BoCC Amber List
Teal *Anas crecca*	Valley mires / permanent ponds	Uncommon, occasional breeder	BoCC Amber List
Montagu's harrier *Circus pygargus*	Dry heath (breeding)	Rare, occasional breeder	W&C Act Schedule 1, BoCC Amber List
Hen harrier *Circus cyaneus*	Dry heath (roost), feeds over heathland, farmland	15 wintering birds in 1980s, latterly reduced. Scarce, currently up to 8 individuals	W&C Act Schedule 1, BoCC Red List
Honey buzzard *Pernis apivorus*	Woodland	Rare, 2–5 breeding pairs, 12.5% of UK population	W&C Act Schedule 1, BoCC Amber List
Kestrel *Falco tinnunculus*	Woodland edge / heathland	Moderately common, regular breeder	BoCC Amber List
Merlin *Falco columbarius*	Heathland	Scarce, overwinters	W&C Schedule 1, BoCC Amber List
Black grouse *Tetrao tetrix*	Heathland	Extinct in the Forest since 1930s	BoCC Red List
Ringed plover *Charadrius hiaticula*	Dry grassland / bare stony ground	Uncommon, scarce breeder	BoCC Amber List
Lapwing *Vanellus vanellus*	Valley mires/ wet grassland / permanent and temporary ponds	Common, regular breeder	BoCC Red List
Curlew *Numenius arquata*	Valley mires / wet grassland / permanent and temporary ponds	Moderately common, regular breeder	BoCC Amber List
Redshank *Tringa totanus*	Valley mires / wet grassland / permanent and temporary ponds	Uncommon, scarce breeder	BoCC Amber List
Snipe *Gallinago gallinago*	Valley mires / wet grassland / permanent and temporary ponds	Moderately common, regular breeder	BoCC Amber List
Nightjar *Caprimulgus europaeus*	Heathland mosaic	647 churring males, 15.7% of UK population	BoCC Red List
Kingfisher *Alcedo atthis*	Rivers and streams	Uncommon, up to 10 pairs	BoCC Amber List
Wryneck *Jynx torquilla*	Woodland	Extinct, last seen in the 1940s	W&C Act Schedule 1, BoCC Red List
Green woodpecker *Picus viridis*	Woodland / grassland mosaic	Common, regular breeder	BoCC Amber List
Dunnock *Prunella modularis*	Woodland edge / scrub	Common, regular breeder	BoCC Amber List
Skylark *Alauda arvensis*	Heathland / grassland	Moderately common, regular breeder	BoCC Red List
Woodlark *Lullula arborea*	Dry heath / dry grassland	Moderately common,163 pairs in 2006, 9.3% of UK population	W&C Schedule 1, BoCC Amber List
Nightingale *Luscinia megarhynchos*	Woodland edge / dense scrub	Very scarce, no recent records of breeding in the Forest	BoCC Amber List
Redstart *Phoenicurus phoenicurus*	Woodland	Common, regular breeder	BoCC Amber List
Stonechat *Saxicola torquata*	Dry heath	Common, regular breeder	BoCC Green List
Song thrush *Turdus philomelos*	Grassland	Common, regular breeder	BoCC Red List
Grasshopper warbler *Locustella naevia*	Heathland	Very scarce, no recent records of breeding in the Forest	BoCC Red List
Dartford warbler *Sylvia undata*	Dry heath	420 pairs in 2006, 16% of UK population	W&C Act Schedule 1, BoCC Amber List
Firecrest *Regulus ignicapilla*	Woodland	Moderately common, regular breeder	W&C Act Schedule 1, BoCC Amber List
Marsh tit *Poecile palustris*	Woodland	Common, regular breeder	BoCC Red List
Willow tit *Poecile montanus*	Woodland	Very scarce, no confirmed records of breeding	BoCC Red List
Starling *Sturnus vulgaris*	Woodland / grassland	Common but much declined, regular breeder	BoCC Red List
Red-backed shrike *Lanius collurio*	Woodland edge	Extinct as breeder in the Forest since 1978	W&C Act Schedule 1, BoCC Red List
Hawfinch *Coccothraustes coccothraustes*	Woodland	Local but regular breeder	BoCC Red List
Bullfinch *Pyrrhula pyrrhula*	Woodland	Moderately common, regular breeder	BoCC Amber List
Goldfinch *Carduelis carduelis*	Woodland / grassland	Common, regular breeder	BoCC Green List
Linnet *Carduelis cannabina*	Heathland	Common, regular breeder	BoCC Red List
Crossbill *Loxia curvirostra*	Pine woodland	Local but moderately common, regular breeder	W&C Act Schedule 1, BoCC Amber List

Bird monitoring in the New Forest: a review of current and ongoing schemes

Greg Conway, Simon Wotton and Adrian C. Newton

The Breeding Bird Survey (BBS)

The BBS provides information on population trends for a range of common and widespread bird species in the UK. The scheme is coordinated by the British Trust for Ornithology (BTO), and jointly funded by the BTO, the Joint Nature Conservation Committee (JNCC) and the Royal Society for the Protection of Birds (RSPB). The project is undertaken at the national scale, with some 3,200 sites now being surveyed across the UK by more than 3,000 participants. Survey sites are randomly selected 1-km squares of the Ordnance Survey (OS) National Grid, and are visited by volunteers who record habitat characteristics and the bird species encountered while walking a survey route (two 1-km line transects).

To date (as of 2006), the survey has provided data for 11 1-km squares in the New Forest (Figure 3), in which 98 species have been recorded since 1994. Forty-nine of these species have been found to occur within more than half of the squares. At present, insufficient squares have been surveyed to permit calculation of reliable data on trends in abundance; for this purpose, more than 30 squares would be needed. However, even this limited annual monitoring data do set a baseline against which future changes in species' abundance and occurrence can be measured. This survey therefore provides an example of an ongoing monitoring programme that is likely to be of increasing value as it continues to develop. Its future value for documenting species trends in the New Forest will depend upon the participation of volunteers, which will inevitably determine the scope of the survey.

Figure 3
Results obtained by the Breeding Bird Survey for the New Forest (up to and including 2006). Figures show duration of coverage in years.

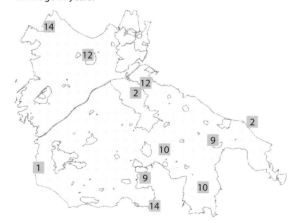

National Nightjar Survey

The Eurasian nightjar is currently declining in many European countries (Burfield and Van Bommel 2004). In Britain, the species is considered to be of high conservation concern, being classified as a Red Listed species with a breeding range decline in excess of 50% between 1972 and 1992 (Gregory *et al.* 2002). Since the 1950s, the geographic range of the species has contracted and it has undergone a marked decline in abundance, as a result of widespread losses of heathland to agriculture, urban development and afforestation. In the UK, the breeding range of nightjars declined from 562 10-km squares in 1968–72 to 241 in 1981, but increased slightly to 268 10-km squares by 1992, still substantially fewer than its former range (Conway *et al.* 2007). The New Forest is still one of the main centres of occupancy of the species, together with other heathland in southern England and the Brecklands and Sandlings of East Anglia. The partial recovery of nightjars in southern and eastern England in the late 1980s can be attributed to an increase in large-scale harvesting of conifer plantations, which increased the availability of suitable habitat (Conway *et al.* 2007).

A national survey of nightjar was undertaken in 2004 on 1-km squares with recent known breeding populations, and a random sample of 1-km squares containing suitable habitat within 10 km of the known range, to detect range expansion. This survey was primarily undertaken by volunteers, but supported by professional ornithologists where needed. A minimum of two visits to a site was required, either at dawn or at dusk, performed between the last week of May and mid-July, with at least three weeks between visits and at least one visit in June. Each surveyor covered no more than 80 ha per visit, being sure to pass within 200 m of all potentially suitable habitat. The locations of 'churring' males were recorded onto 1:2500 scale maps. Additional surveying was also undertaken in 2005 to complete gaps in the national survey coverage.

Results of the national survey indicated an increase in the UK population of nightjars of 36% between 1992 and 2004, which was attributed to habitat protection, management and restoration of heathlands, and the continued availability of clear-fell/young plantations in conifer forests (Conway *et al.* 2007). These national trends were mirrored in the New Forest, where a 28% increase in the number of territories was recorded over the same period (Table 2). It should be noted however, that the New Forest population had never been fully surveyed before 2004. Figures provided for the SPA designated in 1993 were based on a limited survey and extrapolation to other suitable habitat (although most of the Forest was surveyed in 1992). Distribution maps produced for the New Forest indicate a continual expansion in the number of sites colonised from 1981

Figure 4
Distribution of nightjar in the New Forest.

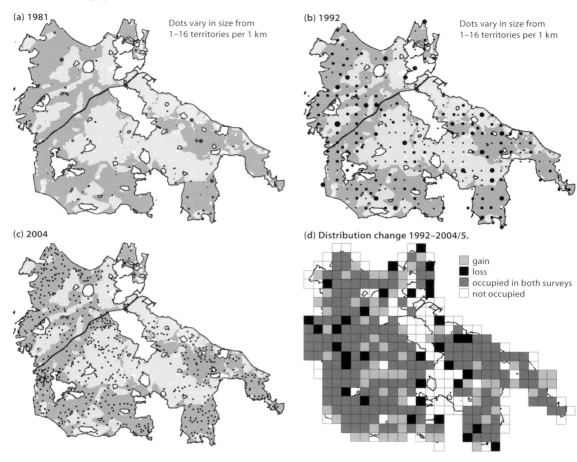

(a) 1981
Dots vary in size from
1–16 territories per 1 km

(b) 1992
Dots vary in size from
1–16 territories per 1 km

(c) 2004

(d) Distribution change 1992–2004/5.

gain
loss
occupied in both surveys
not occupied

onwards, such that the species is now widespread throughout the New Forest heathlands. However, loss of the species from some sites was recorded in the 2004 survey (Figure 4).

Table 2
Trends in the status of nightjar in the New Forest (*actual territories counted)

Year	Number of UK territories*	Number of territories in New Forest (SPA)
1981	1,784	78 (4.3% of UK population)
1992	3,093	313 (10% of UK population)
2004 (2005)	4,131	647 (15.7% of UK population)

National Woodlark Survey

In the UK, the woodlark is at the northern limit of its range in Europe, which appears to be constrained by warm summers and mild winters. European trends for woodlark suggest that a large decline occurred between 1970 and 1990, but numbers have been relatively stable since, although there have been localised increases in countries such as France, Netherlands, Romania and Sweden (Burfield and Van Bommel 2004).

In the UK, the woodlark was widespread across much of southern Britain during the middle of the 20th century, probably peaking in the early 1950s. Subsequently it underwent a dramatic decline in numbers and a contraction in range. An estimate of 200–450 pairs was derived from the 1968–72 breeding bird atlas (Sharrock 1976). In 1981 the population was estimated at 400–430 territories but the hard winter of 1981/82 resulted in a reduction to an estimated 200–250 territories (Sitters 1986).

The first full national survey of the species in 1986 found that the population had declined to a minimum of 241 pairs (Sitters *et al.* 1996), but it then increased once again; the 1988–91 breeding bird atlas produced an estimate of 350 territories (Gibbons *et al.* 1993). The second full survey in 1997 showed that this increase had continued, to 1,426–1,552 pairs, with a range of 90 10-km squares (Wotton and Gillings 2000).

Figure 5
Distribution of woodlark in the New Forest.

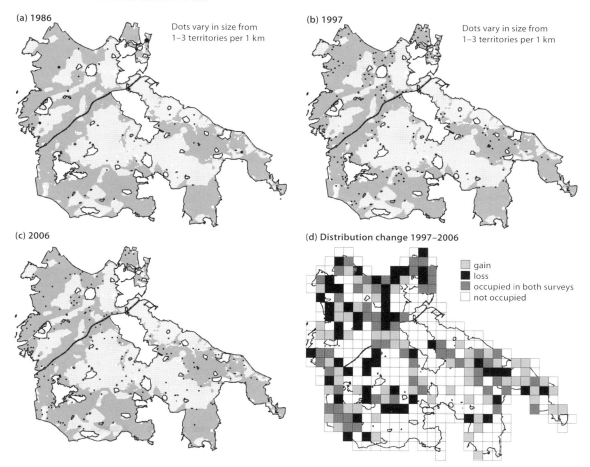

(a) 1986   Dots vary in size from 1–3 territories per 1 km

(b) 1997   Dots vary in size from 1–3 territories per 1 km

(c) 2006

(d) Distribution change 1997–2006

☐ gain
■ loss
▨ occupied in both surveys
☐ not occupied

Conway *et al.* (2009) describe the results of an additional national survey undertaken in 2006. One kilometre squares containing suitable habitat (i.e. lowland heathland, young conifer plantation, farmland, etc.) were surveyed, including previously occupied sites and all potentially suitable habitat for which there was no recent evidence of occupation, occurring within 5-km and 10-km buffers around such sites. Surveyors were also encouraged to visit other sites, such as those historically supporting woodlarks. Additional squares were surveyed that contained potential habitat for woodlarks and entire SPAs designated for this species. Surveys were undertaken during the period 15 February to 31 May, with a minimum of two visits required, ideally at least three weeks apart. Observers were requested to completely cover each 1-km square, walking within 100 m of all areas of suitable habitat to maximise the detection of territorial individuals.

At the national scale, results of the survey identified a strong increase in the breeding population and range of woodlarks in Britain between 1997 and 2006 (Conway *et al.* 2009). A population estimate of 3,064 territories was obtained, giving an increase of 88% since 1997, while the range of occupied 10-km squares had increased by 46%. The majority of territories were associated with two main habitat types; heathland (66.7%) and forest plantation (32.4%), and farmland in the southwest (13.4%). Sandy soils held the majority of territories (80.3%) (Conway *et al.* 2009). This population recovery was attributed to the designation of statutory nature conservation sites, with the majority of breeding woodlarks found on SPAs; together with appropriate restoration and re-creation of heathland and increasingly sympathetic management of key forests (Conway *et al.* 2009). The authors conclude that maintaining the condition of heathland in the face of increasing pressure for development and recreation is imperative for the future population of woodlarks in Britain.

In the New Forest, a similar positive trend in abundance was observed, with a 12.5% increase in the number of territories recorded between 1997 and 2006 (Table 3). Results also indicate that the New Forest

Table 3
Trends in the status of woodlark in the New Forest
(*actual territories counted)

Year	Number of UK territories*	Number of territories in New Forest (SPA)
1986	241	36 (14.9% of UK population)
1997	1,552	183 (11.8% of UK population)
2006	1,747	163 (9.3% of UK population)

continues to be an important stronghold for the species, accounting for 9.3% of the UK population in terms of number of territories located. Distribution maps produced for the New Forest indicate a pronounced expansion in the number of sites colonised between 1986 and 1997, and a slight increase thereafter, such that the species is now widespread throughout the New Forest heathlands. However, loss of the species was recorded from a number of sites in the 2006 survey (Figure 5).

National Dartford Warbler Survey

The Dartford warbler is another species at the northernmost limit of its geographical range in Britain. More than 80% of the world population, of between 1,900,000 and 3,700,000 pairs, is found in Spain (BirdLife International 2004), where it is characteristic of Mediterranean scrub habitats. In the UK the preferred habitat is mature lowland heath, generally with stands of mature gorse (Brown and Grice 2004).

The abundance and geographic range of the species has fluctuated markedly in the UK over the past two centuries, partly reflecting its susceptibility to severe winters, although the species also exhibits an ability to disperse into suitable habitats as conditions become favourable (Wotton et al. 2009). During the 19th century, the breeding distribution probably extended from Cornwall to Kent, with records in Staffordshire and Suffolk (Witherby et al. 1938). By the end of the 19th century, however, the bulk of the population was restricted to Hampshire and Surrey, with the rest of the population mainly located in Berkshire, Dorset, Isle of Wight, Sussex and Wiltshire (Holloway 1996). This range contraction from SW England is probably partly attributable to severe winters in 1880/81 and 1886/87. However, as a result of a succession of mild winters, there were again good numbers on the southern English heaths by the mid-1930s.

The continued loss of lowland heath throughout much of the 20th century, through afforestation, agricultural development and urban development, negatively affected the species, partly through the increasing fragmentation of suitable breeding habitat (Tubbs 1963). Severe winter weather also had an impact, particularly in the early 1960s, when numbers fell from c. 450 pairs in 1961 to just 11 pairs in 1963, following two consecutive hard winters. At this point, the population of Dartford warbler in the New Forest accounted for 55% of the population in the UK (Tubbs 2001; Table 4).

National surveys of the species were undertaken in 1974, 1984 and 1994, and the species is also monitored annually through the Rare Breeding Birds Panel (RBBP) (e.g. Hollings et al. 2008). The 1974 survey indicated that numbers had recovered well from the population crash in the early 1960s, with 560 territories recorded. The 1984 survey showed a slight decline, when 420 territories were recorded, much of the decline being attributed to some harsh winters and to heathland fires (Robins and Bibby 1985). An estimated maximum population of 1,889 territories was recorded in the last national survey in 1994 (Gibbons and Wotton 1996), a more than fourfold increase since 1984.

A fourth national Dartford warbler survey in Britain was undertaken in 2006, as described by Wotton et al. (2009). The aim was to survey all of the 1-km squares occupied in 1994, together with a random selection of squares within 5-km and 10-km buffers around them and entire SPAs designated for this species. As a result of the survey, the population was estimated at 3,214 (95% confidence limits, 2,878–3,591) territories, an increase of 70% since 1994 (Wotton et al. 2009). The number of occupied 10-km squares was 126, an increase of 117% since the previous survey. The main areas of range expansion were in Southwest England and Wales. The species is closely associated with lowland heathland with nearly 90% of the territories found in 2006 recorded in this habitat (Wotton et al. 2009). The positive trend in abundance of the species may partly reflect the considerable work undertaken on the restoration and recreation of lowland heath in recent years in counties such as Dorset, Suffolk and Surrey. However, climatic change may also have been a contributory factor (Wotton et al. 2009).

In the New Forest, the number of Dartford warbler territories declined by 21% between 1994 and 2006, in contrast to the national trend. Analysis of the distribution maps (Figure 6) suggest that this decline has occurred throughout the New Forest, and was not concentrated in a single area. Although the Dartford warbler is currently more than twice as abundant in the New Forest than it was in 1984, the decline recorded over the past decade is significant and should be of concern, particularly as such declines have not been widely recorded in the UK (Wotton et al. 2009). The reasons for the decline are not clear, but might be a consequence of current approaches to heathland management. The influence of climatic factors, and / or increasing recreational pressure are possible factors requiring more research.

Table 4
Trends in the status of Dartford warbler in the New Forest
(*actual territories counted)

Year	Number of UK territories*	Number of territories in New Forest (SPA)
1960	c.460	c.350 (76% of UK population)
1963	11	6 (55% of UK population)
1974	560	c.250 (45% of UK population)
1984	420	187* (45% of UK population)
1994	1,690	535* (32% of UK population)
2006	2,553	420* (16% of UK population)

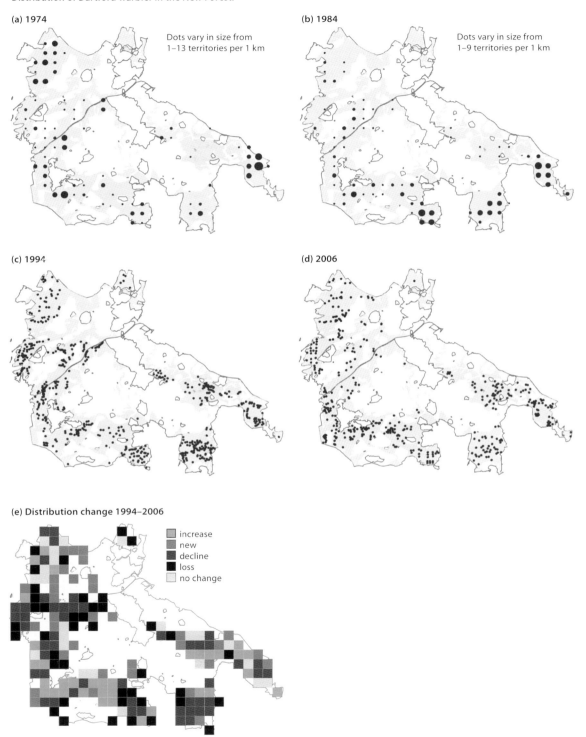

Figure 6
Distribution of Dartford warbler in the New Forest.

(a) 1974

Dots vary in size from
1–13 territories per 1 km

(b) 1984

Dots vary in size from
1–9 territories per 1 km

(c) 1994

(d) 2006

(e) Distribution change 1994–2006

increase
new
decline
loss
no change

New Forest Breeding Wader Surveys

The importance of the New Forest valley mires and wet heaths as valuable habitats for breeding waders has long been recognised (Tubbs 2001). In 1994, Colin and Jennifer Tubbs surveyed the breeding waders in the New Forest's valley mires using a standard, repeatable methodology to assess a random sample of the potential habitat. Results of the survey confirmed the critical importance of the New Forest as a site for breeding lapwings, snipe, curlews and redshanks (Tubbs and Tubbs 1994). With the exception of lapwings, the breeding waders of the New Forest were found to be largely dependent on valley bogs, wet heaths and the wetter humid heaths. Relatively intensive grazing and the continuation of a regime of controlled burning were identified as important habitat management actions for maintenance of populations (Tubbs and Tubbs 1994).

As described by Goater *et al.* (2004), the survey was repeated in 2004, using the same methods as those employed by Tubbs and Tubbs (1994). A sample of 31 of the New Forest's 93 1-km squares holding at least 15 ha of valley bog and/or wet heath vegetation was surveyed. Each 1-km square received three visits, respectively between 10 and 30 April, between 1 and 21 May, and between 22 May and 22 June. A minimum of two weeks separated visits to any one square. Almost all visits commenced at or shortly after sunrise and were concluded within three hours (Goater *et al.* 2004). Results of the survey confirmed that the New Forest mires remain extremely important for breeding snipe, curlews and redshanks. However, comparison with the 1994 results indicated that their numbers have been reduced by 29%, 25% and 22–26%, respectively, over the area surveyed (Goater *et al.* 2004; Figure 7). However, the number of breeding lapwing pairs, a species that is less dependent on mire habitats than the other three species surveyed, increased by 34–39% between 1994 and 2004. These changes may be indicative of Forest-wide trends, but this has yet to be established with certainty.

Further work is suggested to establish whether such trends are indeed widespread over the Forest, and to examine the factors responsible, such as recreational pressure and changes in the condition of wetland habitat (Goater *et al.* 2004). From the results obtained in the 2004 survey, it was difficult to draw any firm conclusions about the possible causes of decline; all of the squares showing the most marked declines in populations seemed, to the surveyors, to contain typical valley mire habitats well suited to breeding waders (Goater *et al.* 2004). The increases in numbers of lapwings recorded may be owed to the burning and cutting programme carried out by the Forestry Commission. As noted by Tubbs and Tubbs (1994), such interventions can increase the area of potential breeding habitat. It should also be noted that these declines in breeding waders mirror those recorded at the national scale (Wilson *et al.* 2005), attributed to loss of grassland to other land uses, and to significant changes in grassland management, including drainage, reseeding and changes in grazing regimes (Wilson *et al.* 2004).

Long-term changes in woodland bird populations

Amar *et al.* (2006) present the findings of a major four-year national-scale project, the Repeat Woodland Bird Survey (RWBS), which investigated trends in breeding bird populations in British broadleaved and mixed woods. Woodland plots were surveyed in 2003 and 2004, repeating previous surveys dating mainly from the 1980s. A total of 406 woodland sites were surveyed throughout the UK. Results indicated that eight out of a total of 34 species showed large national declines (>25%), namely hawfinch, garden warbler, lesser redpoll, lesser spotted woodpecker, spotted flycatcher, tree pipit, willow tit, willow warbler and wood warbler. A further eleven species showed large national increases (>25%) in both datasets: blackcap, blue tit, chiffchaff, coal tit, great spotted woodpecker, great tit, green woodpecker, goldcrest, robin, treecreeper and wren. Overall, more species breeding in woodland were found to have increased rather than decreased, and patterns of population change differed across groups of species. For example, all long-distance migrants have declined, whereas the two medium-distance migrants, blackcap and chiffchaff, have increased. Common species (such as blue tit and great spotted woodpecker) tended to fare better than less common ones (such as willow tit and lesser spotted woodpecker) (Amar *et al.* 2006). These trends reflect factors such as changes in the structure of early successional and understorey vegetation within

Figure 7
Trends in abundance of breeding waders between 1994 and 2004 (using data from Goater *et al.* 2004). ■ 1994 ▨ 2004

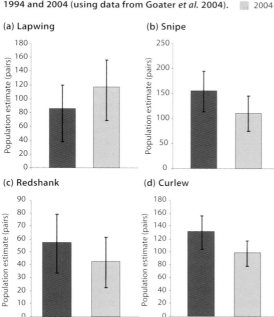

Figure 8
Changes in the abundance of selected woodland bird species between 1985 and 2004, compared to national
trends, derived from the Repeat Woodland Bird Survey (RWBS) (Amar *et al.* 2006).

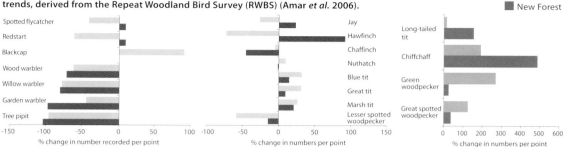

(a) Percentage change in selected woodland migrants

(b) Percentage change in selected woodland residents

(c) Percentage change in selected species that have undergone substantial change in abundance

woodland, climate change, reductions in invertebrates, and wider patterns of changing land-use and predation (Fuller *et al.* 2007).

In the New Forest, 21 New Forest woods were surveyed in 1985; these were resurveyed in 2003/04, using a series of counts at randomly selected points throughout the study woods. Results highlighted contrasting trends in a number of species, with some (such as tree pipit, garden warbler, willow warbler and wood warbler) demonstrating marked declines in New Forest woodlands, consistent with trends recorded nationally (Figure 8a). Others, such as jay and hawfinch, demonstrated increases in the New Forest, in contrast to national trends (Figure 8b). Woodland species that have undergone particularly marked changes in the New Forest included green woodpecker, great spotted woodpecker, chiffchaff and long-tailed tit, all of which were consistent with national trends (Figure 8c). Again, the precise reasons for these changes remain unclear.

Conclusions and implications for management

The various monitoring schemes presented here have provided a rich source of information regarding the status of trends of selected bird species in the New Forest, and also provide a valuable baseline against which future change can be evaluated. The results obtained highlight the contrasting fortunes of different bird species in the area. Some species of conservation concern, such as woodlark and nightjar, have increased markedly in recent years, suggesting that management approaches have been effective. Other species, notably Dartford warbler and the breeding waders snipe, curlew and redshank, appear to be undergoing significant declines, suggesting that management approaches may need to be amended. It is difficult to separate the impacts of local-scale management approaches from regional- or global-scale processes that may also be influential, such as climate change and external impacts on migratory species. However, it is important that the specific needs of declining species are considered when developing management proposals.

The SAC management plan provides the overarching policy and guidance that all the subsequent management plans take consideration of, and the Crown lands management plan (Forestry Commission 2007) forms one of these (see Chapter 19).

A recent focus has been on monitoring the impacts of visitor movements, and managing visitors through the seasonal closure of car parks and laybys, coupled with greater use of interpretation. The draft National Park Plan (NPA 2008) similarly places particular emphasis on visitor management, reflecting the growing concern about the effects of disturbance on ground nesting birds. Recent research has indicated that recreational use can have an adverse effect on nightjar (Langston *et al.* 2007, Liley and Clarke 2003), woodlark (Mallord *et al.* 2007) and Dartford warbler (Murison *et al.* 2007). For example, in the case of the latter, Murison *et al.* (2007) showed that increased recreational disturbance can adversely affect breeding productivity, at least in heather-dominated territories.

In the New Forest, Sharp *et al.* (2008) have recently examined current and projected visitor numbers, and explored the potential impacts on bird species. Housing development forecasts in local regions are likely to result in a significant increase in visitor numbers in the future. The three heathland Annex I bird species (nightjar, woodlark and Dartford warbler) are notable in that their densities within the New Forest National Park are relatively low when compared with other heathland areas (such as Dorset and Thames Basin Heaths). Preliminary analyses provided tentative evidence that areas of high visitor pressure are being avoided (particularly by woodlarks). As noted by Sharp *et al.* (2008), further research is clearly needed to understand the generally low densities and to determine the specific impacts of recreational disturbance. It may be that low densities are associated with particular aspects of habitat structure in the New Forest, associated with high grazing pressure and other management interventions. For example, the combination of burning, cutting and grazing can reduce the suitability of habitats for Dartford warblers, by inhibiting gorse regeneration (Bibby 1979), but can greatly increase woodlark and lapwing breeding territories.

Tubbs (2001) also refers to the negative impacts of human disturbance on breeding waders (lapwing, redshank, curlew, snipe and ringed plover). Observations made by Tubbs and co-workers suggested that declines have occurred in those areas where the level of recreational use has increased most steeply. Some former concentrations of breeding birds that have diminished greatly in size were located close to popular car parks and were heavily visited by people and their dogs (Tubbs and Tubbs 1996). There is also concern that breeding waders associated with coastal SPA and Ramsar sites are also being adversely affected by human disturbance (NPA 2008). Again, further research and monitoring work is required to evaluate the relative effects of human disturbance and other factors that might account for bird declines, such as habitat structure, invertebrate abundance and climate change.

Acknowledgements

The following contributions are gratefully acknowledged: BTO: Ian Henderson and Mike Raven; RSPB: Mark Eaton, Rowena Langston, John Mallord, Nigel Symes, Liz Taylor and Carrie Temple; Natural England: Allan Drewitt, Phil Grice and Diana Westerhoff; Forestry Commission: Fred Currie, Simon Weymouth and Nick Gibbons.

References

Amar, A., Hewson, C. M., Thewlis, R. M., Smith, K. W., Fuller, R. J., Lindsell, J. A., Conway, G., Butler, S. and MacDonald, M. A. (2006). *What's Happening to our woodland birds? Long-term changes in the populations of woodland birds.* Royal Society for the Protection of Birds (RSPB), Sandy; British Trust for Ornithology (BTO), Thetford.

Bibby, C. J. (1979). Conservation of the Dartford Warbler on English Lowland heaths: a review. *Biological Conservation,* 13, 299–307.

BirdLife International. (2004). *Birds in Europe: population estimates, trends, and conservation status.* BirdLife International, Cambridge.

Brown, A. F. and Grice, P. V. (2004). *Birds in England.* Poyser, London.

Burfield, I. and Van Bommel, F. (2004). *Birds in Europe: population estimates, trends and conservation status.* BirdLife International, Cambridge.

Conway, G., Wotton, S., Henderson, I., Langston, R., Drewitt, A. and Currie, F. (2007). Status and distribution of European Nightjars *Caprimulgus europaeus* in the UK in 2004. *Bird Study,* 54, 98–111.

Conway, G., Wotton, S., Henderson, I., Eaton, M., Drewitt, A. and Spencer, J. (2009). The status of breeding Woodlarks *Lullula arborea* in Britain in 2006. *Bird Study.* 56:3, 310–325.

Eaton, M. A., Brown, A. F., Noble, D. G., Musgrove, A. J., Hearn, R. D., Aebischer, N. J., Gibbons, D. W., Evans, A. and Gregory, R. D. Birds of Conservation Concern 3. The population status of birds in the United Kingdom, Channel Islands and Isle of Man. *British Birds,* 102, 296–341.

Forestry Commission (2007). *Management Plan. Part B: The Crown Lands. Draft, November 2007.* http://www.forestry.gov.uk/newforest

Fuller R. J., Smith K. W., Grice P. V., Currie F. A. and Quine C. P. (2007). Habitat change and woodland birds in Britain: implications for management and future research. *Ibis,* 149 (Suppl. 2), 261–268.

Gibbons, D. W., Reid, J. B. and Chapman, R. A. (1993). *The New Atlas of Breeding Birds in Britain and Ireland: 1988–1991.* Poyser, Calton.

Gibbons, D. W and Wotton, S. (1996). The Dartford Warbler in the United Kingdom in 1994. *British Birds,* 89, 203–212.

Goater, R. D., Houghton, D. and Temple, C. (2004) *New Forest Breeding Waders Survey 2004. A Survey of breeding waders in the New Forest valley mires, Hampshire.* RSPB, Sandy, Bedfordshire.

Gregory, R. D., Wilkinson, N. I., Noble, D. G., Robinson, J. A., Brown, A. F., Hughes, J., Procter, D. A., Gibbons, D. W. and Galbraith, C. A. (2002). The population status of birds in the United Kingdom, Channel Islands and Isle of Man: an analysis of conservation concern 2002–2007. *British Birds,* 95, 410–450.

Holling, M. and the Rare Breeding Birds Panel. (2008). Rare breeding birds in the United Kingdom in 2005. *British Birds,* 101, 276–316.

Holloway, S. (1996). *The historical atlas of breeding birds in Britain and Ireland: 1875–1900.* Poyser, London.

Langston, R. H. W., Liley, D., Murison, G., Woodfield, E. and Clarke, R. T. (2007). What effects do walkers and dogs have on the distribution and productivity of breeding European Nightjar *Caprimulgus europaeus? Ibis,* 149 (Suppl. 1), 27–36.

Liley, D. and Clarke, R. T. (2003). The impact of urban development and human disturbance on the numbers of nightjar *Caprimulgus europaeus* on heathland in Dorset, England. *Biological Conservation,* 114, 219–230.

Mallord, J. W., Dolman, P. M., Brown, A. F. and Sutherland, W. J. (2007). Linking recreational disturbance to population size in a ground-nesting passerine. *Journal of Applied Ecology,* 44, 185–195.

Murison, G., Bullock, J. M., Underhill-Day, J., Langston, R., Brown, A. F. and Sutherland, W. J. (2007). Habitat type determines the effects of disturbance on the breeding productivity of the Dartford Warbler *Sylvia undata. Ibis,* 149 (Suppl. 1), 16–26.

New Forest National Park Authority (NPA) (2008). *New Forest National Park Plan Consultation Draft. National Park Management Plan and Local Development Framework Core Strategy and Development Policies.* New Forest National Park Authority, Lymington.

Robins, M. and Bibby, C. J. (1985). Dartford Warblers in 1984 Britain. *British Birds,* 78, 269–280.

Sharp, J., Lowen, J. and Liley, D. (2008). *Changing patterns of visitor numbers within the New Forest National Park, with particular reference to the New Forest SPA.* Unpublished report, Footprint Ecology. © Footprint Ecology Ltd.

Sharrock, J. T. R. (1976). *The atlas of breeding birds in Britain and Ireland.* Poyser, Calton.

Sitters, H. P. (1986). Woodlarks in Britain, 1968–83. *British Birds,* 79, 105–116.

Sitters, H. P., Fuller, R. G., Hoblyn, R. A., Wright, M. T., Cowie, N. and Bowden, C. G. R. (1996). The Woodlark *Lullula arborea* in Britain: population trends, distribution and habitat occupancy. *Bird Study,* 43, 172–187.

Tubbs, C. R. (1963). The significance of the New Forest to the status of the Dartford Warbler in England. *British Birds*, 56, 41–48.

Tubbs, C. R. (2001). *The New Forest. History, ecology and conservation*. New Forest Ninth Centenary Trust, Lyndhurst, Hampshire.

Tubbs, C. R. and Tubbs, J. M. (1994). *New Forest Waders 1994: a survey of breeding waders in the New Forest valley mires, Hampshire*. RSPB, South East Regional Office, Brighton.

Tubbs, C. R. and Tubbs, J. M. (1996). Breeding waders and their habitat in the New Forest, Hampshire, England. *Wader Study Group Bulletin*, 79, 82–86.

Wilson, A. M., Ausden, M. and Milson, T. P. (2004). Changes in breeding wader populations on lowland wet grasslands in England and Wales: causes and potential solutions. *Ibis*, 146 (s2), 32–40.

Wilson, A. M., Vickery, J. A., Brown, A. Langston, R. H. W., Smallshire, D., Wotton, S. and Vanhinsbergh, D. (2005). Changes in the numbers of breeding waders on lowland wet grasslands in England and Wales between 1982 and 2002. *Bird Study*, 52, 55–69.

Witherby, H. F., Jourdain, F. C. R, Ticehurst, N. F. and Tucker, B. W. (1938). *The handbook of British birds*. Witherby, London.

Wotton, S. R. and Gillings, S. (2000). The status of breeding Woodlarks *Lullula arborea* in Britain in 1997. *Bird Study*, 47, 212–224.

Wotton, S., Conway, G., Eaton, M., Henderson, I. and Grice, P. (2009). The status of the Dartford Warbler *Sylvia undata* in the UK and the Channel Islands in 2006. *British Birds*, 102, 230–246.

Wright, R.N. and Westerhoff, D.V. (2001). *New Forest SAC Management Plan*. English Nature, Lyndhurst.

B Bird monitoring in the New Forest: raptors

Andrew Page

Introduction

Covering over 250 square kilometres of mixed conifer plantation, ancient broadleaved woodland, heaths, and wetlands, the New Forest has long been recognised as a special place for birds and not least of these would be its diurnal raptors. With the possibility of up to eight species breeding and another six being encountered at other times, it is inevitable that the area attracts its share of bird watchers generally and raptor enthusiasts specifically.

The Forestry Commission, as the major land managers of the Forest, have the difficult job of accommodating numerous potentially conflicting interests, from large-scale timber felling and cut and burn heathland management, to permissioning a host of recreational activity, and all in a way that is compatible with its unique nature conservation interest and status.

Key to this is a knowledge and understanding of what we have, where it is, and how it can be safeguarded from these activities where possible. To this end, a host of contributors both within and outside the organisation, both professional and amateur, assist and update the biological records that form a working document for the most heavily managed areas of the Forest. In the author's twenty years with the Forestry Commission, a small group of New Forest Keepers and enthusiastic and committed volunteers have monitored some of the area's raptor species. Many other visiting bird watchers have also provided casual observations, or have gathered notes and observations, some of which filters through to official bodies. Sadly, some potentially useful information for land managers is also lost, fragmented or not archived for the county.

Because of the huge task involved, much of the monitoring effort has been targeted at those species most vulnerable to commercial timber felling during the breeding season, particularly buzzard and sparrowhawk. A breeding attempt cannot be protected without knowing where the nest is. At the height of the studies, when time and fitness permitted, this progressed to recording nest success, ringing young, and removing addled and unhatched eggs for analysis at the Institute of Terrestrial Ecology (ITE, now the Centre for Ecology and Hydrology, CEH) at Monks Wood, Huntingdon.

It is important to stress that all activities involving Schedule One or specially protected bird species require the appropriate licences from the relevant agency (e.g. Natural England) and/or the BTO, and work carried out also needs consent from the landowner. Over the years the methods and equipment have been modified and fine-tuned, so that the climbing, nest data collection and ringing are conducted quickly, efficiently and professionally to minimise disturbance. Members of the climbing team are trained in arboricultural techniques and standards of safety.

Most monitoring visits occur when young are in the nest; very often, parent birds are far away hunting and not even aware a nest inspection has taken place. Some birds are more tolerant of disturbance than others and there is variability within individuals and at different stages of the nesting cycle. As a general rule, most birds are more tolerant of nest disturbance with young than they are with eggs, but there is no substitute for good fieldwork and the ability to interpret behaviour to guide the process of learning about different species.

As with any monitoring work, although desirable, achieving total coverage and population estimates that are completely accurate is rarely possible or even provable, and the reports and records summarised in this chapter make no such claims. They represent the culmination of fieldwork and reliable reports drawn together from various sources and observers over each season. Throughout this chapter references to territories, unless stated, are defined as the area around the nest that is defended by the pair against others of its species, and contains the nest and roost areas, but does not include the whole of its hunting range.

Sparrowhawk *Accipiter nisus*

Since 1988 we have found and recorded information on five hundred nesting attempts by sparrowhawk pairs in the New Forest. The vast majority of fieldwork was concentrated on the coniferous forest areas and also excluded the south-east corner of the Forest. From the outset we accepted that this focus on conifer habitats had the capacity to produce a significant bias in population estimates. Over time new sites were added from records submitted when young were heard calling, post fledging, but interestingly records for sites in broadleaved woodland remain very few, and are probably not as numerically important as first thought.

Nearly 100 different sites have held breeding pairs at some time over this period, but no more than 36 nests have ever been recorded in any one year, with nearer 25 nests per year on average. Within each site, pairs have moved, vacated the site permanently or have been absent in some years. Very few sites have been consistently occupied throughout the study period.

Unlike other larger raptor species, long periods of observation of suitable habitat reveal little to aid the process of finding sparrowhawk nests, and the only reasonably reliable method is systematic searching of suitable woodland. Our early studies quickly identified a preference for Scots pine of a certain age and thinning density, but as the Inclosures have been further thinned and opened up, the number of these prime blocks available for breeding has been reduced.

Our fieldwork coverage until very recently has been consistent and had revealed a relatively stable population, albeit with local fluctuations. However our observations suggest the occurrence of a dip in population size in recent years, which could be attributable to a number of factors, none of which are easily determined. One possibility is that the density of the tree stand used for nesting is more important than we first envisaged. It was our opinion that as with most species, providing they have a relatively rich food source available within the territory, then finding a suitable nest site should not be a limiting factor. Studies elsewhere show that commercial forests go through different stages of suitability for breeding sparrowhawks, being largely unsuitable at thicket and final cropping stages but highly suitable in mid-growth thinning phases.

The New Forest has undergone some major changes within its timber Inclosures during recent years, particularly in stands dominated by conifers.

Driven by changing conservation priorities and commercial pressures, heavy thinning and clearfells for reversion to broadleaf have rendered large areas unsuitable as potential nest sites for hawks. This increase in forestry activity, while making some nesting compartments unsuitable, compel those birds that are present to move to a different nesting site. This makes relocation more difficult and can also cause neighbouring pairs to move, as they spatially adjust within the population. Our efforts therefore have had to be extended to cover new ground, and we may be failing to relocate a number of pairs.

Finally, with a new and expanding goshawk population in the Forest, there may be an influence of direct predation affecting the resident sparrowhawks. We have found at least two instances of sparrowhawk remains being found at goshawk sites. Further monitoring is required to determine whether this perceived decline in numbers is real, whether it simply represents a result of reduced survey effort, or whether it is the result of a combination of the factors mentioned above. That said, there is generally greater availability of prey around the periphery of the Forest and around villages, and consequently the density of pairs can be slightly higher in such areas than in mainly coniferous forest blocks, where food availability is believed to be lower.

It was our opinion that the New Forest population of sparrowhawks numbered between 30 and 40 pairs in any one year, but in recent years the total number has been as low as 25 pairs in some years. Any long-term monitoring project has the advantage of bring able to differentiate normal fluctuations in population size from genuine increases in numbers or density, or conversely, long-term declines that may be the subject of concern. Recording nest and fledging success can show whether declines are linked to increased adult mortality, or a sustained drop in fledging success owing to change or loss in habitat quality.

The nest

Sparrowhawks build a new nest every year but often build on a platform that was already in place. This can be the base of an old squirrel drey, woodpigeon nest or just a few sticks lodged in a tree. Less than 2% of all nests found were the result of refurbishing an old sparrowhawk nest, and these records were almost entirely attributable to one site in broadleaved woodland.

As mentioned above, the main determining factor with respect to nest location is the density of the tree stand within the area chosen. It was at first thought that forestry stock maps could provide the information needed to aid nest finding, and although a useful source of information with respect to tree spacing, the different growth rates and thinning regimes can vary substantially from compartment to compartment, which in turn effect tree density. Within the Forest there has been a high preference for sparrowhawk nesting in Scots pine (Figure 9). This could however be a reflection of the prevalence of this tree species within the Forest, rather than it being a superior tree as a nest choice.

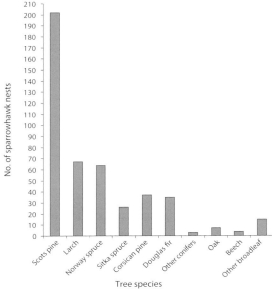

Figure 9
The number of sparrowhawk nests recorded in different tree species in the New Forest.

Almost all nests were constructed from twigs found immediately adjacent to the nest. Therefore nests in Scots pine were constructed of Scots pine twigs, those in larch were constructed of larch twigs, and those in spruce were constructed of spruce twigs. A number of nests, particularly those in broadleaved woodland, contained birch twigs. Larch was the only material that on occasions was brought longer distances, and this undoubtedly is because of its unique ability to hold together in a strong and durable platform. Larch nests were also the largest, consistently measuring 55 cm × 45 cm. Many Scots pine nests measured only 45 cm × 35 cm, and a few were as small as 30 cm × 30 cm.

Of a sample of 242 nests, 230 were positioned on branch whorls against the main trunk, which is by far the preferred position. The remaining 12 nests were in main forks or crotches, out on a limb or in the crown of a tree. Aspect was recorded for those nests positioned on branch whorls and against the main trunk, by taking a compass reading directly away from the tree through the centre of the nest. Results highlight the tendency of nests to be located on south-facing parts of the tree (Figure 10).

Figure 10
The number of sparrowhawk nests falling within each of the eight 45° segments, and also expressed as a percentage of the total sample of 297 nests.

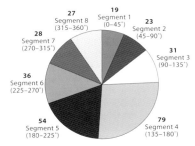

Completed nests were lined with flakes of Scots pine or spruce bark to prevent the eggs from working down through the framework of twigs during incubation and so becoming chilled. With failed nests, this was used as a measure of whether eggs had been laid. Throughout incubation, an accumulation of downy under-feathers from the sitting female gathers on the nest twigs and the immediate vicinity, and is diagnostic in confirming an occupied nest. Nest heights varied between sites, with those in broadleaved woodland featuring amongst the lowest (Figure 11). The highest nest we have recorded was at 23 m and the lowest was at 6.2 m, with the commonest category being 12–14 m (Figure 11).

Figure 11
The number of sparrowhawk nests in each of the height ranges measured directly from nest to ground, in a sample of 351 nests.

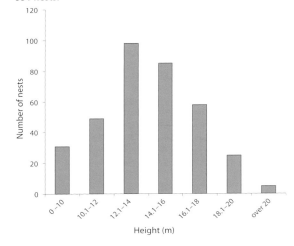

Clutch size

Very little recording of clutch size was undertaken, but the generally accepted range of 3–6 eggs seemed the norm from subsequently observed brood sizes. One clutch of seven was recorded and a nest containing nine eggs that failed was the product of two separate hens. In over a dozen nests we have recorded complete clutch failures, despite the incubating female often continuing to sit into early July.

Around 500 nests have been found over the past 20 years, from a minimum of 19 nests in 2007 to a maximum of 36 in 1999. Of these known nests, 396 were successful and 103 failed at either the egg or the chick stage as a result of a variety of different factors. Over an 18 year period, 240 unhatched eggs were removed from nests and forwarded to ITE / CEH for chemical analysis. Owing to financial cutbacks in recent years many eggs were not analysed, but have been stored for possible future work. Of those eggs that were analysed, no significantly harmful chemical residues were found, although increased concentrations were found in a number of samples.

Chicks

The sexual dimorphism exhibited in sparrowhawks means that males and females carry a differently sized leg ring. For nest inspection to include ringing therefore requires that the young be sufficiently grown to enable accurate sexing to take place. Over the years we have aimed to begin our monitoring from 1 July. As with all species, there is variation in the earliest and latest fledging dates, and this inevitably means that there will be occasional early nests in which the young are too advanced to attempt climbing and ringing, and others that will require a subsequent visit because they are too small. In general, however, the majority of work can be successfully completed during the first week in July. Our latest record for a potentially successful nest was one that contained small young on 19 July.

The optimum age for sexing the young is between two and three weeks of age. Problems can occur with large broods where, because of staggered hatching days, young that are a fortnight old may be found in the same nest as those that are only a few days old. The number of young fledged from successful nests has varied from as few as one to as many as six. The annual productivity of successful nests has ranged from 3.2 to 4.2 with a mean of 3.6. These figures suggest that any population changes are not attributable to poor productivity. A total of 1,012 young have been ringed as part of the survey, including 489 males and 523 females. Tawny owls were occasionally responsible for predating young hawks in the nest, and where possible sparrowhawks seemed to avoid nesting in areas regularly used for roosting by tawny owls.

Prey

As one would expect, our records of prey remains found at plucking posts and at nests reflect a cross-section of the birds most abundant in that environment. During incubation, tit species, robins, wrens, chaffinches, etc., feature highly in what the male is provisioning. During the latter period of chick growth, when the female begins hunting, slightly larger prey features, including a predominance of blackbird and song thrush and often great spotted woodpecker. At one nest where the young had already fledged, a climb to the empty nest revealed a number of fresh and partly plucked carcases including two song thrush, one blackbird, one woodcock and two green woodpeckers. Unusual items occasionally occur such as snipe and hawfinch, and during 2007 plucks of lesser spotted woodpecker were found at three separate sites. This was a significant number given the current scarcity of this species in the New Forest.

Ringing recoveries

Over 30 ringing recoveries have been reported; although most of these involve only short distances and occur within the bird's first year, some recoveries demonstrate the dispersal distances that some young hawks undertake. A female ringed in the nest within the Forest on 6 July 1991 was found dead in Chepstow, Gwent, a distance of 116 km, and a male was found dead at Chippenham, Wiltshire, 80 km away and only 45 days after it was ringed as a nestling. Another female was released alive from a pigeon loft near Newbury during its first winter. The longest-lived bird identified from recovery was a female ringed at Manor Wood near Lyndhurst on 8 July 1999 and found dead at Brook Wood, Bramshaw, on 13 July 2005. A high proportion of recorded fatalities occur after impacts with windows, patio doors, etc.

Northern goshawk *Accipiter gentilis*

As a native breeding species, the goshawk was eradicated from the UK during the early 19th century, primarily as a result of persecution. Its perceived conflict with game rearing and shooting interests is still responsible for its absence from parts of Britain today. Its return as a breeding bird, initially to the large and remote forests of northern and western Britain, has been as a direct result of deliberate and accidental releases of birds kept for falconry purposes. Despite many rumours to the contrary, until 2002 Hampshire Ornithological Society recorded goshawk as 'a bird with few substantiated records and not proven to breed in the County'. This was also the conclusion we reached for our fieldwork in the New Forest, with occasional confirmed sightings but no proof of attempted breeding.

Sightings of an individual during the summer of 2001 were the precursor to a major change to this situation in 2002, when intensive fieldwork from January to March led to the discovery of two separate pairs in display, and subsequently nest building, laying, and eventually successfully fledging of young. That three of the four parent birds exhibited streaked brown plumage in first-year birds indicated that these were probably the first colonisers of the county from a known breeding source in south Wiltshire. It must be said that the original source of these birds is questionable and is rumoured to have originated from birds imported without the correct paperwork and illegally released.

For a large raptor, the goshawk can be extremely unobtrusive for much of the year. Even with young to feed, their hunting forays to and from the nest are not easily observed. During the late winter months, however, male goshawks can regularly be seen in display and soaring flight, over and around their preferred nesting areas. Late morning with blustery, cloudy conditions seems to be preferable to still clear days and interaction with neighbouring males produces the most vigorous and prolonged display. Sightings of the females are not so frequent and decline considerably as egg laying approaches. Indeed at some sites a number of sustained visits have been required to prove that some males occupying territories have a mate.

The year 2003 saw three pairs successfully raise young in the Forest, the two pioneer pairs plus a third new pair. During 2007 at least 10 sites were occupied by either pairs or single birds. Eight pairs raised a minimum of 18 young with the brood of a further pair failing during incubation. To date, a minimum of 52

Figure 12
The gradual increase in goshawk numbers in the New Forest.

(a) Numbers of breeding pairs and individuals. Light grey, number of breeding pairs; filled bars, singles or pairs holding territory but not breeding.

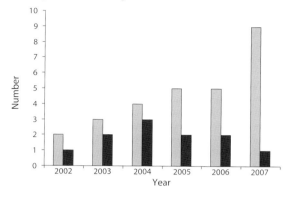

(b) Number of breeding pairs and numbers of fledged young. Filled bars, successful pairs; dark grey, failed pairs; light grey, minimum number of young fledged.

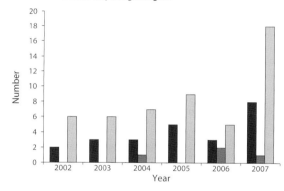

(c) Tree species used by goshawk as nesting sites in the New Forest.

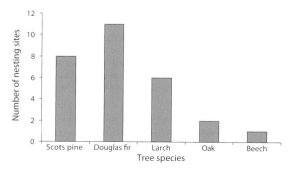

young have fledged within the protection of the Crown lands (Figure 12). This report excludes individuals or pairs that may be residing or breeding outside of the Crown lands. As the population expands to encompass private land, this will inevitably cause potential conflicts with game-rearing interests. It is hoped that cooperation and understanding will enable these issues to be better understood and any conflict minimised.

Montagu's harrier *Circus pygargus*

In 1995 the New Forest was the focus of local ornithological attention when a pair of rare Montagu's harriers took up residence in the north of the forest after an absence of 30 years, and proceeded to nest. This summer visitor is scarce and highly mobile, needing large areas of productive hunting ground, just the right height and structure of nesting habitat and, being a ground-nesting bird, a large slice of luck where natural predation is concerned. Where the Forestry Commission could assist was in ensuring that casual human disturbance was minimised, and that bird watchers generally could watch and enjoy the birds without adversely affecting them.

Large clutches and the ability to repeat lay are both strategies of birds with increased chances of natural predation or nest loss, and both were illustrated by the Forest pair. The majority of Montagu's harrier nests found in the UK today occur in arable or farmed environments, so it was pleasing to have the chance to observe nesting attempts at close quarters in a more natural heathland environment. However a harrier just needs a suitably high sward of rough vegetation, be it heather or a stand of growing barley.

The relatively late arrival date of these birds in the Forest strongly suggests a failed breeding attempt at their more regular or preferred site. In 1995 an adult male was first observed on 12 May and between 17 and 21 May, a pair was seen in courtship and undertaking nest site selection. The first egg was laid on 23 May, but by 26 May it was evident that the part clutch had been predated. Fortunately the birds selected a second site some 20 metres away and resumed completion of the clutch, laying another three eggs. Two hatched and successfully fledged, with the remaining egg being addled.

The nest itself consisted of a small pad of *Molinia* grass, constructed in an opening in the heather approximately 30 cm across, and was added to regularly throughout the incubation period. The observation of food being taken to the nest on 25 June indicated hatching of the first chick. Fledging of the eldest chick was noted on 23 July, and the adults and two young were last seen in the area on 29 August. As is normal with most raptors, the male did most of the food provisioning, with the female not seen to commence hunting until 11 July and then only locally and infrequently. Identification of prey was almost impossible but on one occasion a male nightjar was brought in, and repeated visits locally to a single spot were almost certainly the depletion of a brood of nestling birds such as stonechat or pipit. Voles and lizards were also identifiable on occasion.

In 1996 the female returned on 17 April and the male on 26 April. Breeding again commenced in the same general area as in 1995, but unfortunately the four well-grown young were taken by a fox on 28 June. In 1997 the female was first observed on 11 April, quartering the Black Gutter valley and paying particular attention to the areas previously used for nesting. The adult male of previous seasons failed to return and the female was joined by a second-summer male on 1 May. A number of visiting ornithologists were of the opinion that the male was too young to breed successfully but this was disproved when prey was seen going into the nest site on 11 June. By 9 July, two young could be seen standing on the heather and their first short flight was made early on 11 July. These two juveniles went on to fledge successfully, with an addled egg remaining in the empty nest. Of 123 recorded visits by the male with food for the incubating female, only two occurred before 8 am; 37 were between 8 am and midday, 54 were between midday and 4 pm, and 30 between 4 pm and 8 pm.

Contentious as it may be, the decision was taken to carry out crow and fox control in the nest area following the losses occurring in 1996, with a total of 21 foxes being accounted for in the period. This potential predation level for all ground-nesting birds is a thought for quiet reflection. In 1998 the first egg laid was predated by crows; as in the first year, the birds quickly moved site and continued to lay. Unfortunately these eggs were again predated by crows and the birds vacated the area completely. It is highly probable that the same scenario that saw their arrival in the Forest during 1995 was repeated here, and the birds moved to another unknown area and attempted to breed again. It was unfortunate that the area chosen for nesting by the harriers was in a part of the Forest attracting larger than usual numbers of corvids, which were visiting the nearby landfill site. Harsh as those losses seemed at the time, a 50% success rate from nesting attempts is a very good result for harriers generally.

Montagu's harriers are still occasionally seen on passage in the New Forest but to date no more nesting attempts have been recorded. The habitat in the Open Forest is thoughtfully and carefully managed, considering the many functions that it has to fill, and large areas are eminently suitable for Montagu's harrier to again breed in. Pressure from disturbance will always be an issue, particularly when birds are prospecting for potential breeding sites. It has been shown, however, that with a little help, successful breeding and viewing opportunities for the public can be achieved if these birds choose once again to favour the Forest in the future.

Common buzzard *Buteo buteo*

The common buzzard in the New Forest has been the subject of a lengthy and continuing study to monitor overall population and breeding success. Started many years ago by the late Colin Tubbs and others, and the subject of much written and published work by him, the basic elements of this study are still being continued today. Interested readers are strongly encouraged to consult Tubbs' classic work for further details (Tubbs 1974, 2001; Tubbs and Tubbs 1985). It is pleasing that the New Forest Keepers continue to help with sightings and collection of information.

Throughout most of the last century the buzzard was confined to the western half of Britain, being almost totally absent from eastern areas. The New Forest population was therefore at the extreme eastern edge of its known range. This, coupled with the fact that the area is largely free from widespread chemical use, emphasises the importance of population monitoring.

From 1962 until 1973 the New Forest study area held between 33 and 37 pairs of buzzard. From 1973 until 1982, the number of occupied territories dropped to between 19 and 21 and then remained at this number until 1993. For the next three years the population increased again, reaching a then maximum for the area of 38 pairs. Since then, numbers have continued to increase (Figure 13).

As with a number of other raptor species, the common buzzard is currently undergoing a period of range expansion and increase in abundance, but is still subject to fluctuating breeding success owing to variation in the weather and prey availability. A point not widely appreciated is that prey availability and sometimes weather are often far more crucial in the pre-laying period, for the female to gain good breeding condition, than they are in determining the survival of any hatched or dependant young. Good mast years boost the small mammal population within the New Forest, which in turn boosts the breeding buzzard population the following Spring. This was particularly evident in 2006 when a number of buzzard pairs failed to progress past nest building, despite having established and held territory throughout the year.

Figure 13
Numbers of common buzzard in the New Forest. Note that the 1997 data are incomplete and the number of occupied territories in 2006 is an estimate. Filled bars, occupied territories; dark grey, successful nests; light grey, failed nests or outcome unknown.

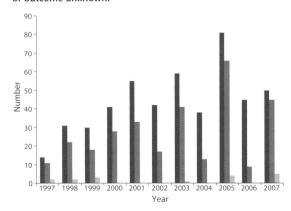

Analysis of the data obtained in 2005, when numbers were particularly high, indicated that of the 81 occupied territories, 69 held breeding pairs, leaving a maximum of 12 sites held by non-breeders. Sixty-five pairs successfully raised 112 young and four pairs failed to do so. Of the successful broods 31 had two chicks, 26 had one chick and eight had broods of three.

Honey buzzard *Pernis apivorus*

Unquestionably the most mysterious and elusive raptor of renowned association with the New Forest is the honey buzzard. Until recently almost nothing of any note had been published on this species in this country, and most records here and elsewhere were heavily suppressed from the birding world as a whole. Much of this was wholly justified for what was, and still is, a very scarce and fluctuating population, which is now known to be scattered throughout England, Scotland and Wales (Roberts and Lewis 2003). The difficulties involved in gathering quantitative data on the species have resulted in some previously written work of dubious merit and much assumption unsupported by evidence.

In the New Forest, numbers vary from odd individuals to a handful of scattered pairs, which are often non-breeding (Figure 14). Slowly, our many hundreds of hours of observation on this species are adding to the national picture through communication with field workers elsewhere, and are improving our knowledge of the ecology of the species. Dedicated watchers and enthusiasts have always monitored the small population known in the Forest. Historically a target for illegal egg collectors, much of the early pioneering work was aimed at nest protection, and suspicion and suppression were rife.

In today's more enlightened environment, it is recognised that there is still much to learn about this species in the UK. However, the huge time commitment demanded of honey buzzard watchers means that accumulation of information is a slow and painstaking task. This is obviously reflected in the completeness of the records and information that follows, and by no means can a complete knowledge of the breeding population every year be inferred from the information that has been gathered. New advances in radio and satellite tracking are opening up areas of study that will hopefully increase the pace of our understanding of individual and pair behaviour.

Honey buzzards arrive back in the Forest in early to mid-May, and adult birds that have bred in previous years will commence nest building or refurbishment almost immediately. For the bird watcher, visual sightings are rare before the third week of May as the birds are very discreet at this time. They are also recovering from the rigours of migration and replenishing lost body mass. It is believed that frogs form a large part of the diet at this time, as the nests of the social insects that form a large part of their diet later in the season are only in their early stages of development at this time of year.

Display from breeding pairs is nowhere near as common as much of the literature would indicate. Unmated birds however display vigorously and regularly towards neighbouring birds. Nest selection and building is rarely witnessed but re-occupation of old nests occurs relatively frequently, which enables us to monitor and protect a site in the extremely difficult locating-period around the early stages of incubation. As with common buzzard, some nests are large structures copiously decorated with green shoots and branches, while others can be quite small affairs and not exhibiting much in the way of visible greenery from below. The nest cup itself is however usually well lined with fresh greenery.

Two eggs make up the normal clutch, although ones and threes are occasionally recorded. Laying dates here in the Forest are normally from the last week of May to the end of the first week of June. Incubation is shared by both sexes, although the female is probably responsible for the greater share, with the off-duty bird foraging and feeding for itself. It is assumed but not proven that some of the off-duty bird's time is spent in locating the nests of wasp species for future plundering.

Contrary to some literature, we have no reason to think that weather plays a significant part in honey buzzard reproductive success, although the results of the 2007 season may appear to cast a small query over this view. Even in prolonged wet conditions the birds seem well capable of finding and excavating the nests of a variety of wasp species including hornets. This has also been proven for pairs nesting in the more adverse wet conditions found in North Wales and Scotland. The difficulties of finding nests early in the breeding cycle can obviously bias the information in favour of successful pairs and undoubtedly some pairs fail in incubation. However, we have only recorded one definite failure to date, and this was due to the two eggs being infertile. Known breeding attempts invariably lead to successful fledging.

Figure 14
Numbers of honey buzzard in the New Forest. This includes birds living or nesting outside the area but known to use the Forest for foraging at various times. Filled bars, number of pairs known to attempt breeding; open bars, sites containing singles or pairs but not thought to be breeding.

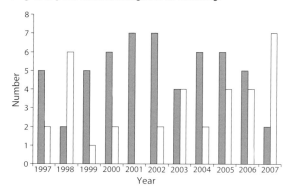

What seems more significant in determining successful breeding is whether the birds establish a pair bond. New pairs or established individuals trying to attract a new mate often spend their first summer together in mutual fights and territory familiarisation, without attempting breeding. Nest building often occurs late in the season and is known as a 'summer nest'. These structures are often half-hearted affairs but can also be more substantial constructions. If the same pair of young or non-breeders return the following year, then successful breeding is much more likely and the previous year's summer nest can become the focus for the pair, often being refurbished and then used for a full breeding attempt. Some pairs can be quite long-lived and can continue to occupy a territory for some years. Once this pair is lost, however, it can be many years before successful breeding is re-established in the area.

Kestrel *Falco tinnunculus*

One of the least common raptors in the forest is the kestrel. Primarily feeding on a range of small mammals, grazing of the New Forest by cattle, ponies and deer prevents the development of long rough grass favoured by these animals. Many of the kestrels seen hunting the Forest are ranging from more suitable marginal land around the edge, and are hunting lizards and larger insects. Unlike the rest of the raptor species, the numbers of kestrel in the UK have shown a recent decline, thought to be linked to declines in several species of farmland bird associated with more intensive agriculture. Between 1961 and 1981, the New Forest population fluctuated between 16 and 24 pairs.

Hobby *Falco subbuteo*

The summer-visiting and breeding hobby is a bird with an historic association with the lowland heaths of southern Britain, which continues to this day. As it is a most difficult and time-consuming bird to find at the nest, accurate assessment of the breeding population is difficult. Tubbs (1974) suggests a New Forest population of around 19 pairs, whereas Parr (1985), in his study of the ecology of the hobby partly undertaken in the New Forest during 1981 and 1982, found 12 and 16 pairs in these years respectively. During the last twenty years I have known over 20 separate sites that have held breeding hobbies, but how many are occupied in any one year I am unable to say with certainty. Given normal fluctuations in the number of breeding territory holders and non-breeding territory holders, I have no reason to believe the current population is significantly different to that assessed by Parr (1985) and probably numbers around 12–14 pairs. That said, 2007 seems to have been a particularly poor year for hobbies, with a number of sites seemingly devoid of birds.

As with many raptors, hobbies exhibit a high preference for traditional sites, with many clumps or belts of trees that held nesting birds fifty or more years ago still holding birds today. Hobbies arrive from their African wintering quarters around mid- to late April and on warm sunny afternoons in May can be observed feeding low over the heaths and mire, hunting day-flying moths, dragonflies and other insects. Some of the more productive areas of the Forest can become a magnet for a number of feeding hobbies, and I have watched up to 13 birds feeding in the Bishops Dyke, Denny area at one time. Emperor and fox moths are caught effortlessly by this superbly agile falcon, and provide high-energy food in return for low-energy hunting, which is key to the birds gaining breeding condition after the rigours of migration. Latterly the abundance of many of these larger moth species appear to have declined markedly, and the length of time spent hunting this food source has dropped correspondingly. Feeding observations such as these were almost non-existent through the very poor weather conditions of 2007.

Hobbies are the last of all our raptors to begin breeding. They make no nest themselves but select an old or recently vacated nest of a crow or other suitable structure. New Forest pairs have a strong preference for using crow nests, which in turn have a preference for choosing Scots pine. It is somewhat debatable how much choice is involved in nest selection by a species that uses another bird's nest, but as breeding crow numbers are significantly higher than hobby it can be assumed that a degree of choice is available. Preferred sites are often older, open-grown Scots pine or 'mother' trees occurring in clumps on the open forest, or belts of trees adjacent to heath, large clearings, clearfells or suchlike, and usually command a good view over the surrounding area.

Laying dates of hobbies are fairly precise and commence in early to mid-June. Two or three eggs form the normal clutch, and incubation is 28 days. Fledging occurs after a further 28–30 days. Some pairs can be extremely noisy around the nest site and vigorously defend it against other birds, particularly buzzards. On the other hand, some can be extremely unobtrusive and are easily overlooked.

Peregrine falcon *Falco peregrinus*

Until fairly recently, any sightings of peregrine falcon would have largely been confined to the winter months, and only then made very sporadically. In recent years any reasonable period of raptor observation is likely to yield a sighting of a peregrine. With known breeding sites now scattered around the edge of the Forest, their hunting forays regularly make them observable to serious raptor watchers. Most nest sites are high on pylons or other tall man-made structures, but it is anticipated that in future a tree-nesting pair might be located high on a woodland or heathland edge, in an old crow or raven nest.

In recent years 1994 was the first recorded breeding in the county, with two pairs breeding in 1995.

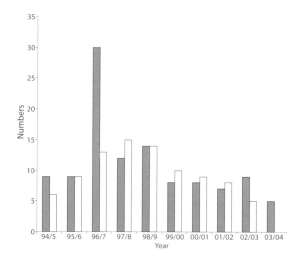

Figure 15
Numbers of hen harriers in the New Forest.

(a) Peak forest counts from Hampshire bird reports (produced by the Hampshire Ornithological Society) for three monthly winter periods. Note that the exceptional influx observed in late December 1996 was the result of a very harsh cold spell of weather moving birds south. Filled bars, October–December; open bars, January–March.

Peak monthly counts of hen harriers using the northern New Forest roost. Filled bars, grey males; open bars, ringtails.

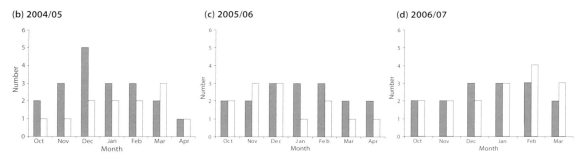

(b) 2004/05   (c) 2005/06   (d) 2006/07

Hen harrier *Circus cyaneus*

During the winter months a few hen harriers still grace the heaths with their distinctive low-quartering flight. Still a much-persecuted bird on their breeding grounds, it is sad to report a decline in the numbers frequenting the known roost areas in the Forest. During the late 1980s and early 1990s, up to six areas of the Forest held roosts, although only two of these north of the A31 regularly held birds. All sites were in heather and in the same localities each year. Sadly, in recent years this situation has regressed further and only the very northern roost is regularly used (Figure 15). It is known that birds are occasionally using other sites within the Forest, and work needs to be done to evaluate these irregular roost areas and record the frequency and number of individuals present. The current heathland management burning programme is examining the maintenance of some of these preferred roost sites past normal rotation to assist the birds.

Merlin *Falco columbarius*

Another regular winter visitor to watch out for is the small and easily overlooked merlin. Never a common

bird in the New Forest, it can be seen with perseverance in very small numbers hunting pipits and finches on the heaths and around the woodland edges. Although many of these birds are hunting well beyond the boundaries of the Forest, particularly along the coast, three to four small roosts have been known to occur annually since the 1970s. The number of records of this species seems to have increased slightly in recent years. With three or four birds probably occurring in the north of the Forest, similar numbers are thought to occur along the coastal strip between Calshot and Lymington, and two or three more along the Avon Valley.

The future

These are exciting times for raptor watchers in the New Forest, with common buzzard, sparrowhawk, honey buzzard and hobby populations fairly stable or increasing, peregrine now regularly observed, goshawk added to the list of breeding birds and the increasing possibility that red kite may soon colonise the area. Although never a place that features highly for rare migrants or vagrants, there is always the possibility that osprey, marsh and Montagu's harrrier can be seen, and in most years there are occasional records of red-footed falcon.

Increasing demands for more recreational time, and tolerance to more varied pursuits within the New Forest environment place increasing pressure on all our wildlife and wild places. We all have an obligation to understand how our presence in the Forest can impact both positively and negatively on a range of species, both intentionally and unintentionally. Our interest in wildlife does not exclude us from the equation, and needs to be borne in mind whenever we are out enjoying those special places, such as the New Forest.

Acknowledgements

The Forestry Commission are thanked for supporting my work. Thanks also to Alan Lucas, Wayne Percy, Diana and Gerald Westerhoff and Richard Jacobs for committing enormous numbers of hours to fieldwork; Jenni Tubbs for coordinating the Common Buzzard Survey; Dave Ransom for his diligence in recording the Winter Harrier roost data; Matthew Davies, Tim Creed, John Gulliver and Robert Colin-Stokes for their climbing skills and data collection; and Forest keepers and other individuals who pass on useful sightings and information that aid completion of the annual raptor data.

References

Parr, S. J. (1985). The breeding ecology and diet of the hobby (*Falco subbuteo*) in southern England. *Ibis*, 127, 60–73.

Roberts, S. J. and Lewis, J. M. S. (2003). Observations of European Honey buzzard breeding density in Britain. *British Birds*, 96, 37–39.

Tubbs, C. R. (1974). *The Buzzard*. David and Charles, Newton Abbot.

Tubbs, C. R. (2001). *The New Forest. History, ecology and conservation*. New Forest Ninth Centenary Trust, Lyndhurst, Hampshire.

Tubbs, C. R. and Tubbs, J. M. (1985). Buzzards (*Buteo buteo*) and land use in the New Forest, Hampshire, England. *Biological Conservation*, 31, 41–65.

2 Bats

Colleen Mainstone

Introduction

Bechstein's bat *Myotis bechsteinii* and the barbastelle bat *Barbastellus barbastella* are two of the rarest bats in Europe. Both species have specialist ecological niches, and seem to require areas of mature deciduous woodland for roosting. Until recently only a handful of colonies of either species were known in the UK. Much of the New Forest is suitable for both species and there are a handful of historical and more recent local records of their presence. Considering these factors, its extent and its position within the more southerly UK ranges of these bats, it is possible that the New Forest could support significant populations of these species. A project was established by Hampshire Bat Group in 2005 to establish the distribution of both species in the area. This chapter provides a summary of current understanding of the ecology and distribution of these rare bats in the UK and highlights some of the results of preliminary surveys of them in the New Forest. In addition, to provide context, an overview is presented of the current status of other bat species in Hampshire.

Status and distribution of bats in Hampshire

There are 16 species of bat resident and breeding in the UK, of which most have been recorded in Hampshire within the past 100 years (Table 5).

Greater and lesser horseshoe bats were once more widely distributed in Hampshire with records from Lyndhurst, Romsey, Winchester, Portsmouth and Southampton as well as Christchurch and Boscombe (now in the county of Dorset) (Vesey Fitzgerald 1944). A greater horseshoe roost survived as late as 1926; this was divided between Winchester Cathedral and a church to its west (Robert Stebbings, pers. comm.). A greater horseshoe roost in the far west of Hampshire has only supported a few males in the past 20 years; Stebbings (pers. comm.) remembers the site supporting a colony at one time. Stebbings also knew Sdeuard Bisserot, who spent most of his life in the New Forest, and stated that with the exception of the loss of a vast Daubenton's roost in Christchurch Priory, bat populations had not changed much over time. The greater mouse-eared bat *Myotis myotis* is possibly extinct in the UK, with only localised records of an

Table 5
UK status and distribution of bats recorded in Hampshire.

Species	Status in the UK (Entwistle *et al.* 2001)	Hampshire records since 1940
Bechstein's bat *Myotis bechsteinii*	Rare and restricted	New Forest and woodland in south-east of county (also Isle of Wight)
Barbastelle *Barbastella barbastellus*	Rare and widespread	New Forest and Mottisfont woodlands (also Isle of Wight). Detector records for south and north of county
Greater horseshoe bat *Rhinolophus ferrumequinum*	Rare and restricted	Three recent records of individuals in south-west and south-east of the New Forest. Last known maternity colony in Winchester Cathedral 1944*
Lesser horseshoe bat *Rhinolophus hipposideros*	Rare and restricted	No recent records with exception of grounded bat in Portsmouth
Grey long-eared bat *Plecotus austriacus*	Rare and restricted	Only one record in SW of the New Forest (Isle of Wight appears to be a stronghold)
Brown long- eared bat *Plecotus auritus*	Common and widespread	Likely to be common and widespread
Common pipistrelle *Pipistrellus pipistrellus*	Common and widespread	Likely to be common and widespread
Soprano pipsitrelle *Pipistrellus pygmaeus*	Common and widespread	Likely to be common and widespread
Nathusius' pipistrelle *Pipistrellus nathusii*	Rare and restricted occasional records elsewhere in Hampshire	Bat detector records from New Forest and
Noctule *Nyctalus noctula*	Frequent and widespread	Likely to be frequent and widespread
Leisler's bat *Nyctalus leislerii*	Rare outside Ireland, otherwise frequent and widespread	Historical records in east Hampshire and more recent very occasional bat detector records central and south-west Hampshire
Whiskered bat *Myotis mystacinus*	Scarce/widespread	Too few data to evaluate
Brandt's bat *Myotis brandtii*	Scarce/widespread	Too few data to evaluate
Daubenton's bat *Myotis daubentonii*	Common and widespread	Too few data to evaluate
Natterer's bat *Myotis nattereri*	Frequent and widespread	Too few data to evaluate
Serotine *Eptesicus serotinus*	Frequent and widespread	Too few data to evaluate but believed to have declined recently

individual in neighbouring West Sussex after a known roost site was destroyed.

Harris *et al.* (1995) estimated the pre-breeding population of Bechstein's bat to be 1500 in England. At the time, however, there had been no evidence of the species breeding in the UK (and the species had not then been recorded in Wales). Vesey Fitzgerald (1944) reviewed the status of bats in Hampshire and described Bechstein's bat as 'very rare', noting its distribution in Hampshire as the Isle of Wight (1909); Burley, New Forest (1834); Brockenhurst, New Forest (1886); and Harewood Forest near Marlborough (1939). He also noted the earliest records of barbastelle in the county, describing them as 'not uncommon, but nowhere plentiful', mainly occurring in the south of the county and in the Isle of Wight, but with 10 records for the mid and north of the county.

A small number of both Bechstein's and barbastelle bats have been accidentally caught in the New Forest in more recent years during the course of mist netting surveys for birds. A few records were also obtained during surveys to assess the viability of moving the some of the campsites in 2003 (at Hollands Wood, Round Hill and New Park), and incidental records have been obtained during public bat walks, bat box checks and from a few casualties handed to New Forest Keepers. In the mid-1990s, English Nature (now Natural England) undertook a bat detector survey of a sample area of 72 km² of the New Forest, confirming it as 'outstandingly rich in bats' (Tubbs 2001). In the late 1990s, English Nature erected some bat boxes near to a record of an injured female Bechstein's bat at Hollands Wood near Lyndhurst, but no Bechstein's or barbastelle bats were ever recorded in them.

Overview of bat ecology

All bats in the UK are insectivorous, using echolocation to locate prey and to navigate. Some bats, however, use vision for both purposes and to varying degrees. Bats roost in crevices, cracks and cavities in trees, caves and man-made structures such as buildings, bridges, tunnels and mines. Female bats congregate in maternity roosts in summer to give birth and raise what is normally a single youngster. Pups are born blind and naked but are able to fly at between three and six weeks of age depending on the species. Bats mate mainly in autumn, the females exhibiting delayed fertilisation. After copulation females retain the sperm during the hibernation period, which lasts between November and March in most species. Fertilisation then occurs in springtime after the ovum has been released from the ovary, birth occurring in midsummer.

In general all species of bat have declined since the 1900s (Harris *et al.* 1995, Stebbings 1988). The principal causes of decline are habitat loss and fragmentation, modern silvicultural practices, agricultural intensification, use of pesticides and infrastructural development leading to loss of traditional roost sites. Modern building methods and materials do not leave gaps that can allow bats (and

birds) into cavities in new and renovated buildings. This bodes very badly for future bat populations, many of which have adapted to roost in lofts, cellars, cavity walls, underneath tiles or slates and in the soffit boxes of buildings, often favouring heated domestic dwellings to raise their young in summer.

All bats in the UK are protected by law (i.e. Conservation (Natural Habitats) Regulations (as amended) and the Wildlife and Countryside Act 1981), and it is an offence to kill, injure or disturb a bat or to block access to, damage or destroy its place of shelter (roost site). Because bats frequently use multiple roost sites throughout the year, a roost site is protected even when a bat is not present. If works are necessary that would contravene the legislation, then a licence must be obtained from the statutory nature conservation agency. Survey licences may also be required for certain survey techniques or where bats may be disturbed.

Ecology of Bechstein's and barbastelle bats

Much of the published information on Bechstein's and barbastelle bats in the UK has been written by David Hill and Frank Greenaway based on research in southern England, and woodlands in West Sussex in particular. This review draws upon findings from these studies but also includes reference to some emerging research and observational accounts in the UK (by G. Billington, J. Flanders, M. Zeale, C. Mainstone and P. Hope). Reference is also made to research on both species in Germany and Switzerland.

Bechstein's bat is one of Europe's rarest bats and is confined in the UK mainly to the south of the country at altitudes less than 150 m (Hill and Greenaway 2006), although it is found at higher altitudes in mainland Europe. It is widespread within its range, which stretches from the Iberian Peninsula to the Ukraine, and is at the northern border of its range in the UK. Although it is widespread in Europe, its populations are believed to be low (although local densities can be high). Its population has declined throughout its range and it is considered 'Vulnerable' (IUCN 2001). It was probably common in Neolithic times when its woodland habitat was very much more widespread, as fossil remains in Grimes Graves in Norfolk suggest (Yalden 1992).

During 2005 and 2006, Hill and Greenaway reviewed the probable distribution of Bechstein's bats in southern England using a combination of GIS mapping and field surveys. In 2005 they surveyed a suitable woodland in each of 52 10-km squares across Hampshire, Surrey, East and West Sussex and Kent. Ten Bechstein's and one barbastelle bat were captured out of a total of 143 bats (11 species). In 2006, 15 Bechstein's and one barbastelle were captured out of 128 bats (11 species) from sites in East and West Sussex (Hill and Greenaway 2008).

A replicable survey protocol has now been established to develop baseline data on the national distribution of Bechstein's bat in conjunction with the Bat Conservation Trust (BCT) and some local bat groups. This project is planned to be phased throughout the region and will run from 2008 to 2010/2011.

In the UK, Bechstein's bats show a significant preference for trees as roost sites, although bat boxes have successfully attracted bats and there are two records of roosts in buildings. Roost sites are most commonly found in cavities excavated by woodpeckers in oak *Quercus* sp. (or ash *Fraxinus excelsior* on the Isle of Wight). Greenaway and Hill (2004) describe an ideal Bechstein's wood to be deciduous, uneven in age, 40–50 ha in extent and to be semi-natural or ancient in origin, with a dense understorey and a watercourse. They state that areas of continuous high forest or smaller woodlands linked by suitable hedgerows could also support Bechstein's, however populations may be almost exclusively male or non-breeding females. Where they occur in prime habitat, the density of Bechstein's bats can be high, with multiple colonies found within a 10-km square.

In the UK, Greenaway and Hill (2004) also suggested that Bechstein's colonies could survive in oak and mixed hardwood forest plantations, as long as there were adequate suitable roost sites and a dense understorey. They cited three oak plantations with an 80–180 year-old class, which exhibited thick understorey layers that supported thriving Bechstein's populations. They also noted that within this habitat, the presence of conifers seemed to have no detrimental effect; in fact small areas of conifers may even have advantages in certain circumstances (Greenaway and Hill 2004). Hill and Greenaway (2008) caution that an entire community of woodland bats could be adversely affected by understorey clearance and that such management should only proceed after a thorough survey of the woodland for bats.

Female Bechstein's bats rear their young in maternity roosts between May and early July, with births beginning towards the end of June (Fitzimmons *et al.* 2002). Group sizes within roost sites vary as individuals regularly split off and regroup within the colony range. This constant 'fission–fusion' behaviour makes population estimates difficult, but average colony size is believed to be 15–40 animals, with a maximum of 80 (Kerth and Konig 1999). Day roost selection and an individual's choice of roost mates is believed to be influenced by reproductive status rather than relatedness, animals gaining mutual benefit from body warmth, grooming and shared knowledge about roosts (Kerth and Konig 1999).

Kerth and Morf (2004) undertook intensive behavioural studies of adjacent Bechstein's colonies roosting in bat boxes in Bavaria, where individuals were fitted with subcutaneously implanted transponders (PIT-tags). This allowed intensive monitoring of individuals on a daily basis without disturbing roosts and affecting behaviour. Some individuals were also radio tracked. In one colony (Blutsee) adult females (18 in number) used 68 roosts and adult males 69 roosts during the three-year survey period. Twenty-eight roosts were exclusive to females and 27 exclusive to males; 41 were used by both sexes, although mixed use was rare, occurring on only 37/515

census days and mostly in autumn or spring. No adult males were ever observed roosting together.

Genetic analysis and mark–recapture studies have shown that Bechstein's females show absolute natal philopatry, forming independent breeding colonies composed of maternally closely related bats (Kerth *et al.* 2002). Females were observed attacking 'foreign' females as they attempted to enter their roost. In Germany, four colonies whose genetic pedigree was known were studied over a five-year period. Despite considerable fluctuations in population size, no immigration to individual colonies was found during that time. Individual bats roosted with most other colony members at some time, but most females had significant positive associations with several other particular individuals (Kerth and Morf, 2004). In the UK, Bechstein's bats forage mainly in deciduous woodland but they also forage and roost in mature orchards on mainland Europe. Use of hedgerows and parkland habitats for foraging has also been recorded in recent years (P. Hope and C. Mainstone, pers. obs.).

The core foraging area of individual female Bechstein's bats is smaller than for most other species of bat. Schofield and Morris (2000) and Kerth *et al.* (2000) calculated mean foraging areas for individual Bechstein's bats to be 21.9 ha (range 6.9–50.5) and 21 ha (range 9.9–37.5), respectively. In the West Sussex study (Fitzsimons *et al.* 2002) these were somewhat smaller; five bats tracked on foot used foraging areas ranging from 0.7 to 2.5 ha. However, account was taken of different methodologies used between the two studies, and after recalculating data to ensure comparability, the mean foraging area in the West Sussex study was still small, calculated to be 11.4 ha per bat (range 5.5–17.2). The maximum distance between foraging area and the main roost site of females during the radio tracking period in this study was 1.4 km. The foraging areas and maximum distance travelled to them from roost sites for Bechstein's bats studied at sites in southern England and the Isle of Wight were similar to those of Fitzsimons (C. Mainstone and P. Hope, pers. obs. 2008/9). Kerth *et al.* (2001) in their studies suggested that young female Bechstein's may inherit foraging areas from their mothers and remain faithful to them.

Siemers and Swift (2006) studied resource partitioning between Bechstein's and Natterer's bats, two species that are morphologically similar, although Bechstein's bats have longer ear length (19–29 mm) than Natterer's bats (13–20 mm). Their studies supported the idea that Bechstein's bats hunt by listening for prey, whereas Natterer's bats use echolocation and associative learning. In their study, Bechstein's bats foraged mainly on moths, flies and earwigs, harvestmen and crickets (i.e. 'louder' prey) whereas Natterer's bats foraged mainly on diurnal flies, spiders and longhorn flies (i.e. more 'silent' prey). There were considerably more tympanate moths in the diet of Bechstein's than in that of Natterer's bats. Tympanate moths are known to be able to 'hear' echolocation and take evasive action to avoid capture.

Bats in the genus *Myotis*, such as Bechstein's, demonstrate autumnal (and sometimes springtime) swarming. This has been observed mainly at underground sites and is believed to be at least partly related to mating. Swarming may assist with gene flow in these otherwise socially closed societies (Kerth et al. 2002). If, as has been suggested, females range further in autumn then this could also assist in genetic mixing.

Kerth and Morf (2004) concluded that most genetic mixing occurs at swarming sites to which males and females must travel great distances, frequently flying across open non-forested areas. They also suggested a much less common phenomenon for gene dispersal may be by females colonising new areas, probably by small groups of females moving to new areas adjacent to their former colonies. This may occur in response to changes in habitat, allowing new areas to become available.

The barbastelle bat is also one of the rarest bats in Western Europe and has also declined within its range in recent years. It occurs from southern Scandinavia south to Morocco, and east towards Turkey and the Caucasus. In continental Europe it is a bat of forested uplands; in the UK it is believed to be confined to lowland woodlands and river valleys. It is also considered 'Vulnerable' (IUCN 2001).

Harris et al. (1995) estimated the UK population of barbastelles to be in the region of 5,000 (4,500 in England and 500 in Wales). Arnold (1993) noted its UK distribution to be south of a line between the Tees, although Millais (1904) noted its presence in Cumbria in 1904–06. Even in suitable woods such as Ebernoe Common in West Sussex, the density of barbastelle bats is low, with fewer than one female or juvenile per 6 km^2 (although this does include large areas of unusable arable land) (Greenaway 2004).

Barbastelle roosts are most commonly found in oak and beech Fagus sylvatica woodland, bats frequently making use of apparently fragile roost locations behind flaking bark. Although most records of roost sites are in trees, some building roosts have also been recorded (mainly in barns). Cavities in trees accessed by small holes are also used, as are crevices in split and torn limbs and trunks, normally in areas of humid unmanaged woodland (e.g. non-intervention areas of ancient semi natural woodland or derelict coppice). Greenaway and Hill (2004) also found that in the UK, barbastelle maternity colonies tend to roost on the northern or north-western side of the brows of low wooded hills, normally in ancient or semi-natural woodland, and frequently with a high humidity associated with a dense understorey. Similarly, Russo et al. (2004 and 2005, in Switzerland) suggested that barbastelle bats avoided roosting in wood pasture with a homogenously loose canopy cover, preferring different vertical layers in a woodland with dominant, codominant and intermediate trees. Greenaway (2004) suggested that the holly understorey in the colony area studied in West Sussex helped to generate these conditions, providing a wide range of microclimates together with a mixture of roost sites. On the continent, Rydell et al. (1996) studied the foraging habits of three barbastelle colonies (in Germany and Switzerland) where roost sites were located in villages 'surrounded by agricultural land, mostly unfertilised grassland and patches of woodland'.

Greenaway (2004) found that barbastelle bats in West Sussex roosted deep in massive hollow trunks during cold winters, within areas of dense evergreen vegetation (i.e. the understorey of holly). Severe cold may have driven them underground or into buildings. In spring and autumn they were frequently located roosting behind loose bark, often low down in deep cover. Dead tree stumps projecting above holly were sometimes used to gain warmth from sunshine during warmer conditions, enabling them to move roost locations according to changing daily conditions. In late spring, pregnant females returned from more dispersed areas to form communal day roosts, but returned to individual foraging territories at night. Communal roosting bats changed roost sites more frequently than in springtime but similar sites were used. Extreme hot weather resulted in a move towards areas with dense cover around the roost site presumably used to buffer the microclimate. As pregnancy advanced bats moved to roost sites that were more protected, frequently using cracks in large boughs. The cracks chosen were commonly those where the tree had tried to repair the injury, and where growth around the crack had formed a more protected site for the bats. After birth, mothers remove youngsters to form splinter groups, frequenting roost sites in splits and behind loose bark. By early August these splinter groups reformed to one large group, still regularly moving between roost sites before disbanding in late August or September. Juveniles often remained in the area long after dispersal of adults, and some adults remained to overwinter (Greenaway 2001).

Barbastelle bats feed almost exclusively on moths, probably captured in flight, although some other prey items such as spiders may be gleaned (Vaughan 1997, Rydell et al. 1996). The diet of barbastelles is unusual because of the high percentage of moths, which require a specialised foraging strategy (i.e. gleaning like long-eared or Bechstein's bats, or flutter detection using very high frequencies like horseshoe bats). Barbastelles probably use both gleaning and aerial hawking techniques (Rydell et al. 1996).

Barbastelle bats have a unique echolocation call using two contrasting types of pulse while foraging. A short relatively weak broadband frequency sweep (maximum 42 kHz) follows a stronger narrowband pulse at 32 kHz, followed by a steep frequency sweep (Rydell et al. 1996). Barbastelle bats may use either or both pulses alternately to suit the situation. Barbastelles can also emit echolocation pulses through their nose (Kolb 1970). Their large, forward-pointing ears are also typical of species that echolocate in clutter. Sierro and Arlettaz (1997) describe barbastelle as a 'typical aerial-hawking species although they hunted exclusively above the forest canopy'. The species has seemingly evolved a peculiar foraging technique to overcome the defence system of its probably tympanate prey. According to these authors, the diet of Barbastella appears one of the narrowest among Palaearctic bats, although Zeale (2008/9 unpublished) recorded a range of macro moths in barbastelle droppings analysed by DNA. As a result of its specialisation in foraging habits, it is probably relatively vulnerable to changes in the abundance of moth populations, compared with other more flexible aerial-hawking bats.

In Greenaway's studies (2004), barbastelle mothers with young foraged within 1 km of roost sites and returned to them frequently. Female bats shared long sections of flight lines and foraging areas but normally these tapered to an area used by a single bat. Later as the young developed, foraging areas increased, with individuals recorded flying up to 30 km per night (although more typically 8 km). Greenaway (2004) noted a seasonal pattern to foraging, with riverine areas preferred in spring, meadows and hedgerows in summer and dense woodland in winter. He noted however that bats could be adaptive when highly productive foraging resources were available, such as a well-used coastal grassland strip used by a colony in Norfolk (Greenaway 2001). He also suggested that where flight routes are not wooded, double hedgerows are important for foraging and commuting.

Billington (2000) radio tracked 17 adult female barbastelle bats during July in Horner Wood NNR (Somerset). He noted favoured foraging areas as headwaters of three local rivers, mainly around scrub and unimproved pasture, particularly in the south and west slopes of coombes bordering moorland and western and southern slopes of woodland and moorland. He noted the most dominant habitat of these areas as European gorse *Ulex europaeus*. Bats also foraged along small tree-lined watercourses and occasionally were recorded foraging over gardens and around low-level street lighting. He also noted that bats commuted and foraged in groups, and had 'socialising places' where they would meet at regular intervals before dispersing more widely. Billington (2000) recorded over 66% of tagged bats together in one place on several occasions.

Hampshire Bat Group Surveys

A project focusing on the New Forest area and Bechstein's and barbastelle bats in particular was instigated after four barbastelles were heard and seen foraging in the canopy of a conifer ride in Burley Inclosure, during a bat group survey in autumn 2005. The project was set up by the current author and Paul Hope of the Hampshire Bat Group with the following aims:

- assess the distribution of barbastelle and Bechstein's bats in the New Forest;
- record roost sites;
- influence positive management of the Forest and surrounding areas for bats;
- train volunteers and land managers in survey techniques;
- raise awareness of the value of the Forest for bats.

There is a range of ways that new volunteers with a varying degree of skills can contribute, but removal of bats from nets and the harp trap is restricted to licence holders or occasionally those training for a licence. Training and support is given where necessary to assist with detector surveys, radio tracking and roost emergence/re-entry counts; all of these are non invasive surveys that with some training and support people may assist with. Promotion of the project has been achieved through a number of talks and presentations, a leaflet and published articles in our own literature/website. The cost of equipment to undertake this work has been provided through grant funding from the New Forest National Park Sustainability Fund and the New Forest Trust. An equipment loan has been gratefully received from Hampshire Bat Group and Ecological Planning & Research.

During bat detector surveys, bat echolocation calls are recorded using time expansion Pettersson D240x detectors and Sony HiMD minidisks. The ability to record calls is valuable, as positive verification of species such as barbastelle can be made by using software analysis of sonograms; in this case the software used is 'Batsound' (Pettersson Electronik). Many woodland specialist species are hard to detect and/or identify using this method, and capture is necessary to confirm their identification to species level. Mist nets and harp trap are used either in dense woodland to capture foraging bats, or along rides and tracks to catch commuting bats. Bechstein's and barbastelle bats are fitted with rings so that they can be identified if recaptured. Surveys began in 2006 and are likely to continue until 2012/13. Females of both species and occasionally males are also radio tracked. Two other rare species with scant records in the Forest, Nathusius' pipistrelle and grey long-eared bat, will also be radio tracked if captured. Nathusius' pipistrelle is rare as a breeding species in the UK, although spring and autumn records suggest that it is more frequently recorded as a migrant visitor.

Bechstein's bats (like long-eared bats) have a quiet echolocation call, and as a canopy feeder they infrequently stray low enough to be within hearing range of a bat detector, and may be less likely than some species to pass within range of mist nets or a harp trap. An effective method recently devised for surveying Bechstein's bat is an 'acoustic lure', which plays ultrasonic, digitally constructed or recorded bat social calls of different species (Hill and Greenaway 2005, 2008). Bats are attracted to the calls and a proportion of these are captured in nearby nets or harp traps. If fitted with radio tags, bats can then be followed back to roost sites and information on the numbers of bats, bat foraging and commuting routes can also be obtained. All of this work is potentially disturbing and is managed to minimise disturbance to local communities of bats by avoiding areas close to potential roost sites and not returning to sites more than three times per year. A licence has been obtained from Natural England (the statutory nature conservation agency in England) to use the acoustic lure, to catch and to fit radio transmitters to bats.

Initial desktop research began with an evaluation of existing records, and a study of Ordnance Survey and Forestry Commission stock maps to evaluate the composition of tree species, woodland management, aspect and the location of waterbodies. Areas with the greatest potential to support maternity colonies of both species were then visited with a view to sampling with bat detectors and capture techniques. It was not possible to undertake a detailed evaluation of the areas owing to the sheer size of the Forest and limitations of the volunteer resource.

Two types of acoustic lure have been used to date, one developed by Sussex University ('Sussex Autobat') that simulated bat social calls played through an amplifier and speaker system ('Ultra Sound Advice', USA), the other using our own pre-recorded calls from a Pettersson D1000x bat detector linked to amplifier and speakers. Data on all species of bat captured are recorded including weight, forearm measurements and other measurements that can help identify cryptic species (for example tragus and thumb length in long-eared bats). Records of any marks on each bat are noted as is the sex and sexual status and general health of each animal. Bats can be aged by examination of the degree of ossification at the joints of the wing bones up until the autumn of their first year. Dropping (faecal) samples are taken from barbastelle bats and sent to Bristol University as part of a wider PhD project on the foraging ecology of the species.

Radio transmitters (tags, provided by Biotrack) are fixed between the scapulae of a bat with an adhesive (Ostomy adhesive solution, Salts Healthcare). These weigh less than 5% of a bats body weight (Aldridge and Brigham 1998). Heavily pregnant bats are not tagged. Because tags are light and small, and battery life is limited to 10–14 days. Signals rarely travel more than 500 m in dense woodland and frequently even less distance where the topography undulates. Bechstein's and barbastelle bats are ringed using 2.9 mm metal rings supplied from the Mammal Society. Sika radio tracking receivers with 3 element flexible Yagi antennae (Biotrack) are used to track bats on foot, whilst magmount omnidirectional antennae fitted to cars are often essential when tracking the fast moving barbastelle. During radio tracking, bat positions are fixed using either triangulation between pairs of surveyors or by closely following the bat (close approach method). Because GPS locations in woodland can be inaccurate, a known reference point is used for taking bearings. The tracking method is normally dictated by the resources available to us at the time, the topography, habitat and bat species.

Once bats have been located, evening emergence and dawn re-entry surveys are undertaken to monitor numbers of bats. As both species make frequent re-entry and re-emergences at dawn and dusk in midsummer, accurate counts are difficult and nightshot video with an infrared illuminator is sometimes used to gain a better estimate of numbers of bats. Each identified roost tree is monitored at dusk (and/or dawn) for at least the lifetime of the tag. Actual roost points on trees are often unclear, particularly where they are high in the canopy, and are often obscured by foliage on lower branches when return visits in the winter are necessary.

Between April 2006 and October 2007, over 40 people were involved in the project although most work has been performed by a core of 8–10 regular volunteers. During this time period 60 individuals of 10 species of bat have been captured. Table 6 shows the number and sex of each species captured during the period including 11 Bechstein's and seven barbastelle bats. Twenty tree roost sites of the two main target species have been located, consisting of 13 Bechstein's and seven barbastelle roosts (Figure 16). (A noctule roost was also located with 27 bats emerging from a well used tree hole in August 2007.) Of the Bechstein's roosts, seven were in oak, six in beech; of the barbastelle roosts four were in oak and three in beech

Figure 16
Map to show distribution of Bechstein's and barbastelle bat records, New Forest, 2006 and 2007.

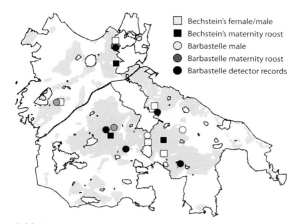

□ Bechstein's female/male
■ Bechstein's maternity roost
○ Barbastelle male
● Barbastelle maternity roost
● Barbastelle detector records

Table 6
Species of bat captured in the New Forest during April 2006–October 2007.

Species	Male	Female	Total
Bechstein's *Myotis bechsteinii*	5	6	11
Barbastelle *Barbastellus barbastella*	2	5	7
Brown long-eared *Plecotus auritus*	5	11	16
Daubenton's *Myotis daubentonii*	2	1	3
Natterer's* *Myotis nattereri*	2	3	5
Noctule *Nyctalus noctula*	1	2	3
Common and soprano pipistrelles *Pipistrellus pipistrellus/pygmaeus*	6	2	8
Serotine *Eptesicus serotinus*	1		1
Whiskered/Brandt's** *Myotis mystacinus/brandtii*	3	2	5
Totals	28	32	60

* 27 Natterer's bats were also ringed from Forestry Commission bat boxes at Castle Hill, Burley.
** Whiskered and Brandt's bats are cryptic species and identification can only be confirmed by DNA analysis. Some features are considered to be suggestive of species and these are used as a guide. During our investigations in the New Forest, the majority of bats encountered so far have shown features that most strongly suggest they were whiskered bats.

(Tables 7 and 8). All of the Bechstein's maternity roost sites were in cavities accessed by holes; one in a rot hole in an oak, the rest in woodpecker holes in oak and beech. Of the barbastelle maternity roosts four were crevices in beech or oak, two under flaking bark (oak) and one unknown. Barbastelle bats have not been recorded using woodpecker or rot holes during our studies so far.

Taken together with records of greater horseshoe, Nathusius' pipsistrelle and grey long-eared bat, the presence of 13/14 species of bat were confirmed in the New Forest during the period autumn 2005–October 2007. By the end of October 2007, three breeding colonies of Bechstein's bats had been located

(Anderwood, Fritham, and Matley Ridge near Denny) and two barbastelle colonies (Mark Ash and Red Shoot). The minimum distance between groups of Bechstein's maternity roost trees which we have recorded has been 5 km (average 7 km); because of the small range of this species, we consider each maternity roost and/or pregnant or lactating female we have captured between mid May and August to represent a separate colony. Barbastelles have a much larger range and such judgements are therefore more difficult to make. Two groups of trees were located that were used by barbastelle bats during the peak maternity periods, separated by a distance of 7 km. We found approximately 45 and 60 bats present at both sites

Table 7
Characteristics of roost sites in the New Forest used by more than five bats.

Observation dates while roost site occupied	Species	No of bats (range during period counted)	Tree species	Roost feature
4–6 June 2006	Bechstein's	1–6	Oak	Not seen (high in canopy)
6–10 August 2006	Bechstein's	3–30	Oak	Hole 3 m on north side
28 August 2006– 1 September 2006 (approx 30 bats also present 21 August 2007)	Barbastelle	7–30	Oak	Split 4.5 m on south side
28 August 2006– 1 September 2006	Barbastelle	7–15 7–12	Beech Oak	Split 3.5 m on north side Flaking bark 5 m on east side
29–30 April 2007	Bechstein's	40–41	Beech	Hole 20 m on west side
19–22 August 2007	Barbastelle	20–45	Oak	Split 7 m on underside of north-west lateral bough

Table 8
Number of bats radio-tracked and tagged, and the number of trees used as roost sites during radio-tracking periods.

Capture date	Species	Sex	Ring number	Tag number	Nights tracked/ located	Number of roost sites used in period
28 May 2006	Bechstein's	Male	n/a	173.285	3	3
3 June 2006	Bechstein's	Female	n/a	173.294	3	2
30 June 2006	Bechstein's	Female	n/a	Not tagged/pregnant	n/a	n/a
5 August 2006	Bechstein's Bechstein's	Male Female	n/a n/a	n/a 173.239	n/a 7	n/a 3
11 August 2006	Bechstein's	Male	n/a	n/a	n/a	n/a
27 August 2006	Barbastelle	Female	n/a	173.214	6	3
10 September 2006	Bechstein's Barbastelle	Male Male	n/a n/a	n/a 173.294	n/a bat lost	n/a
10 September 2006	Barbastelle	Male	n/a	n/a	n/a	n/a
10 March 2007	Barbastelle	Male	n/a	173.248	20	3
28 April 2007	Bechstein's Barbastelle	Female Female	4401 4402	173.775 173.309	4 8	3 1
29 April 2007	Bechstein's	Female	4403	173.737	4	2
14 July 2007	Bechstein's	Male	4404	173.774	4	1
19 August 2007	Barbastelle	Female	4405	173.751	4	2 min
22 August 2007	Barbastelle	Female	4406	173.752	n/a	n/a
23 August 2007	Bechstein's	Male	4407	173.970	7	2 min
12 October 2007	Bechstein's	Female	4408	173.799	9	3

Plate 1
Barbastelle early spring roost. Photo: C. Mainstone

Plate 2
Barbastelle maternity roost in beech tree. Photo: C. Mainstone

(Mark Ash and Red Shoot) on the same night in 2007. We have interpreted these to represent two separate colonies.

In addition to female summer roosts, male Bechstein's bats have been captured and tracked to roosts in three locations (Bramshaw, Shave Green and Pinnick Wood) together with a single female just north of Lyndhurst in October 2007. A male Bechstein's bat was captured at Shave Green in May 2008. Male barbastelles have been captured in a number of locations north and south of Lyndhurst and Brockenhurst (Denny Wood, Matley, Ivy Wood, Hollands Wood, Whitley Wood, Water Copse, Rhinefield), and detector surveys have recorded this species in all of the areas where they have been captured, in addition to Bramshaw. Some of these records include late autumn/early winter foraging and roost sites for both species. By the end of September 2008, surveys had been undertaken in approximately 30% of the area planned. Early in May 2009 we located a new barbastelle colony in Godshill Wood in the north-west of the county.

Although the survey is at an early stage, the indications are that both species are present, at least to some degree, throughout the New Forest woodland areas. There appear to be no shortage of natural tree roosting sites for bats in the Forest, however heavy grazing of the understorey, particularly in the A&O woodlands (see Chapter 13) may affect the Forest's ability to support as large a population of these species (and their moth prey) as it otherwise might. In this context, the mixed deciduous woodland areas with small pockets of conifer and unthinned plantation 'understorey' may be important foraging sites for bats roosting in adjacent stands.

Both species are certain to forage outside the wider National Park boundary as well as much of the private land within it; most of this has so far been inaccessible and may remain unsurveyed. We may only be able to extrapolate therefore from the locations and habitat types of these areas as to how they may function, but some areas of deciduous woodland where ponies are excluded may provide rich areas for bats. The barbastelle bat is likely to forage outside the protected areas of the Forest; bats roosting in Red Shoot Wood for example are likely to use the Avon Valley. Bats at Brockenhurst and areas to its east and west are likely to include some of the extensive areas of private land along the Beaulieu and Lymington rivers within their ranges. The relationship between the colony of barbastelle bats at Mottisfont, situated outside the Park and approximately 10 km to its north-eastern edge, and those in the New Forest, is unknown. As well as the private woodland blocks, mature garden trees as well as the extensive network of mature hedgerows and hedgerow trees are also likely to be used by both species. (A female Bechstein's bat we radio-tracked in 2007 moved regularly between Forest and farmland over hedgerows in Fritham village.) Hopefully over time relationships can be built with landowners and confidences gained to allow access to survey some of these areas.

The value of heathland, conifer forest and the edge habitats these create is unknown for both species. In April 2007 we radio-tracked two female Bechstein's bats (from a roost of 42), foraging along heathland/ conifer edge and within conifer woodland at Matley. The tree was exposed with no adjacent canopy cover and very scant understorey, although it was adjacent to denser woodland. It is unclear how representative the radio-tracked bats foraging behaviour was of the

Plate 3
Bechstein's bat main roost tree. Photo: Paul Hope

Plate 4
Bechstein's bat maternity roost. Photo: Paul Hope

group as a whole, however they continued to forage in both habitats almost exclusively during the tracking period.

All of the bats radio-tracked during the project have in fact foraged for periods in areas of conifer and conifer/mixed woodland. In some areas, roost trees appear to be protected by adjacent conifer stands, which may help to shelter mature trees and play a part in maintaining the appropriate microclimates. Coniferous trees (as well as some of the more recent unthinned oak plantations) could also be providing some degree of varied woodland structure, as well as shelter and habitat for invertebrates, particularly during winter. As Greenaway and Hill (2004) noted, Bechstein's can occur in young plantations including areas of conifer as long as roost sites are available (as they evidently are in the New Forest). Other researchers have also found Bechstein's roosting in or in close proximity to conifer woodland. For example two maternity roost trees (Bechstein's bat) were located in conifer woodland and a hedgerow boundary in Dorset; the bats used the conifer to commute between areas of broadleaf, where they appeared to forage (John Flanders, pers. comm.).

Challenges and opportunities for the future

The New Forest is indisputably a special place for a range of rare as well as common species of flora and fauna. Whether or not habitats are managed, they will change over time, reflecting an environment that is naturally in a constant state of flux. The need to accommodate the increasing pressures from recreational use (see Chapter 1) and a silvicultural output from the Forest are increasing.

A number of conservation objectives require management within the New Forest. Management in the A&O woodlands is kept to a minimum, but some management does occur, notably removal of non-native species such as rhododendron and pollarding of holly. Some of the holly management has been instigated to protect and enhance internationally important lichen communities (see Chapter 9), but pollarding around roosting sites and in key foraging areas is likely to have a negative affect on the microclimates of the habitats used by woodland bats, at least in the short term. Clearly, an understanding of the tolerances of all of the species likely to be affected and a management approach combining the needs of these is required.

An extensive programme of wetland and watercourse management is underway, much of it within mixed woodland blocks (see Chapter 17). Both of these programmes are vital to maintain the important floral and faunal communities of the Forest and will ultimately benefit woodland bats. There is however a danger that too much intensive felling and removal of vegetation along streamsides could again have at least a short term negative effect on bat species such as Bechstein's, and a longer term approach to management of areas (perhaps in rotation) would be advisable. Large areas of conifers have been removed from the Forest and a programme of further removal is planned, largely to recreate heaths and lawns on sites where these were formerly present. Again an understanding and appreciation of the role that some of these areas play for woodland bats should be incorporated in and inform any management planned over a period of time.

Management of the plantations in the Inclosures is ultimately for a timber crop, and methods and timing of extraction and thinning are largely influenced by economics. Some of the plantation oaks have a dense understorey that will provide foraging resources for bats where this may be depleted in adjacent areas such as the A&O woodlands. Again an appreciation of those areas utilised by some of the more important roosts (e.g. maternity sites) could play an important role in the management of such a large and complex area. A planned approach to the positive management of some of these young and semi-mature oak plantations could be adopted to encourage recruitment of new colonies of bats or extension of existing adjacent colony ranges over time. Similarly, management practices such as linking or maintaining links between colonies, between roosts and foraging sites and improving habitat where it has become or is becoming degraded, could also be integrated.

Raising awareness of the ecological needs of bats and gaining confidences with private landowners could help to achieve a positive gain for a wide range of species, not just bats. The incorporation of management for bats within existing incentive schemes is probably something that has not been fully capitalised upon, and could be an important tool in for the protection and enhancement of these habitats in the future. The role of habitats adjacent to but outside the Forest may become increasingly important in the longer term given some of the projections of the impacts of climate change, particularly on sea level rise and on the potential demise of tree species such as beech. Incentive schemes outside the National Park itself therefore should also be utilised to promote positive and informed land management for both species.

The New Forest is a unique and fascinating place with a complex suite of habitats. It faces increasing pressures both from the demands from the public for recreation and threats to some of its traditional rural communities from modern day economics. There are large gaps in our knowledge about the needs and tolerances of not only bats but a wide range of species. This lack of knowledge must be tackled and communications improved so that the most appropriate collaborative management decisions can be made to enable the biodiversity of the Forest and its surroundings to thrive. The Hampshire Bat Group will continue surveys over the coming years. The Group looks forward to the contribution it can make towards unravelling some of the mysteries of our rare bats.

Acknowledgements

Many people have helped with volunteer time, equipment and advice but a particular mention of thanks should go to the following: Paul Hope, Manny Hinge, Steve Trotter and Ian Barker (New Forest National Park), Tim Creed, Andy Page, Claire Gingell and Emma Rigglesworth (National Park Sustainability Fund), Andrew Bell and Katie Burrough (National Park mapping team), Richard Manley (New Forest Trust), Ecological Planning & Research (EPR Ltd.), David Hill (Sussex University), Bob Stebbings, Geoff Billington, Roy Champion, Brian Harrison, John Kaczanow, Nick Knight and Nicola Pyle.

References

Aldridge, H. and Brigham, R. (1998). Load carrying and manoeuvrability in an insectivorous bat: a test of the 5% "rule" of radio-telemetry. *Journal of Mammology* 69, 2, 379–382.

Arnold, H. (1993). *Atlas of mammals in Britain*. HMSO, London.

Billington, G. (2000). *Holnicote Estate, Horner Woods barbastelle bat radio tracking study*. Greena Ecological Consultancy, unpublished.

Entwistle, A. C., Harris, S., Hutson, A. M., Racey, P. A. and Walsh, A. (2001). *Habitat management for bats: a guide for land managers, land owners and their advisors*. JNCC, Peterborough.

Fitzsimons, P., Hill, D. and Greenaway, F. (2002). *Patterns of habitat use by female Bechstein's bats (*Myotis bechsteinii*) from a maternity colony in a British woodland*. School of Biological Sciences, University of Sussex.

Greenaway, F. and Hill, D. (2004). *Woodland management advice for Bechstein's bat and barbastelle bat*. English Nature Research Report no. 658. English Nature, Peterborough.

Greenaway, F. (2001). The barbastelle in Britain. *British Wildlife*, 12, 327–334.

Greenaway, F. (2004). *Advice for the management of flightlines and foraging habitats of the barbastelle bat* Barbastella barbastellus. English Nature Research Report no. 657. English Nature, Peterborough.

Harris, S., Morris, P., Wray, S. and Yalden, D. (1995). *A review of British mammals: population estimates and conservation status of British mammals other than cetaceans*. JNCC, Peterborough.

Hill, D. and Greenaway, F. (2005). Effectiveness of an acoustic lure for surveying bats in British woodlands. *Mammal Review* 35 (1), 116–122.

Hill, D. and Greenaway, F. (2006). *Putting Bechstein's on the map*. Report for the Mammals Trust, UK.

Hill, D. and Greenaway, F. (2008). Conservation of bats in British woodlands. *British Wildlife*, 19(3), 161–169.

IUCN (2001). *IUCN Red List Categories and Criteria: Version 3.1*. IUCN, Gland, Switzerland.

Kerth, G. and Konig, B. (1999). Fission, fusion and nonrandom associations in female Bechstein's bats (*Myotis bechsteinii*). *Behaviour*, 136, 1187–1202.

Kerth, G., Safi, K. and Konig, B. (2002). Mean colony relatedness is a poor predictor of colony structure and female philopatry in the communally breeding Bechstein's bat (*Myotis bechsteinii*). *Behavioral Ecology and Sociobiology*, 52, 203–210.

Kerth, G. and Morf, L. (2004). Behavioural and genetic data suggest that Bechstein's bats predominantly mate outside the breeding habitat. *Ethology*, 110, 987–999.

Kerth, G., Mayer, F. and König, B. (2000). Mitochondrial DNA (mtDNA) reveals that female Bechstein's bats live in closed societies. *Molecular Ecology*, 9, 793–800.

Kerth, G., Weissman, K. and Konig, B. (2001). Day roost selection in female Bechstein's bats (*Myotis bechsteinii*): a field experiment to determine the influence of roost temperature. *Oecologia*, 126, 1–9.

Kerth, G., Mayer, F. and Petit, E. (2002). Extreme sex-biased dispersal in the communally breed, non migratory Bechstein's bat (*Myotis bechsteinii*). *Molecular Ecology*, 11, 1491–1498.

Millais, J. G. (1904). *The mammals of Great Britain and Ireland.* Longmans, Green and Co., London.

Russo, D., Cistrone, l., Jones, G. and Massoleni, S. (2004). Roost selection by barbastelle bats (*Barbastella barbastellus* Chiroptera: Vespertilionidae) in beech woodlands of central Italy: consequences for conservation. *Biological Conservation*, 117, 73–81.

Russo, D., Cistrone, l. and Jones, G. (2005). Spatial and temporal patterns of roost use by tree dwelling barbastelle bats *(Barbastella barbastellus)*. *Ecography*, 28, 769–776.

Rydell, J., Natuschke, G., Theiler, A. and Zingg, P. (1996). Food habits of the barbastelle bat *Barbastella barbastellus. Ecography*, 19, 62–66.

Schofield, H. and Morris, C. (2000). *Ranging behaviour and habitat preferences of female Bechstein's bat, Myotis bechsteinii (Kuhl, 1818), in summer.* Vincent Wildlife Trust, Ledbury, Herefordshire.

Sierro, A. and Arlettaz, R. (1997). Barbastelle bats (*Barbastella* spp.) specialise in the predation of moths: implications for foraging tactics and conservation. *Acta Oecologica*, 18(2), 91–106.

Siemers, B. M. and Swift, S. M. (2006). Differences in sensory ecology contribute to the resource partitioning in the bats *Myotis bechsteinii* and *Myotis nattereri* (Chiroptera: Vespertilionidae). *Behavioral Ecology and Sociobiology*, 59, 373–380.

Stebbings, R. E. (1988). *The conservation of European bats.* Christopher Helm, London.

Tubbs, C. R. (2001). *The New Forest.* New Forest 9th Centenary Trust, Lyndhurst, Hampshire.

Vesey Fitzgerald, B. (1944) *The distribution of bats in Hampshire.* Reprinted from *Proceedings of the Hampshire Field Club and Archaeological Society* Vol XVI, Part 1.

Yalden, D. W. (1992). Changing distribution and status of small mammals in Britain. *Mammal Review,* 22, 97–106.

3 Reptiles and amphibians

Martin Noble

Introduction

Geographically, the New Forest is situated in one of the warmest parts of the United Kingdom. However, it has a very poor reptilian and amphibian fauna when compared with the rest of Europe. Even countries with a climate similar to that of the UK, such as The Netherlands, have more species. This of course is mainly due to the fact that the UK is an island, and the natural return of animals exterminated during the last Ice Age was prevented when the land bridge with Europe was finally flooded by rising sea levels, roughly 7,000 years ago. As well as being relatively warm, the New Forest has another advantage in that much of its vegetational structure is relatively stable. This

particularly suits the native herpetofauna, which does not cope well with dramatic changes in habitat. The Forest is also well protected by UK legislation, although local constraints on management do not always work in favour of the herp species.

This chapter provides an overview of the current status and trends of reptiles and amphibians in the New Forest. As well as containing 12 of the 13 native herp species (Table 9), there have been several introductions of European species to the New Forest in recent years, a few of which have become well established; these are also considered below.

Amphibians

Common frog

This species is widely distributed throughout the New Forest. It has been recorded as breeding in c. 70 ponds in the Forest and often spawns in garden ponds. Males and females gather together in large numbers in breeding ponds in February or March. One or two of the ponds have large aggregations in excess of 2,000 individuals but usually numbers are much lower. Spawning ponds are often ephemeral and dry up during summer. However the water in these ponds heats up more quickly than the deeper, more permanent ponds, and development of the tadpoles is much faster. In addition ponds that dry up seasonally generally have fewer predators, such as water beetle and dragonfly larvae, and the tadpole metamorphosis success rate is therefore higher. A wide range of pond pH of 4.5–8.5 has been recorded.

Pool frog

The pool frog was not recognised as a native species in the UK until 2000. Sadly the one and only native population, in Norfolk, became extinct at the same time. Since then English Nature (now Natural England) have established a reintroduction programme at the last known UK site, using stock from Scandinavia. In the meantime, unofficial introductions have been occurring for many years elsewhere in England, and the species is fast becoming established in the UK. Some of these introductions have resulted in breeding success in the New Forest, where it coexists with the closely related edible frog.

Common toad

The common toad is locally common in the New Forest, recorded as breeding in c.50 ponds. It is rather more particular about the water quality of its breeding ponds, where a pH range of 5.5–8.0 has been recorded. The tendency of toads to return to breed in the pond where they were born themselves results in some very large mating aggregations. Over 1,000

Table 9
Reptiles and amphibians recorded in the New Forest.

Amphibians

Native species
Common frog *Rana temporaria*
Pool frog *Pelophylax lessonae*
Common toad *Bufo bufo*
Natterjack toad *Epidalea calamita***
Smooth newt *Lissotriton vulgaris*
Palmate newt *Lissotriton helveticus*
Great crested newt *Triturus cristatus*

Non-native species
Marsh frog *Pelophylax ridibunda*
Edible frog *Pelophylax esculenta*
American bull frog *Lithobates catesbeianus***
European tree frog *Hyla arborea***

** species thought now to be extinct in the New Forest

Reptiles

Native species
Slow worm *Anguis fragilis*
Common lizard *Zootoca vivipara*
Sand lizard *Lacerta agilis*
Adder *Vipera berus*
Grass snake *Natrix natrix*
Smooth snake *Coronella austriaca*

Non-native species
European wall lizard *Podarcis muralis*
Red-eared slider *Trachemys scripta*

The following non-native species have been recorded in the UK but not so far recorded in the New Forest

Amphibians

Yellow-bellied toad *Bombina variegata*
European midwife toad *Alytes obstetricans*
Alpine newt *Mesotriton alpestris*

Reptiles

European green lizard *Lacerta bilineata*
Aesculapian snake *Zamenis longissima*

individuals have been recorded in one pond, most of which were males. In common with many other parts of the UK, numbers have fallen since 1990 for reasons as yet unknown, although research into the possibility of a chytrid fungus being a cause is ongoing.

Natterjack toad

A few early records exist of this species, from Beaulieu and Holmsley in 1946 (B.R.C.) and c.1980 near Burley (D. Thomson, pers. comm.). However, there have been no recent records and the species is now believed to be extinct in the New Forest. There is good terrestrial habitat with sandy substrate and short grazed grass in many places in the Forest, but sadly most ponds on sandy habitat are very acidic and are consequently unsuitable for natterjack breeding. Colonies have been successfully re-established in nearby parts of Dorset, so there may be some prospect of a reintroduction in the New Forest.

Smooth newt

The smooth newt is not common in the New Forest. It has been recorded from only 24 of 144 ponds surveyed. It is far more common in gardens on the more fertile soils around the perimeter of the Forest. Most of the records are from the south-west corner of the Forest where the Headon Clay beds lie close to the surface. A water pH range of 5.6–8.5 has been recorded in inhabited ponds.

Palmate newt

This is by far the most common newt in the New Forest and it is also the smallest of the three native species. It can tolerate a wide range of water quality and has been found in ponds ranging between pH 4.5 and 8.0. Often it is the only amphibian found in valley mire ponds. Some ponds on the more fertile soils may contain many hundreds of individuals.

Great crested newt

The great crested newt is the largest and rarest of the three native species of newt. It has been recorded from 17 ponds in the New Forest plus two on private land. Most of the breeding ponds are on the Headon Clay beds, especially in old marl pits, where a water pH range of 5.6–8.5 has been recorded. The largest population recorded was c.100 individuals.

Marsh and edible frogs

These frogs are natives of Europe but not of the UK. The edible frog is a hybrid between the native pool frog and the marsh frog. Both have been introduced, sometimes in large numbers, to various parts of England over many years and they are now well established, especially in parts of the south-east. There are small populations of each in various ponds in the New Forest. In Western Europe the edible frog tends to coexist with the pool frog, and there is some suggestion that the same scenario is developing in the New Forest.

European tree frog

The tree frog is another introduced species, although there have been claims that it may be native to the New Forest. Anecdotal records suggest that it was brought from somewhere in Europe to a property on the edge of Beaulieu in the early part of the last century, but the first written record is from a Forest pond near Beaulieu in 1962. Between 1962 and 1986 it occurred regularly in or near this pond, but since then there have been no sightings there. However between 1986 and 1993 there were a number of confirmed sightings in various other parts of the Forest. As its name suggests, the species is largely arboreal, favouring thorny shrubs, presumably for protection from predators. The males have a very loud call and gather around the breeding ponds at night during May and June. In Europe it is a great traveller, and populations tend to move frequently from pond to pond. It now appears to be extinct in the New Forest.

American bull frog

The bull frog was introduced in large numbers, mainly as tadpoles, into the pet trade during the 1980s. Unfortunately, while attractive as tadpoles, they are more of a problem when fully grown adults, and many were simply released once they matured. There were a number of reports from garden ponds in the Lymington area during the 1990s, although no evidence of breeding there. However the species appears to have bred successfully on one occasion in a fish hatchery near Sway. Fortunately the owners of the property soon recognised the problem and dealt with it in a rather extreme but effective manner, by draining the breeding pond and later by shooting the returning adults. Importation to the UK is now banned except under licence but individuals may still survive, although there has been no evidence of breeding in recent years. They are large and effective predators and can pose a serious problem for native wildlife. There have been very few reports from the New Forest proper, but one was heard calling from Setley Pond in 1998.

Pond surveys

Between 1986 and 1990, I surveyed some 144 ponds for the presence or absence of amphibians. Measurements of the pH of the water in some of the ponds were taken at the same time. Figure 17 shows the number of ponds occupied by each of the species identified.

Figure 17
Amphibians recorded in a survey of 144 ponds in the New Forest in the years 1986–1990.

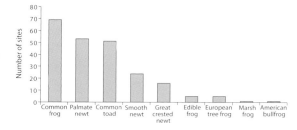

Reptiles

Slow worm

The slow worm is probably the most common reptile in the UK. Recent clearance work involving reptiles on building development sites indicates that even quite small suburban gardens can contain as many as 50 individuals. It is also common in the New Forest, although probably at relatively low densities owing to the poor quality of the soils.

Common lizard

This species is the most frequently seen reptile in the New Forest, although its elusive nature makes it difficult to spot. It is easiest to see in the spring when the males spend more time basking in the sun. It is most frequently found on heathland or woodland margins and is a swift coloniser of clear-fell woodland sites. Females retain their fertilised eggs within the body until they are ready to hatch, which insulates them from many of the adverse environmental factors that affect egg-laying species.

Sand lizard

The sand lizard was extinct over most of its natural range in the UK, including the New Forest, by c.1970. It survived only in parts of Dorset, Surrey and coastal Lancashire. Inappropriate habitat management, principally large-scale heather burning, has been identified as the main cause of its demise in the New Forest. Other factors include afforestation of its heathland habitat and loss of open sand needed for egg-laying. In some parts of the Forest these adverse factors have been eliminated, and a captive breeding programme funded by Natural England and administered by the Herpetological Conservation Trust has now enabled it to be reintroduced to most of its former range. Lizards are bred in captivity and 950 young animals have been released at six selected sites in the south-west of the Forest. These emerging populations are closely monitored with regular transects being walked at each site at three key times of the year. The continued survival of the species has been boosted by strong legal protection and extensive habitat management.

European wall lizard

This species is very common throughout mainland Europe where, as its name implies, it is often associated with man-made structures. More close to home it is native to Jersey and Guernsey in the Channel Islands, and there is a population at Ventnor on the Isle of Wight where written records go back as far as 1841. Colonies elsewhere appear to be of more recent origin, for example Isle of Portland, first recorded in 1986; and Canford Cliffs, Poole, first recorded in 1992. It is now widespread along the Dorset coastline between Southbourne and Portland, with many other smaller colonies scattered throughout England and Wales. Its presence in the New Forest is confined to several gardens, but with no indication so far of colonisation of the surrounding habitat.

European green lizard

This species is native to mainland Europe and Jersey and many attempts have been made over the years to introduce it to England. Most of these have failed, but an attempt at an introduction onto the cliffs at Bournemouth appears to have been more successful. The first recorded breeding there was in 1998. It is an impressive-looking lizard, although surprisingly elusive for such a large animal. So far there have been no records from the New Forest.

Red-eared slider

The red-eared slider, sometimes called the red-eared terrapin, is a North American species that was introduced to the UK via the pet trade around the time of the childrens' craze of *Mutant Ninja Turtles* on television. Most imports were of hatchlings that often quickly outgrew their accommodation and were released by their owners into the countryside. Importation is now controlled, but many already exist in the wild in the UK. There have been no reported cases of successful breeding in the wild but the species is regarded by many as an unwanted predator of native wildlife, especially aquatic larvae. It has been recorded from most of the larger ponds in the New Forest.

Adder

The adder is the only venomous snake in the UK and is locally common in the New Forest. Its bite, although painful and potentially fatal, usually responds well to modern treatments, provided that medical attention is sought at the earliest opportunity. Local hospitals claim not to keep records of people bitten by snakes but telephone discussions I had a few years ago with their registrars suggested that fewer than 50 people were admitted with adder bites in any one year. None of these was reported to have died. However, dogs are more frequently bitten and there are a number of fatalities each year, despite warnings from the Forestry Commission about keeping dogs on leads. The adder's habitual use of traditional hibernating sites makes it relatively easy to locate in the spring. It also exhibits regular seasonal movements between winter and summer areas, which assist monitoring (Dr D. Bull, pers. comm.).

Grass snake

The grass snake is the largest British snake, females often growing up to 1 m in length. It is common throughout the New Forest but is rather elusive and well camouflaged. It is generally associated with aquatic habitats where its prey, predominantly amphibians, can be found. Its habit of seeking out warm places such as compost heaps in which to lay its eggs means that the females are often found in gardens in the summer, where they are often mistaken for adders. They are great travellers and are known to travel considerable distances annually between feeding, egg-laying and hibernating areas.

Smooth snake

This species is widely distributed throughout dry heathland habitats in the New Forest, although nowhere is it very common. It does not compete well with other predators in woodland edge habitats where small mammals are relatively common, but it finds less competition in the extensive dry heathlands where the common lizard is the main vertebrate source of food. The Herpetological Conservation Trust are undertaking a Forest-wide survey of the species, as yet unpublished, which is producing some very useful information on distribution and population size.

New Forest habitats for reptiles and amphibians

Introduction
It is believed by many that the vegetation structure of the UK in Mesolithic times, largely unaltered by humans and extensively grazed by large herbivores, would probably have resembled parts of the present-day New Forest with its patchwork mosaic of woodland, scrub, heathland, grasslands and valley mires. The open structure produced by grazing provides a superb range of habitats for most reptile and amphibian species. In Open Forest areas the vegetation is largely managed by the grazing animals, with minimum need for human interference. However, human intervention still plays a part, for example:

- Most of the amphibian breeding ponds are the result of past human activity, mainly resulting from extraction of minerals such as gravel and marl.
- The present area of heathland is heavily managed by cutting and burning to maintain its existing form.
- Formation of emergent woodland is discouraged by regular felling of pioneer tree species.
- In the Inclosures, management for commercial tree growing has a major impact on the natural vegetation.

However, most of these activities have a beneficial or neutral effect on our native reptiles and amphibians, with the exception of heathland management, which can be very damaging if carried out to excess.

Heathland
Arguably heathland is the most important single habitat, especially for the rare reptiles. It suffers considerable extremes of weather conditions but this is not a problem for reptiles, which can hibernate during the cold periods in winter and take advantage of the extreme heat for developing their embryos. Botanically it has low species diversity but the open structure of the dwarf shrub vegetation provides ideal reptile habitat. On the other hand, poor quality soils result in low productivity of prey, except in late summer when the heather comes into flower. Again this is not necessarily a problem for reptiles, which concentrate their feeding to this time of year.

In the New Forest the two rarest reptiles are dependent on areas of dry heathland. Management techniques of cutting and burning this habitat are controversial and can adversely affect reptile populations. Insensitive burning can be damaging and has already arguably caused the extinction of the sand lizard. However, recent interpretation of the European Habitat Regulations by Natural England suggests that future management of the habitats of the two rare reptiles will need to be much more focused in the New Forest than at present.

Wetlands
In general, the extensive valley mires are too acid for amphibian breeding. Few ponds occur naturally since the extinction of the beaver several hundred years ago; however, the ponds created in the more recent past by the digging of marl or gravel have assumed greater importance for amphibian breeding. Ponds on the Open Forest are well maintained by regular grazing, avoiding the need for much human interference (see also Chapter 16). However, some of the marl pits have become overgrown in recent years and an ongoing programme of scrub and tree clearance has been instigated by the Forestry Commission in association with Natural England and the Hampshire Wildlife Trust. A few new ponds have been created in suitable areas, mainly to benefit the populations of great crested newts. The day-to-day management of the Forest is carried out by the Forestry Commission with advice and support from Natural England and the New Forest Verderers.

Conclusions

The New Forest is one of the most important areas for reptiles and amphibians in the UK, with all except one of the native species present in good numbers. The mosaic of different habitats provides a wide variety of opportunities for both reptiles and amphibians. However, over management of habitats for other species groups can and does impact adversely on reptile population size and may be in breach of the European Habitat Regulations. Heathland management programmes in particular need refining to ensure minimum damage to habitat structure and to minimise the killing of reptiles. Continued grazing by large herbivores is, however, recognised as an essential element of the management programmes for all habitats. The proposed reintroduction of the beaver to England will hopefully in the future provide a wealth of new ponds suitable for amphibian breeding sites.

4 Dragonflies and damselflies

David J. Thompson and Phillip C. Watts

In this chapter we discuss the odonate (dragonfly and damselfly) diversity of the New Forest from a UK perspective, specifically addressing the issue of why there are more species than might be expected given the area and latitude of the National Park. Second, we consider those species resident in the New Forest that are of conservation interest nationally. Finally, we examine in detail the jewel in the crown of the New Forest's odonates, southern damselfy *Coenagrion mercuriale*, which is rare, threatened and protected throughout Europe, and for which the New Forest is an internationally important area.

The New Forest as an area for odonate diversity

The New Forest is a hotspot of biodiversity for dragonflies and damselflies, with 31 of the UK's 45 resident species breeding there. These species are listed in Table 10, together with a broad guide to their habitat and their conservation status within the UK and locally. The Odonata is essentially a tropical group of insects so it is not surprising that the numbers of species found in the UK decreases as latitude increases. Figure 18 shows the numbers of species of odonates recorded on the British Dragonfly Society's database per 10 km square. The most diverse 10-km squares, those that contain between 25 and 33 species, are largely found in southern England and include the whole of the New Forest. However, the diversity observed in the New Forest is not solely a function of latitude, but is also determined by the diversity of freshwater habitats found within the New Forest National Park.

During the Victorian heydays of insect collecting the New Forest was largely famed, with respect to

Table 10
The breeding dragonflies and damselflies of the New Forest together with their broad habitat type and their current UK IUCN threat category, after Daguet *et al.* (2007) and an assessment of their national and local status after Taverner *et al.* (2004)

Family	Species	Habitat	2007 IUCN threat category	2004 status
Calopterygidae	Banded demoiselle *Calopteryx splendens*	Stream		
	Beautiful demoiselle *Calopteryx virgo*	Stream/river		
Lestidae	Emerald damselfly *Lestes sponsa*	Pond		
Platycnemidae	White-legged damselfly *Platycnemis pennipes*	River		CR
Coenagrionidae	Azure damselfly *Coenagrion puella*	Pond		
	Variable damselfly *Coenagrion pulchellum*	Pond	NT	NS, CR
	Southern damselfly *Coenagrion mercuriale*	Stream/valley mire	EN	IR, CS
	Common blue damselfly *Enallagma cyathigerum*	Pond		
	Blue-tailed damselfly *Ischnura elegans*	Pond		
	Scarce blue-tailed damselfly *Ischnura pumilio*	Stream/valley mire	NT	NS, CS
	Large red damselfly *Pyrrhosoma nymphula*	Pond		
	Red-eyed damselfly *Erythromma najas*	Pond		
	Small red-eyed damselfly *Erythromma viridulum*	Pond		
	Small red damselfly *Ceriagrion tenellum*	Valley mire		NS
Aeshnidae	Emperor dragonfly *Anax imperator*	Pond		
	Common hawker *Aeshna juncea*	Pond		
	Southern hawker *Aeshna cyanea*	Pond		
	Brown hawker *Aeshna grandis*	Pond		
	Migrant hawker *Aeshna mixta*	Pond		
	Hairy dragonfly *Brachytron pratense*	Pond		NS, CS
Cordulidae	Downy emerald *Cordulia aenea*	Pond		NS
Gomphidae	Club-tailed dragonfly *Gomphus vulgatissimus*	River	NT	NS County extinct?
Cordulegasteridae	Golden-ringed dragonfly *Cordulegaster boltonii*	Stream		
Libellulidae	Four-spotted chaser *Libellula quadrimaculata*	Pond		
	Broad-bodied chaser *Libellula depressa*	Pond		
	Scarce chaser *Libellula fulva*	River	NT	NR, CR
	Keeled skimmer *Orthetrum coerulescens*	Valley mire		
	Black-tailed skimmer *Orthetrum cancellatum*	Pond		
	Common darter *Sympetrum striolatum*	Pond		
	Ruddy darter *Sympetrum sanguineum*	Pond		
	Black darter *Sympetrum danae*	Pond		

2007 IUCN threat category: EN=endangered, NT=near threatened,
2004 status: NR=nationally rare, NS=nationally scarce, CR=county rare, CS=county scarce and IR=internationally rare; blank indicates 'least concern' (2007) or 'not listed' (2004).

aquatic insects, for species occupying running water. In the 1920s and 1930s manual drainage schemes and in the 1950s and 1960s mechanical drainage schemes changed the character of many New Forest streams for the worse (see also Chapter 15). The canalisation of streams and the formation of levees were detrimental to several odonate species, most notably club-tailed dragonfly *Gomphus vulgatissimus* and white-legged damselfly *Platycnemis pennipes*.

The New Forest also contains a selection of other good odonate habitats. The Forest never contained natural large ponds or lakes. Three of the most notable large water bodies are all artificial. Eyeworth Pond was constructed in the early part of the 18th century to provide a head of water for a gunpowder mill (see Chapter 15). Hatchet Pond, probably the best known of the Forest's large ponds, was constructed at the end of the 18th century by building a causeway to dam Hatchet Stream, which runs off Beaulieu Heath. The original aim was to flood a series of gravel and marl pits (see below) and provide another hammer mill. Sowley Pond began life as a 14th century monastic fish pond. By the 18th century it, too, served as a hammer pond for an ironworks. Sowley Pond occurs on a

private estate and even the eminent entomologist Col. F.C. Fraser feared being 'pulled over as a trespasser' if he ventured too close (cited in Taverner *et al.* 2004). Each of these ponds contributes to the odonate diversity of the Forest. Eyeworth and Sowley are to a large extent wooded (as is Hatchet to a lesser extent), and all three hold good populations of downy emerald *Cordulia aenea*. In addition Eyeworth holds the Forest's largest population of red-eyed damselfly *Erythromma najas*, while Sowley is the only known site in the Forest for the nationally declining variable damselfly *Coenagrion pulchellum*; it also contains the scarce but increasing hairy dragonfly *Brachytron pratense*.

There are many collections of marl pits scattered around the Forest. A loamy clay was extracted from these pits, but the practice effectively ceased at the beginning of the 20th century and the pits, once excellent habitat for odonates, generally became covered by scrub unless actively managed. During World War II more small ponds were created by German bombers depositing unused bombs prior to leaving England. Their fate mirrors that of the marl pits; they are extant if managed. A further source of small ponds appeared in the 1960s when 'flight' ponds

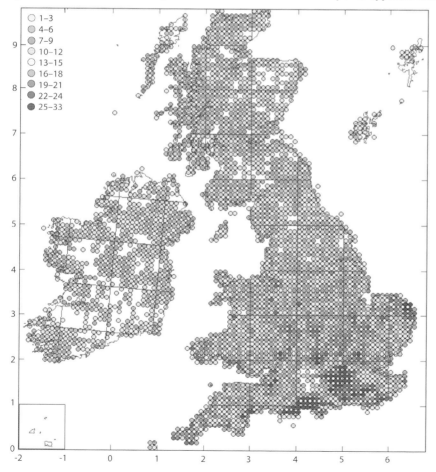

Figure 18
The diversity of odonate species in the British Isles by 10-km square (from the British Dragonfly Society database, with permission).

Legend:
○ 1–3
◐ 4–6
◐ 7–9
○ 10–12
○ 13–15
◐ 16–18
◐ 19–21
◐ 22–24
● 25–33

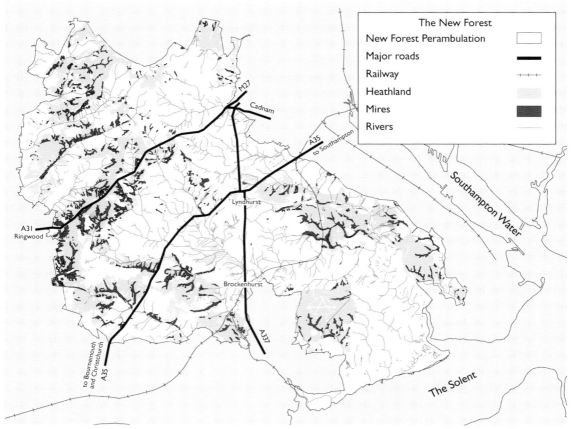

Figure 19
The distribution of heathland, valley mires and major streams within the New Forest. From Taverner *et al.* (2004).

were dug, usually at the head of valley mires, in order to attract wildfowl. Some of these proved to be excellent ponds for odonates. Finally, gravel extraction for building work around the periphery of the Forest has left a large number of gravel pits, many of which have become excellent wildlife habitat. Some of these lakes provide a source of dragonflies that would otherwise be rare in the Forest (Taverner *et al.* 2004), notably brown hawker *Aeshna grandis* and migrant hawker *A. mixta*.

Since the onset of Inclosures in the Forest in 1851, odonate habitats have been in something of a state of flux. The one constant feature of the New Forest's odonate habitats has been the valley mires. Figure 19 shows the distribution of streams and valley mire habitat. It is within these mires that the species of highest conservation value are to be found, and are what really separates the New Forest from the rest of southern Britain.

Odonates of national conservation interest

Taverner *et al.* (2004) quote Fraser in stating (of club-tailed dragonfly *Gomphus vulgatissimus*) *'its true home is in the New Forest where, in the course of a morning's walk, more specimens may be seen than the total records for the whole of the other localities'*, meaning the rest of the UK. As if to demonstrate that fact, he took 120 specimens himself in 1935! The last substantial records came in 1959, when 38 exuviae were found upstream of Puttles Bridge. It is considered extinct in the Forest at present, although there are three records that date back to as recently as 1990–1996 (Figure 20). The canalisation and levees referred to above gave rise to scrub along the most appropriate streams for this species and rendered them unsuitable. The same is also true for another riverine/stream species, white-legged damselfly, which Fraser also described as a common insect in the Forest, particularly on the Ober Water and parts of the Avon Water. This species is still hanging on at one or two locations on the Ober Water.

Scarce chaser *Libellula fulva* is essentially a species of river floodplains, water meadows and, increasingly frequently, gravel pits. It is not mentioned at all by Fraser (1950), but there have been more records in the New Forest in recent years (Figure 21). Unlike club-tailed dragonfly, which is declining nationally, scarce chaser is increasing and the extensive gravel pits referred to above have probably contributed to the number of sightings within the Forest. The stronghold for scarce chaser in the region is the Moors River, which is just outside the National Park to the west.

Variable damselfly is a nationally scarce species and is declining. Its UK distribution (Figure 22) is patchy, scattered over many parts of England and Wales, and extending into Scotland (Brooks and Lewington 2002). Often colonies are restricted to small areas that seem outwardly no different to the surrounding countryside. Water quality is thought to be a determining factor in their long term persistence. Goodyear (1989) found variable damselfly on Sowley Pond and this remains the only Forest record, though there are occasional records from sites bordering the Forest. Although there has been speculation that its decline is the result of hybridisation with azure damselfly *C. puella*, this is considered highly unlikely (Lowe *et al.* 2008).

Scarce blue-tailed damselfly *Ischnura pumilio* occurs in shallow water with a low flow-rate, at a variety of natural and man-made sites. It is an enigmatic damselfly. Fraser (1941) commented: *'I do not know of any other British dragonfly which has offered so much difficulty in identification or over which so many errors have been made'*. At the end of the 19th century, it was considered by Lucas (1900) to be almost extinct in Britain. However, records suggest that historically it was more widespread than records account for, owing

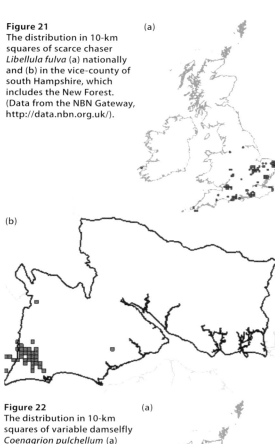

Figure 21
The distribution in 10-km squares of scarce chaser *Libellula fulva* (a) nationally and (b) in the vice-county of south Hampshire, which includes the New Forest. (Data from the NBN Gateway, http://data.nbn.org.uk/).

Figure 20
The distribution in 10-km squares of club-tailed dragonfly *Gomphus vulgatissimus* (a) nationally and (b) in the vice-county of south Hampshire, which includes the New Forest. (Data from the NBN Gateway, http://data.nbn.org.uk/).

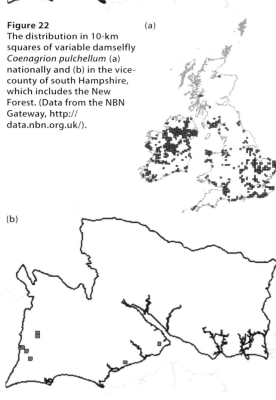

Figure 22
The distribution in 10-km squares of variable damselfly *Coenagrion pulchellum* (a) nationally and (b) in the vice-county of south Hampshire, which includes the New Forest. (Data from the NBN Gateway, http://data.nbn.org.uk/).

to the small-scale and transient nature of its preferred habitat (Figure 23).

Fox and Cham (1994) concluded that the important habitat features for scarce blue-tailed damselfly in the UK are low water velocity, a limited amount of emergent vegetation for oviposition without the water becoming 'choked' with plants, and a varying but considerable degree of habitat disturbance. In fact it seems this species responds exceptionally well to disturbance, particularly that caused by human activity. Numerous colonies have been recorded in areas of mineral extraction, where shallow springs and pools are formed with little vegetation cover, but conditions can be highly unstable (Fox and Cham 1994). In these artificially created sites, colonies rarely persist for more than a few years as vegetation soon encroaches, particularly where water flow is low. However, where there is a continual supply of water and a degree of openness is maintained, persistence is increased (Fox and Cham 1994). The openness is maintained in the Forest by grazing by ponies, deer and cattle. What some see as overgrazing in the Forest, and therefore a bad thing, is advantageous to those species whose abundance depends on the prevalence of early successional habitat. Scarce blue-tailed damselfly is one such species.

Small red damselfly *Ceriagrion tenellum* is the third damselfly species, along with scarce blue-tailed and

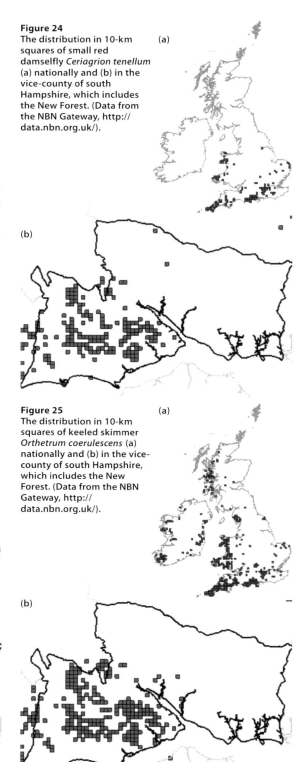

Figure 24
The distribution in 10-km squares of small red damselfly *Ceriagrion tenellum* (a) nationally and (b) in the vice-county of south Hampshire, which includes the New Forest. (Data from the NBN Gateway, http://data.nbn.org.uk/).

Figure 23
The distribution in 10-km squares of scarce blue-tailed damselfly *Ischnura pumilio* (a) nationally and (b) in the vice-county of south Hampshire, which includes the New Forest. (Data from the NBN Gateway, http://data.nbn.org.uk/).

Figure 25
The distribution in 10-km squares of keeled skimmer *Orthetrum coerulescens* (a) nationally and (b) in the vice-county of south Hampshire, which includes the New Forest. (Data from the NBN Gateway, http://data.nbn.org.uk/).

southern damselflies, that is found in the Forest's valley mires. Its distribution in the UK (Figure 24) indicates that it is nationally threatened, and its distribution within the Forest follows closely that of the valley mires (Figure 19). Like southern and scarce blue-tailed damselflies, it is essentially a Mediterranean species, which is on the edge of its range in the UK. Unlike the other two its larvae are often found among *Sphagnum* mats, so that it can emerge from areas without standing water.

Keeled skimmer *Orthetrum coerulescens* is the dragonfly most closely associated with the valley mires and found with the three damselflies described above (Figure 25). It is locally common in the Forest and forms an important food source for one of the Forest's specialist birds of prey, the hobby (see Chapter 1).

The most important odonate species in the New Forest from a national and international perspective is southern damselfly. This species has been the subject of intensive research in the past 10 years, some of which is summarised in the next section.

Southern damselfly

This section is concerned with the population structure of southern damselfly in its UK stronghold, the New Forest. This species has a somewhat fragmented population structure throughout its European range and this is even more apparent at its range margin in the UK. Some preliminary results from a multi-site mark–release–recapture (MRR) project are discussed together with genotype data at 14 genetic markers (microsatellite loci). Together, the results give an indication of the likely structure of the New Forest populations both from short-term (ecological) and historical (genetic) perspectives. They also point the way towards resolving potential conservation problems in the medium to long term.

Southern damselfly is one of Europe's highest-profile damselfly species from a conservation perspective. It is restricted at both global and national scales. It is mainly limited to the south and west of Europe and has populations of unknown status in northern Africa. Populations in Italy and northern Africa consist of different subspecies (*Coenagrion mercuriale castellani* and *C. m. hermeticum*, respectively) to those found in the rest of Europe (Askew 1988). Southern damselfly is protected within Europe as a whole and several European countries have taken complementary legislative measures for protection at a national or regional level. The UK distribution of southern damselfly is shown in Figure 26. There are population strongholds in the New Forest, the Test and Itchen Valleys, the heathlands of Dorset and the Preseli hills of Pembrokeshire, with isolated populations in Anglesey, the Gower, Oxfordshire, the east Devon pebble beds and Dartmoor. The species has suffered a 30% decline in UK distribution since 1960 (Thompson *et al.* 2003). It has been lost from Cornwall, some Devon and Dorset sites and from St. David's peninsula in Pembrokeshire. Even within the New Forest it has

disappeared from some sites (Blackwell Common, Rowbarrow Pond, Applemore Stream, the Forest's most easterly sites) since the last exhaustive survey (Stevens and Thurner 1999).

Estimates of population size

Southern damselfly on Beaulieu Heath inhabits a network of small flushes, runnels and streams that may be subdivided into seven central areas and four peripheral sites (Figure 27). A mark–release–recapture (MRR) programme was undertaken on Beaulieu Heath in 2002. It operated over five weeks during the peak of the flight season and employed 16 field assistants. It was the largest odonate MMR study ever attempted. As well as marking animals by writing numbers on the wing at each capture and subsequent recapture, the

Figure 26
The distribution in 10-km squares of southern damselfly *Coenagrion mercuriale* (a) nationally and (b) in the vice-county of south Hampshire, which includes the New Forest. Note that *C. mercuriale* also occurs in the water meadows surrounding the Rivers Test and Itchen, its only riverine UK sites. The different shades of the symbols represent different centres of population and are retained in later analysis (see Figure 30). (Data for (b) from the NBN Gateway, http://data.nbn.org.uk/).

(a)

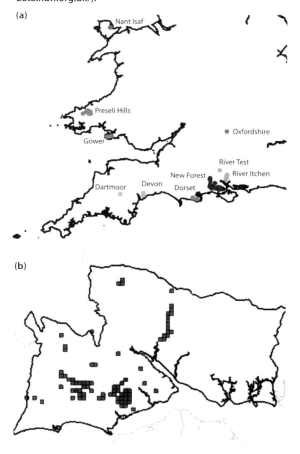

(b)

exact location of each animal was recorded using a Global Positioning System (GPS) calibrated to the UK Ordnance Survey. The estimates of daily population size (±SE) at Beaulieu Heath are shown in Figure 28. The numbers of males reached a maximum of some 5,000–6,000 individuals per day (during late June). Using a mean mature adult lifespan of 5.93 days provided an estimate of the total number of individuals on Beaulieu Heath during the summer of 2002 of 39,913. This calculation is based on the 10,259 (4,158) individuals actually marked (and recaptured) during the study. The relative population sizes at each Beaulieu Heath sub-site (Figure 27) were estimated as the proportion of marked animals at each site. The smallest populations were at the peripheral sites Bagshot Moor, Greenmoor and Hatchet Stream.

Figure 27
Location and movement of southern damselfly *Coenagrion mercuriale* between subsites on Beaulieu Heath, New Forest. The diameter of the circles represents the estimated population sizes of the sites. The arrows indicate the direction and the number of individuals that moved.

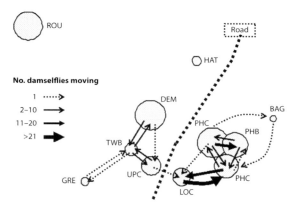

Figure 28
Daily estimates (± standard errors) of male population size of southern damselfly *Coenagrion mercuriale* on Beaulieu Heath, New Forest, southern England. Estimates were made by using a full Jolly–Seber model. Open circles and solid line are estimated data extrapolated from the daily estimates.

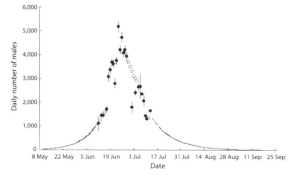

These data suggest that the Beaulieu Heath metapopulation is relatively healthy. It is likely that habitat loss/degradation poses a more immediate threat to the persistence of this species at Beaulieu Heath. These data on Beaulieu Heath are the only quantitative estimates of the abundance of southern damselfly anywhere in the UK (or indeed the rest of its European range). There is a clear need for future work to correlate these estimates of population size with standardised transect counts so that the population demography of this species may be monitored with some quantitative meaning.

Pattern of movement

In the MRR study we were looking primarily at the dispersal potential of southern damselfly in heathland. The overall pattern of movement between the sub-sites on Beaulieu Heath (Figure 27) resulted in a limited interchange among most pairs of populations, except among the three Peaked Hill sites and Lower Crockford. Interchange was limited to neighbouring areas in almost all cases. The large population at Round Hill (NW of Beaulieu Heath) and the next most northerly population at Hatchet Stream proved to be isolated, at least during the present study. The central sites on Beaulieu Heath (Figure 27) that did not prevent movement. This finding was in agreement with Purse *et al.* (2003) who also recorded movement across the road. However, dispersal was limited to a single individual and only in the direction indicated. Single damselflies were observed moving in and out of the small, isolated populations at Greenmoor and Bagshot Moor.

Figure 29 shows net lifetime movement (defined as the distance between first and last sighting) of mature adult (both sexes) of southern damselfly on Beaulieu Heath in the New Forest. Seventy per cent of mature adults moved less than 50 m in their mature adult lifetimes and 85 % moved less than 100 m. However, five individuals (0.12 %) moved more than 1 km, with 1.25 km the greatest distance moved in this study. In a parallel study in the more linear habitat of water meadow ditch systems the pattern was generally similar, with the longest recorded distance being 1.79 km (Watts *et al.* 2004c).

Southern damselfly is a species that occurs in an even more fragmented landscape than most other damselfly species because of its rather particular habitat requirements (Thompson *et al.* 2003). It is one of the smallest of the blue damselflies and body size has been correlated with dispersal capability in some odonates (Conrad *et al.* 1999, Angelibert and Giani 2003). From the present study and that of Purse *et al.* (2003) it is clear that most individuals do not move more than 100 m during their mature adult lifespans. There was relatively little movement between many of the patches of suitable habitat connected by the same stream (which provided a corridor for movement), and where movement was observed, it was almost exclusively between adjacent sites (Figure 10). Given that many sites are separated by more than several kilometres of unsuitable (forested) habitat, we would

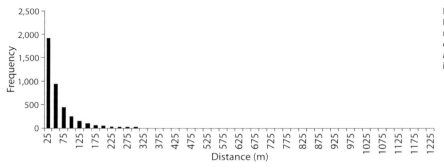

Figure 29
Net lifetime movement in mature adult southern damselfly *Coenagrion mercuriale* on Beaulieu Heath in the New Forest.

expect to find a large number of more or less isolated populations within the New Forest and this is supported by genetic analysis (see below). On the other hand, although most individuals do not move far, a small percentage does move up to about 1.2 km; if these animals breed then gene flow between sites separated by 1–2 km seems assured. Rouquette and Thompson (2007) in a parallel study in the Itchen Valley, in a water meadow ditch system surrounding chalk streams, found similar patterns of movement. Hunger and Röske (2001) also observed limited movement by adult southern damselflies.

Population genetic structure

We took tissue samples from up to 90 individuals from all of the UK's southern damselfly populations. One hind leg per individual was taken and stored in 100% ethanol until analysis. Full details of the PCR and genotyping procedures using an automated sequencer are given by Watts *et al.* (2004a, b, c). We have used the microsatellite data in two ways. First, by principal components analysis (PCA). A plot of the sample scores (eigenvectors) of significant principal components offers a convenient representation of the overall spatial variation in data as long as the principal components still account for a significant amount of the total between-sample variation. Second, the population genetic structure of the New Forest samples was assessed in more detail using the model-based clustering approach implemented by STRUCTURE v. 2.0 (Pritchard *et al.* 2000). This approach simultaneously identifies clusters (populations) and assigns individuals to populations using a Bayesian approach.

The first two principal components (Figure 30) accounted for 24% and 17% of the variation within the data and were significant ($P < 0.001$ for each axis). The PCA plot is based on allele frequencies, that is, shared or similar alleles. It has little real 'genetic interpretation' other than that more closely related populations might be expected to share alleles. The New Forest populations generally occur in the centre of the plot because they contain more genetic variation than other populations. Those from Dorset are the closest in allele frequencies to the majority of the New Forest populations and there is some overlap. In general, populations from similar geographical areas have, for the most part, clustered together (Figure 30).

For example, the Pembrokeshire populations are grouped in the top left quadrant, while small, isolated populations fall furthest away from the New Forest, for example, with the Anglesey population (2002 and 2003 datasets) falling in the top right of the top right quadrant. There are, however, some exceptions whereby some New Forest populations are separate, notably Acres Down, Shobley, Common Moor and Kingston Great Common, while at least one isolated population, Oxfordshire (2002 and 2003 datasets), is positioned with the main New Forest cluster (Figure 30).

With respect to the New Forest itself, the lowest posterior probability of the data (PPD) indicate that the New Forest appears to contain five distinct genetic 'clusters' (average Ln PPD = -30,991 for K=5). The three 'best defined' clusters (with regard to the proportion of membership of individuals) include samples identified by PCA (Figure 30) as being quite distinct: Acres Down, Shobley and Common Moor. Also similar to the latter sample are other populations that drain into

Figure 30
Principal components analysis plot showing spatial pattern of allele frequencies in the UK southern damselfly *Coenagrion mercuriale* populations. The coloured symbols reflect different centres of population. One French population (from Normandy – SSG) is also plotted. Two Devon populations (Moortown Gidleigh Common and Aylesbeare Common), the Anglesey and Oxfordshire populations have two points representing sampling across two years.

PEM=Pembrokeshire, GOW=Gower, FOU=Foulford, SHO=Shobley, ITC=Itchen Valley, NAI= Anglesey, MAM=Mariner's Meadow, COM=Common Moor, KGC=Kingston Great Common, OXF=Oxfordshire, AYL=Aylesbeare Common, ACD=Acres Down.

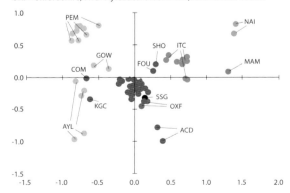

Mill Lawn Brook (the Ober Water) plus Stony Moors. The fourth cluster comprises populations at Setley Plain, Three Beech Bottom, Widden Bottom, and also Kingston Great Common. The final cluster includes samples from Gypsy Hollies and Foulford and almost 'by default', a poorly defined group comprising all Beaulieu Heath sites that were included in the MRR study. Future analyses will determine whether the northern populations flowing into Millersford Brook and Latchmore Brook proves to be distinct or not. With caution, these data may be summarised by the proportion of membership of individuals from each of the predefined populations to each of the five model clusters. Again, the most distinct populations are Acres Down, Common Moor and Shobley where 82%, 78% and 67 % of individuals respectively are assigned to a particular cluster. Individuals from three sites (Mill Lawn, Stag Brake Bog, Stony Moors) near Common Moor are also predominantly assigned (26–37%) to the 'Common Moor' cluster, while those from Setley Plain form the fourth group whereby 42–48% of individuals from the samples are assigned to that cluster. In contrast, both Foulford and Kingston Great Common sites show genetic differences to nearby populations. The Beaulieu Heath samples are similar in that they all show no strong affinity to any of the five model clusters; hence, while two Peaked Hill sites appear to be similar to the 'Acres Down' cluster this simply reflects some 3% of the sample (c.1 individual) clustering with Acres Down rather than within the 'Foulford – Kingston Great Common' group.

A more detailed look at the New Forest highlights the effects of genetic drift, but at a more localised scale. The Beaulieu Heath sites, separated by several kilometres, were not all linked during the MRR study but are indistinguishable genetically. This indicates that this population is behaving like a metapopulation with the strong central sub-sites providing a source for the smaller peripheral sites. It is important to recognise that apparently separated populations will not show substantial genetic divergence when there is gene flow between intermediate populations. Appropriate management of streams (cutting down trees and shrubs) so that ponies can get closer to graze, at further peripheral subsites, is likely to lead to re-establishment of southern damselfly there. The population at the apparently isolated site of Round Hill does not show substantial genetic differentiation, probably because it is large and also as there has been insufficient time for substantial genetic drift. We do not exclude the possibility (more so for Hatchet Stream) that there is occasional immigration from the main Beaulieu Heath populations. The Setley Plain and Mill Lawn clusters probably behave in a similar way.

The two populations that seem not to resemble any others, Acres Down and Shobley, are particularly interesting. Acres Down is a small isolated population, at a higher altitude (70 m) than any of the other New Forest populations. The site is small, never likely to have held a large population, and was probably founded by a few individuals and seldom replenished genetically, if at all. We do not know whether southern

damselfly in this or even other small, isolated sites (Watts *et al.* 2005) suffer from inbreeding depression, but if so its long-term survival would probably be enhanced by translocation of individuals from the nearest, genetically similar populations at Beaulieu Heath. The Shobley population is more 'problematic'. Although no MRR study or monitoring work has ever been carried out there (the site was only discovered in 2002), it is a large population. It is less than 1 km from the Foulford site (also discovered in 2002) but separated by a long high ridge carrying the main trunk road through the New Forest. The Shobley and Foulford sites are genetically dissimilar. Some combination of the ridge and road are evidently a barrier to movement between these two sites. Here, the effect of the road as a barrier contrasts with movement observed on the Crockford stream (see also Watts *et al.* 2004c) where water flow was still maintained between 'separated' sites by a bridge.

To summarise, in the UK southern damselfly exists as a number of isolated population fragments at the northern edge of its distribution. This species is a relatively sedentary damselfly, a characteristic that combined with specialised habitat requirements makes it susceptible to the detrimental effects of habitat loss and fragmentation. Despite concerns about its conservation, MRR data reveal the New Forest to sustain a large population. Bayesian genetic analysis provides evidence that the New Forest stronghold is subdivided into several distinct genetic units and this needs to be considered for future biodiversity management.

Acknowledgements

The work on southern damselfly described in this chapter was funded by the Natural Environment Research Council (grant no. NER/A/S/2000/01322) and the Environment Agency. Southern damselfly is protected under Schedule 5 of the 1981 Wildlife and Countryside Act in the UK. All work was carried out under licence from Natural England. We thank Alan Hold, Derek Jenkins and Dave Winsland for welcoming us onto their patch and Tim Sykes for his energetic and creative chairmanship of the *Coenagrion mercuriale* BAP Steering Group. We are grateful to the British Dragonfly Society for permission to use the distribution maps supplied to the NBN Gateway and for providing Figure 1.

References

Angelibert, S. and Giani, N. (2003). Dispersal characteristics of three odonate species in a patchy habitat. *Ecography*, 26, 13–20.

Askew, R. R. (1988). *The dragonflies of Europe*. Harley Books, Colchester.

Brooks, S. and Lewington, R. (2002). *Field Guide to the dragonflies and damselflies of Great Britain and Ireland*. British Wildlife Publishing, Hampshire.

Conrad, K. F., Willson, K. H., Harvey, I. F., Thomas, C. J. and Sherratt, T. N. (1999). Dispersal characteristics of seven odonate species in an agricultural landscape. *Ecography*, 22, 524–531.

Daguet, C. A., French, G. C. and Taylor, P. (2007). *The Odonata Red Data List for Great Britain. Species Status x*; 1–31. Joint Nature Conservation Committee, Peterborough.

Fox, A. D. and Cham, S. A. (1994). Status, habitat use and conservation of the scarce blue-tailed damselfly *Ischnura pumilio* (Charpentier) (Odonata: Coenagrionidae) in Britain and Ireland. *Biological Conservation*, 68, 115–122.

Fraser, F. C. (1941). The nymph of *Ischnura pumilio* Charpentier (Order Odonata). *Proceedings of the Royal Entomological Society of London*, A18, 50–56.

Goodyear, K. G. (1989). The dragonflies (Odonata) of Sowley Pond, New Forest, Hampshire. *Journal of the British Dragonfly Society*, 5, 8–14.

Hunger, H. and Röske, W. (2001) Short-range dispersal of the southern damselfly (*Coenagrion mercuriale*: Odonata) defined experimentally using UV fluorescent ink. *Zeitschrift für Okologie und Naturshutz*, 9, 181–187.

Lowe, C. D., Thompson, D. J., Harvey, I. F. and Watts, P. C. (2008). Strong genetic divergence indicates that congeneric damselflies *Coenagrion puella* and *C. pulchellum* (Odonata: Zygoptera: Coenagrionidae) do not hybridise *Hydrobiologia*, 605, 55–63.

Lucas, W. J. (1900). *British Dragonflies (Odonata)*. Upcott Gill, London.

Pritchard, J. K., Stephens, M. and Donnelly, P. (2000). Inference of population structure using multilocus genotype data. *Genetics*, 155, 945–959.

Purse, B. V., Hopkins, G. W., Day, K. J. and Thompson, D. J. (2003). Dispersal characteristics and management of a rare damselfly. *Journal of Applied Ecology*, 40, 716–728.

Rouquette, J. R. and Thompson, D. J. (2007). Patterns of movement and dispersal in an endangered damselfly with implications for its management. *Journal of Applied Ecology*, 44, 692–701.

Stevens, J. and Thurner, M. (1999). *A 1998 survey to investigate the status and distribution of the Southern Damselfly (Coenagrion mercuriale) in Hampshire*. Environment Agency, Colden Common.

Taverner, J., Cham, S. and Hold, A. (2004). *The Dragonflies of Hampshire*. Pisces Publications, Hampshire.

Thompson, D. J., Rouquette, J. R. and Purse, B. V. (2003). *Ecology of the Southern Damselfly, Coenagrion mercuriale*. Conserving Natura 2000 Rivers Ecology Series No. 8. English Nature, Peterborough.

Watts, P. C., Thompson, D. J. and Kemp, S. J. (2004a). Cross-species amplification of microsatellite loci in some European zygopteran species (Odonata: Coenagrionidae). *International Journal of Odonatology*, 7, 87–96.

Watts, P. C., Hong-Wu, J., Westgarth, C., Thompson, D. J. and Kemp, S. J. (2004b). A panel of microsatellite loci for the Southern Damselfly, *Coenagrion mercuriale* (Odonata: Coenagrionidae). *Conservation Genetics*, 5, 117–119.

Watts, P. C., Kemp, S. J., Saccheri, I. J. and Thompson, D. J. (2005). Conservation implications of genetic variation between spatially and temporally distinct colonies of the damselfly *Coenagrion mercuriale*. *Ecological Entomology*, 30, 541–547.

Watts, P. C., Rouquette, J. R., Saccheri, I. J., Kemp, S. J. and Thompson, D. J. (2004c). Molecular and ecological evidence for small-scale isolation by distance in the endangered damselfly, *Coenagrion mercuriale*. *Molecular Ecology*, 13, 2931–2944.

5 Saproxylic beetles

Keith Alexander

Introduction

The New Forest has long been known to be one of the richest parts of Britain for saproxylic beetles, i.e. those species that are dependent on the fungal decay of dead woody tissues (see below). This importance has been recognised at a European scale (Speight 1989). The earliest records date back to the early 19th century and perhaps earlier – Stephens (1830), for example, makes frequent reference to the New Forest as the source of many rare click beetles (Elateridae). Remarkably, the beetle fauna of the Forest remains poorly documented – a manuscript list (in the possession of R. C. Welch) was compiled by A. E. Gardner (d. 1976) and others, but has never been published or even updated. Harding (1978) compiled records of key species known from the Forest and drew on the Gardner manuscript. The Harding compilation formed the basis of subsequent site assessments (Harding and Alexander 1993, Alexander 2004). The New Forest LIFE Project provided new impetus for beetle recording, which resulted in a large effort covering the period 1999–2002 (M. Salmon, pers. comm.).

The following analysis is based on data on British saproxylic beetles accumulated by the author over many years, particularly formally published information but also records made available through the Invertebrate Site Register (Nature Conservancy Council and more latterly English Nature) and the New Forest LIFE project.

What are saproxylic beetles?

The term saproxylic is used to describe the community of species that are dependent on the process of fungal decay of wood and the products of that decay (Speight 1989, Alexander 2008). It encompasses the full spectrum of situations from undecayed wood through to the debris left after decay, which may effectively be indistinguishable from soil rich in organic material. It also includes the species which feed on the mycelium and/or fruit bodies of the decay fungi, plus the predators and parasites which specialise on that species. Decay may occur within a wide variety of situations within otherwise living trees as well as in dead trees, fallen wood, stumps and dead roots within the soil.

The succession from undecayed wood through to the end debris is exploited by a different suite of invertebrate species at each stage. The early successional species are unique to saproxylic situations but decaying wood is increasingly colonised by species more typical of organic-rich soil as breakdown reaches the more advanced stages. Similarly the early successional saproxylic invertebrates include species

specific to particular tree species or groups of tree species, while decaying and decayed wood is more characterised by saproxylic invertebrates associated with particular decay fungi species or the main types of decay – white-rot or red/brown-rot. Thus there is a trend from tree associates through fungi associates eventually to soil associates. Other important factors influencing the species composition are moisture and temperature.

How many saproxylic beetles are known from the New Forest?

There are currently 781 saproxylic beetle species known to have been breeding in the wild in Britain and Ireland at some stage during the past 150 years (Alexander 2002, plus updates). This total includes so-called natives as well as accidental introductions and recent colonists. Unfortunately there appears to be no complete list of which of these has been found in the New Forest. However, the Site Quality Index (SQI) website (http://thasos.users.btopenworld.com/ sqi.htm) includes a total of SQI qualifying species for the Forest of 326, using data complete to 2000. The SQI species are a listing (Fowles *et al.* 1999) of species that aims to confine itself primarily to long-established native species – although it is by no means complete. The full SQI list is of 598 species and so the New Forest is known to support 55% of these species. It seems reasonable to extrapolate that this represents slightly more than half of the saproxylic beetles known from Britain. Only one other British site has a longer list: Windsor Great Park and Forest, with 364 species, i.e. 61%.

How important is the New Forest for saproxylic beetles?

Two indices have been devised for site assessment of saproxylic communities, both based on beetles alone: the Index of Ecological Continuity (IEC) and the Site Quality Index (SQI). These measure two different aspects – species-richness of relict old growth species (IEC) and proportion of rare species present (SQI). The IEC (Alexander 2004) is a cumulative index and so provides a minimum figure for a particular site. Indices of 80 or greater are suggested as indicating European significance – the IEC value for the New Forest is 194, considerably exceeding this threshold. Only one British site has a higher IEC value: Windsor Great Park and Forest (249) (Table 11). The SQI (Fowles *et al.* 1999), being based on the proportion of rare species known from the site, may increase or decrease with additional recording, which makes interpretation

Table 11
The top British sites for saproxylic beetles as assessed using the Index of Ecological Continuity and the Site Quality Index.

Index of Ecological Continuity		Site Quality Index	
Windsor Great Park & Forest	249	New Forest	856
New Forest	194	Windsor	847
Richmond Park	140	Langley Park	757
Moccas Park	125	Silwood Park	685
Bredon Hill	120	Richmond Park	641
Sherwood Forest	100	Moccas Park	638

Table 12
Saproxylic beetles with British Red Data Book status (Hyman 1992) known from the New Forest, with dates of most recent reports. * Species for which the New Forest is potentially a key area in Great Britain. N.B. Two species are excluded as almost certainly extinct (see text).

Species	Not recorded for 25 years	Most recent records
Aderus brevicornis*	Pre 1892	
Aeletes atomarius		1999–2002 (LIFE)
Amarochara bonnairei	1915	
Ampedus cinnabarinus		1999–2002 (LIFE)
Ampedus nigerrimus		1999–2002 (LIFE)
Anoplodera (Leptura) sexguttata*		1999–2002 (LIFE)
Colydium elongatum		1999–2002 (LIFE)
Cryptophagus micaceus		1985
Diaperus boleti		2005
Epierus comptus		1999–2002 (LIFE)
Epuraea neglecta	1966	
Eucnemis capucina*	1973	
Euplectus tholini	19th century	
Eutheia formicetorum	1964	
Eutheia linearis	1977	
Euryusa optabilis	1964	
Gnorimus nobilis noble chafer*		2000
Grammoptera ustulata		1999–2002 (LIFE)
Gyrophaena munsteri		1999–2002 (LIFE)
Gyrophaena pulchella		1999–2002 (LIFE)
Hylis cariniceps*	1966	
Ischnomera caerulea	1934	
Lymexylon navale		2002
Megapenthes lugens*	1971	
Melandrya barbata*		1992
Mesosa nebulosa		1999–2002 (LIFE)
Microrhagus pygmaeus		1999–2002 (LIFE)
Microscydmus minimus	'post 1970'	
Mordellistena neuwaldeggiana	?	
Orthocis coluber*	1917	
Paracorymbia (Leptura) fulva	?	
Paromalus parallelepipedus	1910	
Pedostrangalia revestita*	1917?	
Phyllodrepa nigra	1917?	
Platydema violaceum	1901	
Procraerus tibialis		1999–2002 (LIFE)
Ptenidium turgidum		1999–2002 (LIFE)
Ptinella limbata	19th century	
Scraptia fuscula	?	
Scraptia testacea		1984
Stenichnus godarti		1999–2002 (LIFE)
Stichoglossa semirufa	1969	
Tachinus bipustulatus	Old?	
Trichonyx sulcicollis		1981
Trinodes hirtus	1911	
Triplax lacordairii*		1999–2002 (LIFE)
Tropideres niveirostris	1831	
Tropideres sepicola	1967	
Velleius dilatatus		1999–2002 (LIFE)
Xyletinus longitarsus	1962	
Zyras cognatus	1970	

difficult. European significance is set at an SQI value of 590 or greater. The New Forest currently has the largest SQI of any British site at 856 but is closely followed by Windsor at 847 (Table 11).

Both indices agree that the saproxylic beetle fauna of the New Forest is of European significance. This is in agreement with Speight (1989) who listed the top sites in Europe based on representation of a more restricted list of species, although following the IEC approach rather than SQI.

The New Forest and Windsor Great Park and Forest are clearly the two best sites in Britain. The variation between IEC and SQI partly reflects a key difference between the fauna of these two sites. Windsor is especially rich in relict old growth species confined in Britain to this one area, and hence is favoured by the IEC. The New Forest is, in contrast, notable for its exceptional representation of rare and threatened species characteristic of central and south-eastern England. At least 53 species known from the Forest are given Red Data Book (RDB) status in the British Coleoptera Review (Hyman 1992, 1994), and hence the New Forest is favoured by the SQI. Only two of these rare species have only ever been found in Britain in the New Forest – *Anthaxia nitidula* (Buprestidae) and *Endophloeus markovichianus* (Colydiidae) – and these are both almost certainly now extinct.

Fifty-one of the RDB species are listed in Table 12 together with the date of the most recent reports of sightings – the *Anthaxia* and *Endophloeus* are omitted as these are believed to be extinct in the Forest. This immediately demonstrates that more than 50% of these species (27) have not been reported during the past 25 years, with at least four not reported in the past 100 years. Although not confined to the New Forest, ten of the RDB species have very restricted ranges in Britain with the New Forest remaining a potentially key area. These are indicated by an asterisk.

The above species are all considered to potentially still be present within the New Forest today. The species represented only by very old records are retained in the list as these are very difficult species to find on demand and could conceivably remain overlooked for a very long time. The LIFE project rediscovered many species that had not been reported for many decades. However, at least five apparently native species known from the New Forest historically are thought to be extinct throughout Britain (Table 13, and see later).

Table 13
New Forest saproxylic beetles believed to now be extinct in Britain.

Species	Assemblage	Last date
Ampedus sanguineus	Heartwood	1830
Anthaxia nitidula	Sapwood	1954
Cardiophorus gramineus	Heartwood	19th century
Endophloeus markovichianus	Sapwood	1927
Oxylaemus cylindricus	Sapwood	19th century

Three of the New Forest key species feature in the UK Biodiversity Action Plan as Priority Species: noble chafer *Gnorimus nobilis* has been a BAP species from the very beginning (UK Biodiversity Group 1999), while *Megapenthes lugens* was included as a member of a Grouped Species Statement. The bearded false darkling beetle *Melandrya barbata* is proposed for addition in 2007 (Biodiversity Reporting and Information Group 2007). A fourth species which is known from the forest – the stag beetle *Lucanus cervus* – is also an existing BAP Priority Species.

Ecological requirements of key species

With the New Forest known to support so many different saproxylic beetles, and so many rare ones, the fauna might be considered too unwieldy – too complicated – to cope with at a species conservation level. Standing back from the species level, and focusing at the assemblage level instead, appears to offer a workable way forward. A new system for undertaking Common Standards Monitoring for terrestrial and freshwater invertebrates is under development within English Nature/Natural England (Webb and Lott 2006). A new assemblage classification forms the basis for the site condition assessments. The present author has led on saproxylic assemblages and the fauna has been split on the following basis:
- heartwood decay specialities;
- bark and sapwood specialities;
- fungal fruit body specialities, i.e. species developing within or on the fungal material (as opposed to adults feeding casually);
- more generalist saproxylic species.

Table 14
Key New Forest saproxylic beetles classified by assemblage type.

Assemblage type	Saproxylic beetle species
Heartwood decay	*Aderus brevicornis* *Eucnemis capucina* *Gnorimus nobilis* *Hylis cariniceps* *Megapenthes lugens* *Melandrya barbata*
Bark and sapwood decay	*Anoplodera sexguttata* *Pedostrangalia revestita*
Fungal fruit bodies	*Orthocis coluber* *Triplax lacordairii*
More generalist species	*Lucanus cervus*, wood within soil

The intention is to facilitate surveying as well as analysis, as the second and third specialist assemblages are more readily surveyed than the first.

If this approach is applied to the four BAP Priority Species and the other key species identified in Table 12, then it becomes very clear which assemblage is the most important for saproxylic beetles in the New Forest (Table 14).

Heartwood decay is the most significant specialist saproxylic habitat for rare and threatened beetles throughout Britain and the rest of Europe, so this result is not surprising. The succession of habitats provided as fungal decay of heartwood within living trees proceeds requires the affected trees to be at least of mature age, to have been colonised by specialist heartwood decay fungi, and for that decay to proceed right through to final trunk hollowing and accumulation of composted debris in the base of the tree. For trees to survive through to this stage they generally need to be in open-grown situations, as canopy competition from neighbouring younger trees is likely to cause premature death of the older tree through overshading. There is therefore a requirement both for time and space, and the probability of the tree surviving to provide suitable habitat for the key species is therefore low in the modern countryside, with so many conflicting demands – particularly the all-too-common ill-informed paranoia about 'dangerous' trees and forest hygiene. It is easy to understand why heartwood decay species are rare and threatened in Britain today.

Which are the most significant species?

The most sensible guide to which of the many rare and threatened New Forest saproxylic beetles are considered to be the most significant species for nature conservation action is the UK Biodiversity Action Plan (www.ukbap.org.uk). Four species have been identified for Species Action Plans: stag beetle *Lucanus cervus*, noble chafer *Gnorimus nobilis*, bearded false darkling beetle *Melandrya barbata* and the click beetle *Megapenthes lugens*. These will be discussed in the following sections. The stag beetle is listed on Annex II of the EC Habitats and Species Directive and has been used to propose the New Forest for Special Area of Conservation (SAC) status. It is the only one of the four species with any legal protection in Britain, it being illegal to sell or exchange.

Stag beetle *Lucanus cervus*
The larvae of the stag beetle develop in moist decaying wood near or below the soil surface, including old decaying stumps and roots but also the bases of fence posts (Alexander 2002). The People's Trust for Endangered Species (PTES) are the UK Lead Partner for the Stag Beetle Species Action Plan (SAP); they initiated a National Stag Beetle Survey in 1998 (Napier 2002) with the aim of promoting deadwood conservation amongst the general population, while at the same time generating fresh data on its British

Figure 31
Distribution of stag beetle records 1998–2002 (source:
People's Trust for Endangered Species).

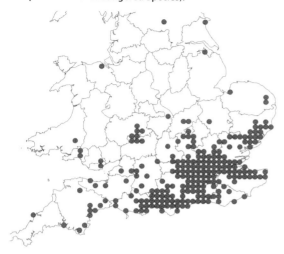

distribution. Expert opinion had suggested that the
species had suffered a significant decline and range
contraction in the latter part of the 20th century.
Survey returns confirmed the previously recorded
distribution of the stag beetle in Britain as a
predominantly south-eastern species with three main
population centres, focused on the lower Thames
basin, the coastal plain between Colchester and
Ipswich, and the Solent basin (see Figure 31). The
records revealed an apparent association with areas on
light free-draining soils, typically composed of sands
and gravels, as well as following river corridors. The
national survey has been repeated in 2002. The
Hampshire Wildlife Trust reported that 725 sightings
were made in and around the New Forest (New Forest
LIFE Partnership 2000).

No evidence for any significant range contraction
has been demonstrated but it is known that local
populations are under continued threat, mostly from
loss of larval habitat through development and
tidiness. It has become too easy to remove old stumps;
stump-grinding equipment is now readily available
and heavy construction equipment makes the removal
of trees and buried wood a relatively easy process. A
methodology for quantifying populations is urgently
needed in order to prove that populations are in
decline owing to human activities. Researchers are
actively investigating the potential for using chemical
attractants for estimating adult population sizes.

Noble chafer *Gnorimus nobilis*
Larvae of the noble chafer develop within
accumulations of moist wood-mould in tree cavities
and especially in the base of hollow old trees (Smith
2002). The PTES are again the UK Lead Partner for this
species. The species is known to develop in a wide
range of broadleaved trees within its European range
but British populations appear to have a more

restricted palate, particularly favouring woody Rosaceae
and especially old orchards. PTES survey work has
revealed that there remains just one very extensive
population associated with the traditional orchard
landscape of Gloucestershire, Herefordshire and
Worcestershire, plus at least three more restricted
populations: New Forest (in old oaks), south Chilterns
(in old cherry trees in woodland boundaries) and Kent
(in old plum orchards). One oak site is also known in
Herefordshire. The larval faecal pellets (frass) are very
distinctive and can be used by experienced surveyors to
identify host trees.

The British range was formerly much wider
(Figure 32) and it is clear that we are currently dealing
with serious fragmentation and isolation of the
surviving populations. Old records came from as far
afield as Devon, Cumbria and Norfolk (Smith 2002).
The New Forest population was first discovered by
G.C. Champion in 1894 (Whitehead 2002) but the
precise locality was not documented. It has
subsequently been reported from Mallard Wood
(1970s and 1996), Matley (1982 and 1996), and
Whitley Wood (1988); details in Smith (2000). PTES
survey work has resulted in a sighting of a single
female in 2000, at hogweed blossom along the A35
east of Lyndhurst (Smith 2000), i.e. towards Mallard
Wood. No trees with developing larvae have so far
been identified and so the precise breeding areas
within the Forest continue to be unknown.

A captive colony established by Owen (1989) from
a pair found in the Forest in 1986 is still viable and is

Figure 32
Distribution of noble chafer (all positive records since 1966).
(Source: People's Trust for Endangered Species).

● Pre-1980 records
● 1981–2008 records

now in the possession of M. N. Smith. The female found in 2000 was kept in captivity for a number of days before being released back into the Forest. Eggs were laid in crumbled rotten cherry wood provided and have formed additional material for the captive rearing programme, which is continuing. It is hoped that this material can be used to start a new colony within the historic range.

Until trees are found supporting larval development it is impossible to assess the extent of the New Forest population or to begin to identify trends. There is a clear need to expand the recording effort in the New Forest but this effort needs to focus on the potential host trees themselves, at least initially. Maps are needed which show the locations of older generation oaks with the potential for advanced heartwood decay, and hence the potential to support developing larvae. This will help target follow-up larval surveys and ensure that host trees are properly documented and their conservation needs assessed and acted upon.

The click beetle *Megapenthes lugens*

Megapenthes is a speciality of the New Forest and Windsor Forest, with older records reported from Epping Forest and various sites in Middlesex, Surrey and Norfolk, where it is presumed to now be extinct. The New Forest population is however very poorly known, with only three areas named in the literature. It was first discovered near Lyndhurst in 1915 (one adult at holly blossom), then found at Ashurst (two at hawthorn blossom in 1946) and Mallard Wood (an adult on a beech tree in 1971 – the most recent reported record). Some details are provided in Allen (1964). The adults and larvae are found within the decaying heartwood of various broadleaved trees – especially elm and beech – and are thought to be specialist feeders on the larvae of cossonine weevils. The adults have been found active on the trunks of host trees after dark and are attracted to the blossom of hawthorn and holly. Most information on the species comes from Windsor where it has been studied by Owen (1990). No methodology for surveying or monitoring this species has been determined other than targeted searching by knowledgeable surveyors.

Bearded false darkling *Melandrya barbata*

Knowledge of this beetle tends to mirror that of *Megapenthes*. It is a speciality of the New Forest but there are also odd records from elsewhere, most notably Chiddingfold Woods in Surrey (1971 – see Allen 1972) but also older ones from Stratfield Turgis, north Hampshire (1914) and Darenth Wood in Kent (19th century). It was discovered in the New Forest in 1823 and has been reported widely since then, although apparently not since 1992. Adults have been found on standing and felled oak and beech trees, and in flight but never from blossom. It is presumed that they develop within decaying heartwood of older generation trees. Named localities are: Brockenhurst (1823 and 1902), Burley Lodge (1923), Denny Promontory (old), Denny Wood (1935), near Pondhead Inclosure and Jones' Inclosure (old), Queen's Bower (1901), Rhinefield (1896) and Whitley Wood (1990). As with *Megapenthes*, no methodology for surveying or monitoring this species has been determined other than targeted searching by knowledgeable surveyors.

Extinct species

It is notoriously difficult to prove that an insect with such a cryptic lifestyle as a saproxylic beetle is genuinely extinct at a national level, let alone a local level. The definition of 'extinct' used by the Joint Nature Conservation Committee in the series of national status reviews is 'native species not recorded since 1900' (Hyman 1992). In some cases, however, it may be reasonable to assume extinction in the absence of sightings over a 50 year period.

The most famous extinct beetle in the New Forest is the jewel beetle *Anthaxia nitidula* (Buprestidae). The larvae develop beneath sappy bark on freshly dead or dying trunks and twigs of various woody Rosaceae, usually in open sunny situations. The adults are attracted to the flowers of *Ranunculus* spp., hawthorn, guelder-rose, etc. The precise larval requirements in terms of age, size and condition of the host stems is not documented. The New Forest formerly supported a colony on blackthorn by Balmer Lawn and which was well known from the 19th century up until 1954. It has not been seen anywhere since the Forestry Commission removed the Balmer Lawn blackthorn stands in the late 1950s. This work is reported to have been carried out on the behalf of the Ministry of Agriculture to improve the grazing on the lawns (C. Chatters, pers. comm.).

Another relatively recent extinction is the beetle *Endophloeus markovichianus* (Colydiidae). This beetle was discovered in the Forest in 1862 (Fowler 1889) and was last seen in 1927 (Hyman 1992). It is a very distinctive species and readily found within its main European range beneath loose bark on dead beech trees standing in sunny situations. It would seem very unlikely that it could be present in the New Forest and have escaped notice for 80 years. Its loss most probably reflects past forestry and commoning practices of removing standing dead beech trees.

Both of these species were only known in Britain from the New Forest and so their local extinction was also national extinction. The probable cause of extinction of the jewel beetle seems undeniably due to grazing improvement works, although it has often been blamed on beetle collectors! The removal of dead trees is the most likely cause of the extinction of the *Endophloeus*. Other important factors that may be causing extinction of saproxylic beetles include increasing shade in the woodlands, and continued loss of natural tree regeneration through the continued scrub clearance by the Forestry Commission on and around the lawns. This is apparently a statutory requirement for grazing maintenance but one that demands review and development of a more sensitive approach.

What needs to be done for saproxylic beetle biodiversity in the New Forest?

Two key issues arise from this review of the saproxylic beetle fauna of the New Forest and both relate to poor knowledge of:

- the key beetle species themselves, both in terms of knowledge of where their breeding sites are and also their detailed habitat requirements, especially structure and composition of the host tree population;
- the natural population dynamics of the host trees and shrubs, including the locations of the older generation trees which are currently supporting the key beetle species, but also positive management of thorn scrub for natural regeneration of the host trees.

In many ways the second issue, the tree demographics, is the highest priority for action.

There is a clear polarisation in the Forest between the common grazings and forestry, between pastures and woodlands, but this is a false division as the two are not separate in reality. The saproxylic beetles are very clearly associated with trees rather than woodland and their conservation demands a tree ecology approach and not conventional woodland ecology. The key factors which determine which saproxylic beetles may or may not be present are:

- age structure of the tree and shrub populations;
- the density of the trees and shrubs, and hence shade levels and the scope for open-grown trees and shrubs;
- the total numbers of trees, with implications to the viability of dependent species such as saproxylic beetles.

A fourth key factor – continuity of suitable habitat conditions in time – can be taken as read in the New Forest. These factors are crucial to determining the fauna which can be supported and yet they do not feature in most woodland ecology textbooks, if any at all. Woodland ecology is basically about managing shade conditions whereas saproxylic beetles require management for light. Woodland ecology is only a small part of tree ecology!

Newton *et al.* (Chapter 13, this volume) have shown that the findings of Mountford *et al.* (1999) with regard to the impacts of grazing on forest structure and composition need to be placed in the context of the whole Forest and not taken in isolation. Denny Wood – the study site of the latter authors – has now been shown to be atypical of the rest of the Forest, representing an extreme case. The conclusions of Mountford *et al.* (1999) are not necessarily generally applicable, and perhaps reflect thinking based on the 'high forest hypothesis', rather than the 'Vera hypothesis' (Vera 2000). Oak regeneration in the Forest takes place amongst thorn scrub in the open areas and not in the woods; exactly as stated by Vera (2000). A landscape-scale approach is therefore needed, not a stand-scale one.

Although 'natural processes' are often seen as the ultimate solution to managing wild habitats, this approach needs to be very well informed by knowledge of species' ecology. There are many ways forwards using 'natural processes' – decisions need to be taken about how 'natural' the processes actually are and whether or not they are actually desirable in relation to other objectives. The Forest is not a natural site – it is a cultural landscape – and so-called 'natural processes' reflect varying levels of human impact. They are not identical to the natural processes that occurred in the prehistoric Wildwood of pre-Neolithic Britain and should not be assumed to be so. Although grazing by large herbivores is a natural process, human management of the herds may or may not be considered so. Mechanical clearance of thorn scrub – along with the natural tree regeneration it has nurtured – is less likely to be considered a natural process. 'Natural processes' can be applied simplistically but the result may be disastrous. Well-informed decisions are vital to the conservation of the Forest's special features.

In the case of saproxylic beetles, there are certainly too many species to deal with effectively individually, but an assemblage type approach is feasible, as outlined above. Knowledge of the Forest's tree demography is vital to the conservation of the Forest's saproxylic beetles. It is essential that the tree population structure is documented and analysed, at local and whole Forest levels (and throughout the Forest, not just in defined 'woodland' or isolated and unrepresentative long-term study sites). This is essential in order that informed decisions can be made on the adequacy or not of tree recruitment rates, and the many factors influencing variations in tree density across the Forest. Mapping of older generation trees will greatly facilitate successful surveying of the Forest's key saproxylic beetle species. A strategic approach involving the gathering of adequate data on the trees as well as their dependent organisms needs to be developed if conservation management is to be at all successful.

Conclusions

Over 300 species of saproxylic (wood-decay) beetle have been reported from the New Forest. This represents more than half of the native fauna of Britain. Site quality is very high and the Forest has been shown to be of European importance for these beetles. The Forest is of especial importance for its sheer abundance of British Red List species – with over 50 species known – including many for which the New Forest is a key core site in a central southern England context. Four species have been identified as priorities under the UK Biodiversity Action Plan. However, about 50% of the Red List species have not been reported in the past 25 years and some are almost certainly now extinct within the Forest.

The analysis presented here has demonstrated that the saproxylic beetle fauna of the New Forest continues to be poorly documented and poorly understood. There is an enormous knowledge gap. Trends in abundance can only be dreamed about – methodologies do not yet exist, let alone any suitable data. A special recording effort as part of the LIFE Project certainly generated a large amount of new information but few of the key species were found. These key species require a more targeted approach and one which is informed by knowledge of the locations of the older generation trees across the Forest. This knowledge is not yet available other than as generalised maps of old growth areas.

Conservation of such a rich and diverse fauna needs to be well-targeted and guided by the known ecological requirements of the species. The majority of the key species require heartwood decay and hollowing of the host trees. This suggests that tree biology and tree demography should be the focus of the conservation plan, rather than conventional concepts of woodland ecology. It follows that the first priority for saproxylic beetle conservation is actually detailed survey work on the tree populations across the Forest. The key factors that require attention are: age structure of the tree population, tree density (open-grown trees provide better quality habitat), and total numbers of trees. A strategic approach is suggested which requires mapping of the older generation trees throughout the Forest, to provide baseline information on tree demographics and to facilitate targeted survey and monitoring of the key beetle species. Recognition of the vital role of thorn scrub in tree regeneration is also required.

Acknowledgements

Data used in this analysis came from a wide variety of sources and over an extended timescale. Acknowledgement needs to be made of Michael Salmon and Michael Darby for making the LIFE Beetle Survey data available, and the People's Trust for Endangered Species for information from their recent work on noble chafer and stag beetle. Thanks also to Chris Palmer for checking data held by Hampshire County Council Museums & Archives Service.

References

Alexander, K. N. A. (2002). *The invertebrates of living & decaying timber in Britain and Ireland – a provisional annotated checklist*. English Nature Research Reports No. 467, Peterborough.

Alexander, K. N. A. (2004). *Revision of the Index of Ecological Continuity as used for saproxylic beetles*. English Nature Research Report No. 574. Peterborough.

Alexander, K. N. A. (2008). Tree biology and saproxylic Coleoptera – issues of definitions and conservation language. In: Vignon, V. (ed) Proceedings of the 4th Symposium and Workshop on the Conservation of Saproxylic Beetles, 27th to 29th of June, 2006. *Revue d'Ecologie (Terre Vie)*, suppt. 10: 9–13.

Allen, A. A. (1964). *Megapenthes lugens* Redt. (Col., Elateridae) in Hants, Glos, etc, with additional notes. *Entomologist's Monthly Magazine,* 100, 95–96.

Allen, A. A. (1972). *Melandrya barbata* (F.) (Col., Serropalpidae) in Surrey, with further notes. *Entomologist's Monthly Magazine,* 108, 239.

Biodiversity Reporting and Information Group (2007). *Report on the Species and Habitat Review.* Report to the UK Biodiversity Partnership. (http://www.ukbap.org.uk/library/BRIG/SHRW/SpeciesandHabitatReviewReport2007.pdf)

Fowles, A. P., Alexander, K. N. A. and Key, R. S. (1999). The Saproxylic Quality Index: evaluating wooded habitats for the conservation of dead-wood Coleoptera. *Coleopterist,* 8 (3), 121–141. See also: http://thasos.users.btopenworld.com/sqi.htm

Fowler, W. W. (1889). *The Coleoptera of the British Islands. III Clavicornia*. L. Reeve & Co, London.

Harding, P. T. (1978). *A bibliography of the occurrence of certain woodland Coleoptera in Britain: with special reference to timber-utilising species associated with old trees in pasture-woodlands.* Nature Conservancy Council CST Report no. 161., Banbury.

Harding, P. T. and Alexander, K. N. A. (1993). The saproxylic invertebrates of historic parklands: progress and problems. In Kirby, K. J. and Drake, C. M. (eds.) *Dead wood matters: the ecology and conservation of saproxylic invertebrates in Britain.* Pp. 58–73. English Nature Science No. 7, Peterborough.

Hyman, P. S. (revised Parsons, M. S.) (1992). *A review of the scarce and threatened Coleoptera of Great Britain*. Part 1. Joint Nature Conservation Committee:UK Nature Conservation: 3, Peterborough.

Hyman, P. S. (revised Parsons, M. S.) (1994). *A review of the scarce and threatened Coleoptera of Great Britain*. Part 2. Joint Nature Conservation Committee: UK Nature Conservation: 12, Peterborough.

Mountford, E. P., Peterken, G. F., Edwards, P. J. and Manners, J. G. (1999). Long-term change in growth, mortality and regeneration of trees in Denny Wood, an old-growth wood-pasture in the New Forest (UK). *Perspectives in Ecology, Evolution & Systematics,* 2, 223–272.

Napier, D. (2002). The Great Stag Hunt – methods and findings of the 1998 National Stag Beetle Survey. In Bowen, C. P. (ed.) *Proceedings of the second pan-European conference on Saproxylic Beetles.* Pp. 32–35. PTES, London.

New Forest Life Partnership (2000). *New Forest Life Project Progress Update 2 – April 2000. Booklet.* Forestry Commission, Lyndhurst.

Owen, J. A. (1989). Breeding *Gnorimus nobilis* Linn. (Col: Scarabaeidae) in captivity. *Entomologist's Record,* 101, 19.

Owen, J. A. (1990). Annual Exhibition: Beetles bred from eggs or reared from larvae. *British Journal of Entomology and Natural History,* 3, 88–90.

Smith, M. (2000). *Noble Chafer* Gnorimus nobilis. *New Forest & Oxfordshire Surveys 2000.* Unpublished report to PTES, London.

Smith, M. N. (2002). Saproxylic beetles in Britain, an overview of the status and distribution of four Biodiversity Action Plan species. In Bowen, C. P. (ed.) *Proceedings of the second pan-European conference on Saproxylic Beetles.* Pp. 47–49. PTES, London.

Speight, M. C. D. (1989). *Saproxylic invertebrates and their conservation*. Council of Europe: Nature and Environment Series No 42, Strasbourg.

Stephens, J. F. (1830). *Illustrations of British Entomology. Mandibulata III*. Baldwin and Cradock, London.

UK Biodiversity Group (1999). *Tranche 2 Action Plans. Volume IV – Invertebrates*. English Nature, Peterborough. http://www.ukbap.org.uk

Vera, F. W. M (2000). *Grazing ecology and forest history*. CABI, Wallingford, UK.

Webb, J. R. and Lott, D. A. (2006). The development of ISIS: a habitat-based invertebrate assemblage classification system for assessing conservation interest in England. *Journal of Insect Conservation*, 10, 179–188.

Whitehead, P. F. (2002). The noble chafer *Aleurostictus nobilis* (L., 1758) (Col. Scarabaeidae) in Britain. Pp. 17–31 in Bowen, C. P. (ed.) *Proceedings of the second pan-European conference on Saproxylic Beetles*. PTES, London.

6 Butterflies and moths

Andrew J. Barker and David Green

Introduction

This chapter reviews the history of Lepidoptera in the New Forest and evaluates the current status and distribution of priority species and broad groupings of Lepidoptera associated with key habitats of the New Forest, most notably woodland and heathland. The foundation for this work was established following a major study carried out by Butterfly Conservation under the LIFE III project on behalf of the Forestry Commission (Green 2000). It has been supplemented by ongoing research and monitoring undertaken by Butterfly Conservation volunteers and various conservation organisations and individuals active in the New Forest. The geographical extent of the original study comprises the then provisional Special Area for Conservation (SAC) boundary, but excluding the coastal areas. The area outside the SAC boundary, but now included in the New Forest National Park, is less well known, but studies are planned to address this.

The richness of the New Forest

The New Forest has been regarded as an area of outstanding national importance for butterflies and moths since at least the mid-19th century (Oates 1996, Oates *et al.* 2000, Goater and Norriss 2001). In his evaluation of macromoth species richness across Britain by Watsonian vice-county, Leverton (2001) found vc11 (south Hampshire), with 678 species, to be second only to vc9 (Dorset). Leverton (2001) made the specific comment that this was in part due to the richness of the New Forest. Considering all Lepidoptera (macromoths, micromoths and butterflies), at least 1,488 species are known to have been recorded from the New Forest study area, approximately two-thirds of all species ever recorded in the British Isles (Green 2000). This is an unparalleled total and gives an indication of the great historical richness of the area for Lepidoptera. This total includes a remarkable 72 Red Data Book and 192 Nationally Notable species.

This unrivalled fauna is due to: the extent and continuity of semi-natural habitat within the New Forest; its geographical location in central southern England providing a mild climate; the varied geology and soil types; the complex mosaics of semi-natural habitats present (at all scales); the continuity of traditional land management practices, particularly livestock grazing.

The changing fortunes of Lepidoptera in the New Forest

There was a general decline in both abundance and diversity of Lepidoptera found in the New Forest during the second half of the 20th century (Oates 1996, Barker *et al.* 2000, Green 2000), as elsewhere in southern England (Fox *et al.* 2006a,b). Clearly, management of the Forest for much of the 20th century failed to deliver effective conservation measures for many species. Over 65% of the Red Data Book and Nationally Notable butterflies and around 50% of the scarce and threatened moths have not been recorded since before 1980, and may now have been lost (Table 15 and Appendix). Many other species including butterflies such as the pearl-bordered fritillary *Boloria euphrosyne*, small pearl-bordered fritillary *Boloria selene*, Duke of Burgundy *Hamearis lucina*, dingy skipper *Erynnis tages* and grizzled skipper *Pyrgus malvae* now survive only as small, relict populations.

The greatest losses have occurred for Lepidoptera species associated with the herb and shrub layers in open woodland habitats, and particularly those species dependent on early succession vegetation (Table 16). This category includes most of the scarcer butterflies mentioned above, and mirrors declines seen throughout southern England (Fox *et al.* 2006a, 2007). There have also been marked declines for those New Forest Lepidoptera species associated with bogs and mires, heath and open grassland areas.

The overall pattern for moths in south-east England is equally concerning, with the long-term trends from Rothamsted traps (1968–2002) revealing that 74% of common and widespread species have substantially decreased in numbers over recent decades (Parsons *et al.* 2005). Fox *et al.* (2006b) considered that the declines of many woodland macromoth species probably related to changing structure, management and composition of woods, especially increased shading, loss of open spaces and decline in plant species diversity. Such factors are undoubtedly

Table 15
The Red Data Book and Nationally Notable Lepidoptera of the New Forest.

Status	All records	Post 1980	% decline
RDB1	16	2	87.5
RDB2	9	4	55.6
RDB3	35	16	54.3
RDB4	2	0	100
RDBI	2	0	100
RDBK	1	0	100
RDB Appendix (Extinct)	7	2	71.4
Total RDB	**72**	**24**	**66.7**
Notable/Na	26	13	50
Notable/Nb	164	95	42.1
Notable	2	0	100
Total Notable	**192**	**108**	**58.5**
Total RDB and Notable	**264**	**132**	**53.57**

Table 16
The Red Data Book and Nationally Notable Lepidoptera of the New Forest by habitat association.

Habitat category	All records	Post 1980	% decline
Mature trees in ancient semi-natural deciduous woodland	49	38	22.5
Shrub layer in open woodland, rides or clearings	41	19	53.7
Herb layer in open woodland, rides or clearings	41	19	53.7
Coniferous woodland	5	2	60
Humid and wet heath, mires, bogs and fens	48	30	37.5
Dry heathland	27	16	40.7
Open grassland habitats	8	4	50
Open bracken habitats	3	3	0
Domestic areas (gardens and houses)	4	1	75

also relevant to the New Forest woods. Species associated with the canopy layer of trees in mature deciduous woodland of the Forest have maintained their status rather better (Table 16), and lichen-feeding species such as the marbled beauty *Cryphia domestica* have shown population increases. Parsons *et al.* (2005) and Fox *et al.* (2006b) relate this to improved air quality and resultant increase in the status and distribution of various lichens (see Chapter 9).

The principal factors driving the declines in New Forest Lepidoptera are considered to be:

- increased levels of herbivore grazing and browsing, particularly in the Inclosures, leading to a loss of structural diversity;
- greater intensity of management for grazing (burning, re-seeding, scrub clearance);
- direct destruction of habitat caused by forestry operations (e.g. conifer planting, surfacing of rides in Inclosures);
- economic pressures driving land use at the Forest margins (e.g. development, pony paddocks, lack of support for traditional woodland management).

The conservation of butterflies and moths in the New Forest

The Lepidoptera declines identified highlight the need for a landscape-scale strategy for the conservation of Lepidoptera in the New Forest. Despite the loss of abundance and diversity, many national rarities do still occur and the area has considerable potential for habitat restoration and improvement. The New Forest is unique, and one of the very few unfragmented landscapes of semi-natural habitats in central southern England. Although it is important to ensure that the needs of individual species are taken into account, management should attempt to provide sufficient areas of diverse habitat types in order to support functioning metapopulations.

There is cause for optimism, not least of which is due to the changing priorities and initiatives undertaken by the Forestry Commission. Their ongoing work to regulate stock numbers, control deer numbers and undertake dynamic and sustainable forest management in selected Inclosures around Brockenhurst has resulted in:

- restoration of a varied vegetation structure;
- increased foodplant resources;
- increased nectar sources;
- maintenance of early successional habitats.

As a result, the pearl-bordered fritillary is thriving and other key Lepidoptera species, all critically reliant on regulation of grazing in the Inclosures, are benefiting. The upturn in fortunes of the pearl-bordered fritillary is particularly encouraging, as it is a species that has fared particularly badly in south-east England over recent decades, with some 55% of all colonies lost over the period 1997–2004 (Fox *et al.* 2006a). There are now perhaps fewer than 10 colonies of this species in the whole of south-east England, and of these, the New Forest populations near Brockenhurst are the only ones currently showing an increase and expansion, and perhaps the only population with long-term viability. The small pearl-bordered fritillary is similarly one of the fastest declining butterflies in England, and now reduced to just a handful of sites in south-east England. The New Forest supports two or three tiny populations, all critically reliant on regulation of grazing within the fenced Inclosures.

The ancient deciduous woods continue to support a suite of rare RDB3 and UKBAP priority canopy-feeding moths, including such rarities as the scarce merveille du jour *Moma alpium*, the light crimson underwing *Catocala promissa* and the dark crimson underwing *Catocala sponsa*. On the heathlands, continuity of grazing, ensuring cycles of heather regeneration, has ensured the survival of nationally important populations of silver-studded blue *Plebejus argus* and shoulder-striped clover *Heliothis maritima*.

Conclusions

The New Forest is recognised as one of the most important areas for Lepidoptera in the whole of Britain, and has been so for more that 150 years. Even with the declines experienced in the second half of the 20th century it remains an area of exceptional species diversity. Not only is the Lepidoptera fauna of the New Forest valuable in its own right, but it provides a vital food source for many other organisms higher in the food chain (e.g. birds, bats). Furthermore, Lepidoptera are shown to be sensitive indicators of environmental change (Thomas *et al.* 2004, Fox *et al.* 2006a,b, 2007, Greatorex-Davies *et al.* 2007), have a positive public profile (even including moths these days!), and are well-studied with good baseline information.

For the conservation of butterflies and moths in the New Forest, the overriding need is to protect the integrity of the Forest as a landscape, with structural and habitat diversity maintained and enhanced at all scales. If these objectives can be achieved we can be confident that the Forest will remain an area of outstanding natural value with species diversity robust enough to accommodate future change. Change is natural; although it is unrealistic to expect to preserve every last species, by conserving the overall condition of the landscape we will ensure that the rich assemblages of today are replaced by equally rich and diverse assemblages of the future. Central to all this is the need for economic support for traditional grazing practices and for conservation-sensitive forest management. Butterfly Conservation looks forward to further collaboration with all its conservation partners to help achieve these aims.

References

Barker, A. J., Fuller, M. and Shreeves, B. (2000). *Butterfly Conservation South-Central England Regional Action Plan*. Butterfly Conservation, Wareham, Dorset.

Fox, R., Asher, J., Brereton, T., Roy, D. and Warren, M. (2006a). *The state of butterflies in Britain and Ireland*. Pisces Publications, Newbury.

Fox, R., Conrad, K. F., Parsons, M. S., Warren, M. S. and Woiwod, I. P. (2006b). *The state of Britain's larger moths*. Butterfly Conservation and Rothamsted Research, Wareham, Dorset.

Fox, R., Warren, M. S., Asher, J., Brereton, T. M. and Roy, D. B. (2007). *The state of Britain's butterflies, 2007*. Butterfly

Conservation and the Centre for Ecology and Hydrology, Wareham, Dorset.

Goater, B. and Norriss, T. (2001). *Moths of Hampshire and the Isle of Wight*. Pisces Publications, Newbury.

Greatorex-Davies, J. N., Brereton, T. B., Roy, D. B., Middlebrook, I. and Cruickshanks, K. L. 2007. *United Kingdom Butterfly Monitoring Scheme Report for 2006*. CEH, Monks Wood, UK.

Green, D. G. (2000). *The status of Lepidoptera in the New Forest*. Report by Butterfly Conservation for the Forestry Commission, Lyndhurst.

Leverton, R. (2001). *Enjoying moths. A practical guide to moths and where to find them and how to breed them*. Poyser Natural History, London.

Oates, M. R. (1996). The demise of butterflies in the New Forest. *British Wildlife*, 7 (4), 205–216.

Oates, M. R., Taverner, J. H. and Green, D. G. (2000). *The butterflies of Hampshire*. Pisces Publications, Newbury.

Parsons, M. S., Fox, R., Conrad, K. F., Woiwod, I. P. and Warren, M. S. (2005). British Moths: throwing light on a new conservation challenge. *British Wildlife*, 16, 386–394.

Parsons, M. S., Green, D. and Sterling, P. H. (2001). The rediscovery of *Scythris empetrella* Karsholt & Nielsen, 1976 (Lepidoptera: Scythrididae) in the New Forest, with notes on the distribution of the species in Britain. *Entomologist's Gazette*, 52(3), 149–150.

Thomas, J. A., Telfer, M. G., Roy, D. B., Preston, C., Greenwood, J. J. D., Asher, J., Fox, R., Clarke, R. T. and Lawton, J. H. (2004). Comparative losses of British butterflies, birds and plants and the global extinction crisis. *Science*, 303, 1879–1881.

Appendix
The 'lost' Lepidoptera of the New Forest.

The 2000 study referred to in the text identified the following Red Data Book and Nationally Notable species that had not been recorded from the New Forest since before 1980, and were considered likely to no longer occur. Species listed in square brackets are considered to require confirmation. There have been further losses since 1980, most notably the UK BAP Priority butterflies, the high brown fritillary *Argynnis adippe* and the marsh fritillary *Euphydryas aurinia* (Oates *et al*. 2000). Conversely, a few species have been re-found, including the RDB1 micromoth *Scythris empetrella*, rediscovered near Lyndhurst after a gap of 167 years (Parsons *et al*. 2001). Losses of species with no UK conservation status have never been quantified. It is hoped that future studies of the Lepidoptera of the New Forest National Park area will allow this list to be updated.

Code	Species	Status	Code	Species	Status
0021	*Ectoedemia sericopeza*	Na	0373	Currant clearwing *Synanthedon tipuliformis*	Nb
0118	*Enteucha acetosae*	Nb	0374	Yellow-legged clearwing *Synanthedon vespiformis*	Nb
0133	Currant shoot borer *Lampronia capitella*	Nb	0375	White-barred clearwing *Synanthedon spheciformis*	Nb
0163	Forester *Adscita statices*	Nb	0377	Sallow clearwing *Synanthedon flaviventris*	Nb
0168	New Forest Burnet *Zygaena viciae*	RDB1	0380	Red-tipped clearwing *Synanthedon formicaeformis*	Nb
0183	*Bacotia claustrella*	Nb	0381	Large red-belted clearwing *Synanthedon culiciformis*	Nb
0188	*Proutia betulina*	Nb	0431	*Yponomeuta sedella*	Nb
0191	*Acanthopsyche atra*	Nb	0457	*Ypsolopha lucella*	Nb
0207	[*Myrmecozela ochraceella*]	Nb	0593	[*Elachista regificella*]	Nb
0220	*Nemapogon clematella*	Nb	0624	*Biselachista trapeziella*	pRDB3
0234	Tapestry Moth *Trichophaga tapetzella*	Nb	0634	*Schiffermuellerina grandis*	pRDB1
0258	*Leucoptera lathyrifoliella*	Nb	0638	*Denisia augustella*	pRDB1
0311	*Dialectica imperialella*	Nb	0645	*Borkhausenia minutella*	pRDB1
0344	*Phyllonorycter strigulatella*	Nb	0668	*Luquetia lobella*	Nb

Code	Species	Status	Code	Species	Status
0680	*Depressaria albipunctella*	Nb	1529	Silver-spotted skipper *Hesperia comma*	RDB3
0715	*Agonopterix capreolella*	pRDB1	1539	Swallowtail *Papilio machaon*	RDB2
0718	*Ethmia dodecea*	Nb	1541	Wood white *Leptidea sinapis*	Nb
0720	*Ethmia bipunctella*	pRDB1	1548	Black-veined white *Aporia crataegi*	Extinct
0744	*Monochroa arundinetella*	pRDB1	1556	Brown hairstreak *Thecla betulae*	Nb
0791	*Chionodes distinctella*	Nb	1559	Black hairstreak *Satyrium pruni*	RDB4
0799	*Neofriseria singula*	pRDB2	1576	Adonis blue *Lysandra bellargus*	Nb
0808	*Platyedra subcinerea*	Na	1578	Mazarine blue *Cyaniris semiargus*	Extinct
0836	*Caryocolum kroesmanniella*	Nb	1594	Large tortoiseshell *Nymphalis polychloros*	Extinct
0851	*Dichomeris alacella*	Nb	1612	Glanville fritillary *Melitaea cinxia*	RDB3
0865	*Dichomeris derasella*	pRDB1	1633	Small eggar *Eriogaster lanestris*	Nb
0877	*Stathmopoda pedella*	Nb	1636	Grass eggar *Lasiocampa trifolii*	Na
0887	*Mompha lacteella*	pRDB3	1644	Kentish glory *Endromis versicolora*	Na
0896	*Cosmopterix orichalcea*	pRDB3	1664	Rest harrow *Aplasta ononaria*	RDB3
0908	*Sorhagenia rhamniella*	Na	1696	Bright wave *Idaea ochrata*	RDB1
0917	*Scythris empetrella*	pRDB1	1714	Portland ribbon wave *Idaea degeneraria*	RDB3
0926	*Phalonidia manniana*	Nb	1718	Oblique striped *Phibalapteryx virgata*	Nb
0930	*Gynnidomorpha alismana*	Nb	1731	Chalk carpet *Scotopteryx bipunctaria*	Nb
0931	*Gynnidomorpha luridana*	Nb	1787	Argent and sable *Rheumaptera hastata*	Nb
0943	*Aethes margarotana*	RDB2	1833	Bleached pug *Eupithecia expallidata*	Nb
0952	*Commophila aeneana*	Nb	1841	Yarrow pug *Eupithecia millefoliata*	Nb
0963	*Cochylis flaviciliana*	Nb	1872	Blomer's rivulet *Discoloxia blomeri*	Nb
0976	*Archips oporana*	pRDB1	1877	Waved carpet *Hydrelia sylvata*	Nb
1034	*Spatalistis bifasciana*	Nb	1878	Drab looper *Minoa murinata*	Nb
1052	*Acleris umbrana*	pRDB1	1908	[Dark bordered beauty *Epione vespertaria*]	RDB3
1069	*Celypha aurofasciana*	Nb	1946	Speckled beauty *Fagivorina arenaria*	Extinct
1100	*Endothenia pullana*	pRDB3	1982	Narrow-bordered bee hawk *Hemaris tityus*	Na
1101	*Endothenia ustulana*	pRDB3	2012	White prominent *Leucodonta bicoloria*	Extinct
1121	*Ancylis upupana*	pRDB3	2013	Plumed prominent *Ptilophora plumigera*	Na
1149	*Epinotia crenana*	pRDB3	2041	Dotted footman *Pelosia muscerda*	RDB3
1164	*Zeiraphera rufimitrana*	Nb	2053	Speckled footman *Coscinia cribraria*	RDB1
1171	*Gypsonoma minutana*	Nb	2062	Water ermine *Spilosoma urticae*	Nb
1180	*Epiblema tetragonana*	Nb	2137	Great brocade *Eurois occulta*	Na
1194	*Eucosma aemulana*	Nb	2148	Pale shining brown *Polia bombycina*	Nb
1206	*Clavigesta sylvestrana*	Nb	2149	Silvery arches *Polia trimaculosa*	Nb
1325	*Platytes alpinella*	pRDB3	2153	Bordered gothic *Heliophobus reticulata*	Na
1341	*Eudonia lineola*	Nb	2191	Double line *Mythimna turca*	Nb
1357	*Evergestis extimalis*	Nb	2242	Sword-grass *Xylena exsoleta*	Nb
1359	*Cynaeda dentalis*	pRDB3	2257	Orange upperwing *Jodia croceago*	RDB1
1373	*Paratalanta pandalis*	Na	2313	Angle-striped sallow *Enargia paleacea*	Nb
1381	*Anania funebris*	Na	2315	Heart moth *Dicycla oo*	RDB3
1396	*Mecyna flavalis*	pRDB2	2317	White-spotted pinion *Cosmia diffinis*	Na
1410	*Agrotera nemoralis*	pRDB1	2325	Crescent striped *Apamea oblonga*	Nb
1465	*Nephopterix angustella*	Nb	2378	Brighton wainscot *Oria musculosa*	Na
1480	*Homoeosoma nebulella*	Nb	2392	Marsh moth *Athetis pallustris*	RDB3
1505	*Stenoptilia pneumonanthes*	RDB2	2393	Reddish buff *Acosmetia caliginosa*	RDB1
1525	Chequered skipper *Carterocephalus palaemon*	RDB4	2465	Four-spotted *Tyta luctuosa*	Na
1528	Lulworth skipper *Thymelicus acteon*	Na	2493	Dotted fan-foot *Macrochilo cribrumalis*	Nb

7 The New Forest cicada and other invertebrates

Bryan J. Pinchen and Lena K. Ward

Introduction

The New Forest supports important populations of a wide range of invertebrates associated with many different habitats. The woodlands are recognised as being of outstanding importance, and one of the ecological characteristics giving them national and international importance is an exceptionally rich invertebrate fauna, particularly the deadwood invertebrate fauna. Inside the Forest perambulation (as opposed to just the SAC) 445 species of Coleoptera, Hemiptera, Diptera, Orthoptera and allies and Hymenoptera (published data to April 1999) that are categorised as Nationally Scarce and Red Data Book (all categories) species (Pinchen 1999) occur, from a UK total of 2,330 species in these groups (see also Table 17 for the SAC totals). This can broken down by habitat into Bog Woodland 17 species, Forestry Inclosures 34, Ancient and Ornamental Woodland 166, Riverine Woodland 20, Dry Heath 70, Wet Heath 40, Mires 41, Temporary and Permanent Pools 31, Rivers and Streams 23, Wet Grassland 22 and Dry Grassland 9 species. (Repetition of species occurs where they may be present in, or dependent on, more than one New Forest habitat.) These figures were pooled from the unpublished invertebrate site registers held by English Nature and the Hampshire Biodiversity Information Centre (Court 1998, English Nature 1985), and largely cover the period between 1970 and 1998. Overall this seems a rather small total when considered against the range of different habitats and the total of 29,262 ha (SAC) of available habitat in this southern county in the UK, where there is a high species richness of other groups. Unfortunately data are not available to compare these figures with other similarly sized individual habitat features (e.g. other Bog Woodlands).

There are serious difficulties in providing an overview of the current status of the invertebrate fauna because, with the exception of Lepidoptera and Odonata (see Chapters 4 and 6), the New Forest seems to have been poorly recorded for invertebrates over recent years. For example, the stag beetle *Lucanus cervus* was recorded as nationally rare (Cox 1997). However, a recent national survey received over 10,000 records (Robb 2001), suggesting that this species should no longer be regarded as nationally rare. This survey also revealed that the species was commoner in local gardens than in the New Forest itself, although the latter has not yet been systematically surveyed for this species (see Chapter 5). Conversely, other rare species have not been recorded for many years and may be extinct.

For many insects a lack of recorder effort may also be related to a reduction in the numbers of specialist entomologists, and to a consensus that there has been a decline in the number of insects to collect, as well as the general unwillingness of many entomologists to undertake surveys because of the need for permit application and Public Liability Insurance now required even to wield a net. Even recent innovations such as the LIFE II and LIFE III Projects (see Chapter 17) have focused on undertaking (often dramatic) habitat management works with little consideration given to surveying the habitats either prior to or after such works are undertaken, to assess their effectiveness in providing 'improved' habitats. Large-scale habitat changes should be more carefully monitored in future.

This chapter first provides an overview of one of the most notable insects associated with the area, the New Forest cicada *Cicadetta montana*. This provides a relatively well documented example of a species that has declined significantly in recent years, apparently as a result of a reduction in habitat availability resulting from changing management practices in the New Forest. In particular, an increase in grazing pressure appears to have had a negative impact on the abundance of this species. The potential impacts of grazing of a range of other invertebrate species, associated with a variety of different habitats, are then considered.

Table 17
Notable invertebrates by group and status, recorded in the New Forest SAC (adapted from Wright and Westerhoff 2001). (RDB refers to Red Data Book).

Status	Coleoptera	Hymenoptera	Diptera	Orthoptera	Hemiptera	Araneae	Crustacea	Annelida	Mollusca
RDB1	16	5	7	1	1	-	-	-	-
RDB2	6	3	13	1	-	-	1	-	-
RDB3	23	17	28	1	5	1	1	1	1
RDBK	6	1	2	-	-	-	-	-	-
Notable A	34	6	-	3	-	-	-	-	-
Notable B	138	8	33	6	3	-	-	-	-
Notable	17	-	17	-	-	-	-	-	-
Total	**240**	**40**	**100**	**12**	**9**	**1**	**2**	**1**	**1**

The New Forest cicada

The problems of understanding the status of a rare insect are illustrated by the New Forest cicada, *Cicadetta montana*. As the only representative of the Cicadidae in Britain, this species is something of a speciality of the New Forest, which is the only area in the country where the insect is now thought to occur. The ecology and conservation of this species are described in detail by Pinchen and Ward (2002), on which this brief account is based.

This species has always been very sporadic in occurrence, being recorded from only 26 New Forest localities since 1812 (Pinchen and Ward 2002). A good site near Brockenhurst was well known to collectors until about 1913, and there were a few records between the two World Wars, but after a sighting in 1941 the species was then thought to be extinct. In 1962 a population of about 100 singing males was discovered in the northern part of the New Forest. This population was monitored and studied for 30 years during its long decline to only a few specimens in the mid-1990s (Grant and Ward 1992, Grant 1972, 1970). Since 1991, when the species was included in the English Nature Species Recovery Programme, there have been publicity campaigns for naturalists to search for this elusive insect, as well as surveys by specialists, but there have been only a very few records of possible song in this period.

The cicada is most closely associated with open deciduous woodland, with scattered bushes and wide clearings. The adult phase typically lasts from two to four weeks, with adults usually on the wing from late May to mid-July. Eggs are oviposited in small-diameter stems of herbaceous plants, bracken, and small trees and bushes. Nymphs have been observed feeding on the roots of purple moor-grass *Molinia caerulea*, and may also feed on other species, although this has not been confirmed in the New Forest; adults feed on small twigs of various trees, where they suck the phloem.

The cicada occupies the successional habitat between open heath or grassland and scrubby woodland, and requires open sunny woodland rides and clearings, bordered by scrub or woodland edge. South-facing, well-drained slopes are preferred, and a structured and mixed flora of herbs and shrubs is essential, to provide food sources and oviposition sites. Heavily grazed sites are wholly unsuitable; as a result, all modern records have been made in relatively ungrazed forestry Inclosures. Adults disperse to found new colonies when the successional habitat of young scrub becomes overgrown, but these new populations are particularly hard to find. This is because colonies may be very small and intermittent, with a long generation time of between six and 10 years underground, as well as the short flight season, often among trees, and the high-frequency male song that is inaudible to most persons over 40 years of age. There have been definite records up to 1996 on the northern known area and around Denny Wood, and there have been other possible records of song since then.

However, numbers of singing males declined markedly at this known northern site from around 100 in 1962 to around four or five in the early 1970s, with only occasional observations made since then.

The decline in the cicada population can be attributed to habitat changes, resulting from succession to woodland, and changing forestry practices; traditional coppice rotations are more likely to provide suitable conditions than the longer rotations employed by modern commercial forestry. The cicada might have moved around in coppice/felled systems, which would have provided a sufficiently long rotation time to complete their life cycle, but we envisage this as a 'hanging-on' situation compared with natural forest glades under intermittent grazing. In more 'natural' systems the cicada and other insects would have been associated with the transitional woodland edge zone where successional scrub of the right size and age would have been present. The preferred cicada habitat is of ungrazed warm glades with small shrubs and taller herbs where oviposition can occur at lower levels in stem diameters of about 5–15 mm. However, shorter, younger scrub, and even blackthorn *Prunus spinosa*, a noted host of ovipositing cicadas in continental Europe, are quite scarce in these situations. This may be why oviposition in bracken occurs in the New Forest (not recorded elsewhere), although this tends to be an unsuitable host because the stems often split before the nymphs emerge in the autumn.

Most significantly, when the cicada was rediscovered in 1962, grazing pressures were less intensive than they are today. Heavy and increased grazing pressure in the Open Forest removed low-growing oviposition sites for females, and the herbs required as a nymphal food source. The graduated transitional zone between open heath and scrub edge and the early successional scrub, which are the favoured habitats, are now relatively rare and are mostly confined to the forestry Inclosures. Proposals to remove Inclosure fences are likely to lead to the loss of lightly grazed scrub, and are likely to have further negative effects on the cicada, as on many other invertebrate species (Pinchen 2000).

The impacts of grazing

Changes to the grazing regime and management of the heaths and woodlands on a significant scale are likely to have had a detrimental effect on various insect species and their habitats. Grazing levels have increased since the fencing and gridding of the Forest perambulation in the early 1960s, and the ways in which the woodlands and heaths are managed have changed considerably since the decline of 'traditional' commoning (e.g. bracken is no longer harvested for bedding or fodder, and turfs are no longer cut/removed). However, as there has been a serious lack of directed quantitative survey and research on the current status of invertebrates, the evidence for declines (or gains) can be hard to establish. A minimal survey was funded in 1998 and 1999 to look at a few

Inclosures that were proposed to be opened to livestock. While the overriding message of the report was that more survey was needed and that opening the Inclosures to the heavy grazing pressure of the Open Forest would be quite detrimental to insects (Pinchen 2000), they were still opened and no further survey or research appears to have been undertaken since then to assess the impact. Searches of historical records prior to this survey produced none more recent than a 1985 NCC Butterfly Survey.

Many entomologists consider that the New Forest is currently under very severe grazing pressure, and as a consequence the habitat quality for many insect groups that were formerly considered typical of the area has degenerated markedly. Very few terrestrial insect species have been recorded in recent entomological surveys on the Open Forest. Even those regarded as being common, widespread and familiar elsewhere are rarely recorded and often absent. However, while the decline of butterflies in the New Forest Inclosures has been highlighted by Oates (1995) (see Chapter 6), care must be exercised when attributing declines in insects solely to increases in grazing pressure on the Open Forest alone. The intensification of farmsteads within the Forest and the loss of small rotationally managed fields must also have had a devastating effect upon insect populations in the Forest, as it has throughout the wider countryside.

Invertebrates in grazed areas (Open Forest)

Stock densities have increased across the Forest as a result of the fencing and gridding of the perambulation. Current levels of pony stocking are at an all-time high with an increase in pony numbers from about 1,700 in 1960 to 3,500–4,000 in the 1990s, although this was initially offset by a decline in the numbers of cattle after the 1960s. By the 1990s the head count of cattle had returned to the figures depastured previously (Tubbs 1997). Some of the responses by commoners (who no longer ran stock on the Forest) to a questionnaire published in 1984 indicated that the quality of grazing had declined (Countryside Commission 1984). In addition to this, the provision of supplementary winter feed (which is allowed in some circumstances, and provided without permission in others) for livestock also suggests both a lack of winter grazing available on the Open Forest, and a lack of sufficient fall-back land to support the numbers of stock. This would suggest that there are either too many animals present for the grazing available or that the winter grazing is of poor quality. Either way the number of depastured livestock needs to be reassessed and ideally significantly reduced. The decline of rotationally managed pastures off the Forest has also had a significant effect, as was seen when the livestock (cattle) were culled during the 2001 Foot and Mouth outbreak, as Forest farmsteads could not support the numbers of livestock depastured (B.J.P., pers. obs.).

Putman (1986) classified New Forest grasslands in relation to grazing as 'short grass' <20 mm, while long grass was described as being within the height range '20–50 mm'! This illustrates the over-grazed nature of the Forest grasslands, as very few herbs are given the opportunity to flower or grow to their normal size and grass tussocks do not form as they would if stocking rates were reduced. In his analysis of the 'effects of the grazing on the Forest's other animals', Putman (1986) does not mention vegetation height in relation to invertebrates, but many of the associated insects would be seriously affected, with immediate damage or loss caused by direct trampling and the removal of eggs, larvae and even adults. At the same time the loss of habitat variously affects feeding, reproduction, sheltering and hibernation sites. Elsewhere it has been shown that species richness of plants peaks in shorter grassland, but the species richness of insects is greater in tall ungrazed (or more lightly grazed) grasslands (Pöyry et al. 2006, Kruess and Tscharntke 2002).

A variety of grassland heights is important in conserving a range of insects; e.g. different turf heights are used by different grassland butterflies, ranging from 0–4 cm for Adonis blue Lysandra bellargus to 20–>30 cm for wood white Leptidea sinapis (Oates 1995). These species are not directly relevant to the New Forest, but illustrate the way in which invertebrates utilise the range of structural variation within grassland habitats. Brown and Searle (1974) described the Orthoptera as being 'very common' in the Forest in 1972, but bush crickets and grasshoppers are now scarce on the Open Forest as there are fewer places for them to feed and their numbers are greatly reduced; because of the increase in grazing and browsing pressure, many now have a patchy distribution. Otherwise widespread species such as the common green grasshopper Omocestus viridulus also appear to have declined since the early 1990s, and records are very scarce in recent times (B.J.P., pers. obs.). The Inclosures that have the best ground flora structure are now probably the main stronghold of this group (Tubbs 1986; B.J.P., pers. obs.). Similarly, Heteroptera appear to be particularly scarce in the New Forest, apart from a few tree and shrub specialists, because of the loss of the herb layer that the majority feed on. Many terrestrial heteropterans feed on plant sap obtained from soft-stemmed herbs or feed on plant seeds. Plants do not grow to any appreciable height owing to the grazing, so that stem availability is reduced, and the removal of flowers eliminates seed production.

This loss of diverse, continuous and varied flower resources seriously affects nectar-feeding and pollinating insects. Indeed, the greatest numbers and diversity of these insects can be found on the road verges within the Forest that are not grazed but are occasionally mown. Good examples with varied structure and a variety of flower-heads can be seen in summer on the A337 (Lyndhurst to Lymington) and the A35 (Lyndhurst to Christchurch) roads that cut through the forest. On these road verges grazing pressure is largely non-existent (mowed twice a year), flowers are plentiful and there is a noticeable variation in the vegetation structure (B.J.P., pers. obs.). Comparative survey of road verges and the open forest would be an interesting subject for future study.

These nectar- and pollen-dependant species are particularly hard hit by heavy and continuous grazing pressure. The most obviously affected species are the Hymenoptera (bees, ants and wasps) and the Diptera (flies). From personal observations, the bulk of Hymenoptera recorded during visits to the Open Forest and the Inclosures are those that provision their nests with paralysed live prey, such as homopteran bugs that have often been collected from trees and shrubs. Limited numbers of adult Hymenoptera are recorded on flowers, including species that are parasitoids or aculeate bees and wasps that nest in standing dead wood, while a few use bare ground. Many of the adult Diptera recorded on flowers develop as larvae in rot holes (e.g. some hoverflies), in the sap-runs of old trees, in decaying plant material or in dung (e.g. robberflies, Asilidae). The large and impressive hornet robberfly *Asilus crabroniformis*, a BAP species, is exceptionally rare on the Open Forest (B.J.P., pers. obs.) but abundant on the grasslands and heaths outside the perambulation to the south near Fawley and across the Dorset heaths. This species requires animal dung for oviposition but preys as an adult on terrestrial and usually highly mobile insects, and is likely to have been affected by the absence of insect prey. Even familiar species such as bumblebees *Bombus* spp. are hard to find because there are so few forage resources available throughout the summer period, and these species need a constant forage source from March through to September.

The spread of bracken on the Open Forest because of its resistance to grazing also has a deleterious effect on insects and invertebrates, e.g. grasshoppers (Ragge 1965). This is due to both the shading of the ground flora reducing host plants and the lowering of the ground temperature, which can have a serious effect on surface and underground stages of many insects (e.g. the cicada).

In recent years a severe threat has appeared to species that nest in bare ground, especially solitary bees and wasps. A recent trend has seen the 'improvement' of sandy footpaths and tracks for access to bicycles and horses by resurfacing them with compacted gravel and clay. Not only does this imprison any species that had already nested, but makes the new surface wholly unsuitable for nest excavation. Between 130 and 180 species of ground-nesting solitary bees and wasps may nest in and around sandy exposures on tracks, footpaths and bridleways, along with as yet undetermined numbers of beetles, flies and bugs. Despite awareness of this damaging practice being raised by the Heathland Fly BAP group, little consideration appears to be paid to the concerns at present (S. Miles, pers. comm.). A survey of invertebrates utilising newly created areas of bare ground at Hyde Common in the north of the New Forest, near Mockbeggar, has shown that species with a dependence on bare ground for nesting can decline in numbers quickly, as the bare areas revegetated after as little as three or four years. These areas need to be regularly disturbed (Pinchen 2007).

The removal of large carrion is another overlooked invertebrate habitat issue that requires some consideration on both the open forest and in the woodlands. When grazing animals die they are removed from the Forest as soon as possible. This therefore prevents the large-mammal carrion invertebrates and their predators from playing their natural part in the ecosystem.

Invertebrates in woodlands (Open Forest and Inclosures)

Here we discuss the current condition of the woodland habitats in relation to insects and invertebrates, and assess some of the threats faced by a range of invertebrate groups. It is useful also to consider the dynamic aspects of woodland communities (see Chapter 13) and how these should be temporally balanced from the earliest seral stages through all ages leading to ancient high forest (Chatters and Sanderson 1994). At the present time the temporal sequence is unbalanced (Tubbs 1986), with a paucity of young regenerating stands and over-representation of ancient dying trees. The New Forest cicada is an example of an insect that is particularly associated with ungrazed seral scrub and woodland edges. Some aspects of recent research (Pinchen and Ward 2002) have led to insights into this diminishing habitat. Other species may be similarly affected, based on anecdotal evidence gathered over a number of years both within and on land immediately outside the New Forest.

There are different woodland types; those woodlands (and grasslands) on shallow sandy soils are likely to have a more impoverished flora compared to those on the richer clays. However, each will have its own unique assemblage of invertebrates that will be adapted to these conditions. Woodlands comprising chiefly beech *Fagus sylvatica* and pine *Pinus sylvestris*, and particularly plantations of conifers, contain fewer flowering plants/fauna owing to their lower light availabilities under the canopy.

Open woodlands with old trees are of particular significance for the saproxylic insect fauna (see Chapter 5). Two UK sites, the New Forest and Windsor Forest and Great Park, have been identified as of potential international importance for their saproxylic invertebrate fauna (and bryophytes) by the Council of Europe (Speight 1989). However, of the 10 species on the grouped JNCC Action Plan (JNCC 2007) none appears to have been recorded in the New Forest post 1970 (but see Chapter 5). Saproxylic habitats in old pasture woodlands are less susceptible to excessive grazing pressure (although the adult stages of many saproxylic invertebrates do also have a requirement for nectar and pollen). The lifetimes of these old tree habitats are relatively long and currently reasonably good, but nevertheless there is a need to maintain a supply of replacement trees, which will eventually be a problem in the New Forest because of the currently uneven age structure of the trees of the forest (Tubbs 1986).

The Inclosures currently provide a habitat with a mixed vegetation structure and availability of the flower resources and taller herbs that are poorly represented elsewhere in the Forest. It is only really in these areas where nectar- and pollen-dependent insects and successional habitat species can survive. However, even these Forestry Inclosures are significantly browsed by deer, as well as grazed by ponies that are not completely excluded by the fencing, so that in practice this habitat component is not well represented. The regeneration of scrub and young trees is almost non-existent and the shrub layer often very poor. This distinct lack of scrub has an effect on invertebrate populations, as also on small mammals and birds (particularly passerines, which can be surprisingly scarce in the Forest woodlands; see Chapter 1). Many adult deadwood (and other) insects can be found at hawthorn *Crataegus* sp. blossom in the spring and the lack of this shrub and other early flowering shrubs may be one reason why there appear to be so few records of adult deadwood insects. The general paucity of many butterflies, particularly woodland species, e.g. silver-washed fritillary *Argynnis paphia* and white admiral *Limenitis camilla* is probably attributable to the lack of flowering brambles *Rubus* spp., brought about by the browsing and grazing pressure that affects many invertebrates (Stewart 2001). At present the Inclosures with least grazing pressure and the woodlands on the outskirts of the Forest perambulation that are being managed with controlled grazing or careful mowing regimes appear to support a greater diversity of insects than the Open Forest and its woodlands (Palmer 2000).

Personal observations and limited survey from two ungrazed/controlled grazed woodlands in the New Forest area have shown a greater diversity of insect species than many of the Forest Inclosures. The two woodlands were Sims Wood (part of the North Solent National Nature Reserve near Beaulieu) and Roydon Wood (Hampshire Wildlife Trust reserve) near Brockenhurst. Sims Wood (SU4101) is a mixed deciduous wood (with some conifers) of 58 ha. Light browsing pressure came from a small population of roe deer *Capreolus capreolus* and the wide, floristically rich rides were cut on a two-year rotation with all cut material being removed. Between 1995 and 1999 31 species of butterfly were recorded on regular transects, including silver-washed fritillary, dark green fritillary *Argynnis aglaja*, pearl-bordered fritillary, grizzled skipper and white admiral, all in high numbers. Limited moth trapping work produced 134 species of macromoth including five Nationally Scarce species. Other groups included 155 species of spider with 15 Nationally Scarce species, seven harvestmen and three pseudoscorpions as well as in excess of 50 hoverfly species including one Red Data Book 1 and five Nationally Scarce species. Seventeen species of Orthoptera and allies were also present (Pinchen 1998,

Jones 1997). Roydon Wood (SU310003) is grazed at varying densities at differing times of the year by a small herd of cattle and contained a floristically rich and well-structured sward, and subsequently high numbers of insects. It was described as being '...a wonderful patchwork of many different habitats... but without the pressures of grazing' (Anon 1992). Many of the species present are dependent upon the controlled management regime and would not be able to survive the heavy grazing pressure of the New Forest. Intensive survey in 1998 recorded 1,105 insect species including 17 Red Data List species and 85 Nationally Scarce species (D. Wicks, pers. comm. in 1999, Palmer 2000).

The high numbers of Nationally Scarce and Red Data List species in these two woodlands are almost certainly a product of their lightly grazed nature and the provision of structural variation and a continuum of flower resources throughout the summer season. The total number of Red Data List and Nationally Scarce species in the small but intensive survey of Roydon Wood is almost one quarter of those recorded for the New Forest as a whole (Pinchen 1999). Of this total for Roydon Wood, Diptera made up five of the Red Data List and 20 of the Nationally Scarce species, with half of these species being deadwood specialists (Palmer 2000). It is concluded that these species, and the other insects recorded, are present because of their dependence on the relatively abundant nectaring resources that are available from spring through to autumn, whereas these are almost absent from the remainder of the New Forest.

Many forest or woodland species have a requirement for sheltered sunny open areas (south-facing slopes) with a varied ground flora and little or no grazing, which is best for a range of species and vegetation heights. The New Forest cicada is one good example of an insect needing this type of habitat, as it sings at temperature >20°C in sunny glades where there are younger shrubs with narrow woody stems for oviposition near ground level, together with underground tree roots for the later instars living underground.

Woodland management and insects

The understorey and woodland floor flora in deciduous woodland is most important to many insect species in the spring, before the canopy closes over. Light grazing of the understorey is sometimes essential to maintain plant diversity, and hence the insect diversity associated with it. Heavy uncontrolled grazing, particularly if this is continual, has been shown to be extremely damaging. Tubbs (1986) describes the rapid destruction of the woodland ground flora in Broomy Inclosure following its partial opening up to grazing by Open Forest stock. Such grazing removes all but the most unpalatable species as flowering components of the understorey/woodland floor, and can also lead to excessive poaching over large areas. Cleanliness in modern forestry techniques is another factor affecting insects. The rarity of the white admiral butterfly can be related to the lack of the larval foodplant, honeysuckle *Lonicera* sp., as this is often removed from forest trees during the brashing stage of forestry management.

Clearfell areas in the New Forest are short of the successional flowering shrubs that are especially good for insects (and birds feeding on the insects), probably because the long years of grazing have eliminated species and also because of the length of the forest rotation. These areas are often large, making them exposed, cool and windy, and although they do provide some flower resources for a brief period they are planted quickly after felling and rapidly become unsuitable for all but a few generalist species. Unlike the old coppice system, where compartments were close together and often linked by wide woodland rides, clearfell blocks are often widely spaced apart and not linked together, leading to colonisation problems because species are physically unable to reach these new areas.

Forest rides
Warm, open forest rides provide good habitats for thermophilous insects (Sparks *et al.* 1996, Greatorex-Davies *et al.* 1994) but in the New Forest Inclosures and other associated woodlands the rides tend to be too narrow, with low light availability and poor gradation of vegetation heights between the woodland floor and the canopy. This has to be balanced against the heavier grazing by livestock or wild deer that is more likely to occur on wider rides. Ideally, a ride should be twice as wide as the tallest tree at its margins. Ride management should ensure that there is a gradation from grassland through scrub to canopy and a small proportion of all narrow, sheltered and shady rides need to be retained as a habitat for species such as carabid beetles.

Rotational management for insects
Favourable small, warm sites for insects are rare in both the Inclosures and the Open Forest today. Clearfell areas can provide suitable conditions, but tend to be ephemeral because of speedy replanting in modern forestry, but the management of seral scrub communities is a specialised nature conservation management technique that could be applied in suitable areas of the New Forest. The early stages of seral change depend on reduction or absence of grazing, the initial community and local seed parents (Ward 1990). Temporary exclosures on various time scales can then be used to achieve these early successions, for example those used to protect newly coppiced areas within woodland (Chatters and Sanderson 1994). This type of management is extremely effective in providing suitable habitat for many insect species associated with woodland, with an option to provide also for the establishment of replacement high forest trees. Rotational management for the grassland (Morris *et al.* 2005) in some of the marginal areas of the Forest should also be considered for insects.

Conclusions
Although there are few data available, anecdotal and personal observations suggest that some insects appear to be surviving well at present under the current regime of management of the New Forest. These include those species associated with trees, such as forest tree feeders, those feeding on dead wood and rotting wood and many associated with the abundant woodland fungi. Insects of very short disturbed grassland and those directly associated with the stock and deer such as dung beetles and insects in the main are relatively common. However, other insects associated with tall herbs and scrub and nectar-bearing flowers are not faring so well. These species need a radical reduction in grazing stock numbers with better successional management of the woodlands, especially the early seral stages. These requirements are not compatible with the current management of the New Forest, and although a range of species requires, or can tolerate, these less than ideal conditions, the question of what proportion of the Forest should be maintained in these relatively species-poor (for invertebrates) conditions must be addressed.

Tubbs (1986) stated that the proportion of Open Forest to total New Forest area was 50%, with the Forestry Inclosures occupying an area of about 25%. Creating open grazing (and conditions similar to those currently available on the Open Forest) to replace the Forest Inclosures should therefore be a low priority. Improved management within the woodlands, including controlled and appropriate grazing, better ride design, and provision of replacement native trees for conservation is of much higher priority. Unless major changes take place it is unlikely that the Forest will ever be as 'good' for insects as it was formerly famous for, and we will not see woodland rides of the quality of those just yards outside the perambulation that are free from the pressures of constant heavy grazing. We know of no other SSSI that would be allowed to be so heavily and continuously grazed and still classified as being in 'favourable condition', particularly at a site where insects are said to be one of the primary groups of international importance.

References
Anon. (1992). *Nature reserves guide*. Hampshire and Isle of Wight Wildlife Trust.

Brown, A. J. and Searle, C. A. (1974). The native Orthoptera of the New Forest. *Entomologists' Gazette*, 25, 85–92.

Chatters, C. and Sanderson, N. (1994). Grazing Lowland Pasture Woods. *British Wildlife*, 6, 78–88.

Countryside Commission. (1984). *The New Forest Commoners*. Countryside Commission Report CCP164.

Court, N. (1998). *Invertebrate Site Register for the New Forest, records to 1995*. Unpublished Data.

Cox, J. (1997). *New Forest Natural Area Profile*. Jonathon Cox Associates, Lymington.

English Nature (1985). *Invertebrate Site Register: The New Forest*. Unpublished report. English Nature, Peterborough.

Grant, J. A. (1970). Search for our insect singer (*Cicadetta montana*). *Countryside. Journal of the English Naturalist's Association*, 21, 301–307.

Grant, J. A. (1972). Conserving Britain's cicada (*Cicadetta montana*). *Countryside. Journal of the English Naturalist's Association*, 22, 8–11.

Grant, J. A. and Ward, L. K. (1992). *English Nature Species Recovery Programme – New Forest cicada (Cicadetta montana Scopoli) (Hemiptera: Cicadidae)*. English Nature/NERC Contract.

Greatorex-Davies, J. N., Sparks, T. H. and Hall, M. L. (1994). The response of Heteroptera and Coleoptera species to shade and aspect in rides of coniferised lowland woods in southern England. *Biological Conservation*, 67, 255–273.

JNCC. (2007). *Biodiversity Action Plans. Grouped statement for saproxylic beetles*. JNCC, Peterborough. www.ukbap.org.uk/UKPlans.aspx?ID=341#4

Jones, D. (1997). *North Solent National Nature Reserve. Compartment 7. Sims Wood SU4101. Arachnological Survey 24 April to 24 October 1997*. Unpublished Report to English Nature.

Kruess A. and Tscharntke, T. (2002). Contrasting responses of plant and insect diversity to variation in grazing intensity. *Biological Conservation*, 106, 293–302.

Morris, M. G., Clarke, R. T. and Rispin, W. E. (2005). The success of a rotational grazing system in conserving the diversity of chalk grassland Auchenorrhyncha. *Journal of Insect Conservation*, 9, 363–374.

Oates, M. R. (1995). Butterfly Conservation within the management of grassland habitats. In Pullin, A. S. (ed.) (1995). *Ecology and conservation of butterflies*, pp. 98–111. Chapman and Hall, London.

Palmer, C. J. (2000). *Roydon Woods Reserve, Brockenhurst, Hampshire: the results of a survey of certain dipteran families undertaken during 1998*. Unpublished report to Hampshire Wildlife Trust.

Pinchen, B. J. (1998). *Butterfly Data, North Solent and Kingston Great Common NNRs, 1994 – 1998*. Unpublished Report for English Nature detailing results of Butterfly and Dragonfly Transect Data 1994–1998.

Pinchen, B. J. (1999). *A summary of New Forest invertebrates. Their status and habitat requirements*. Unpublished Report to English Nature.

Pinchen, B. J. (2000). Evaluation of five inclosures. In *The New Forest for invertebrate conservation and potential impact of grazing*. Unpublished report to the Forestry Commission and English Nature.

Pinchen, B. J. (2007). *Hyde Common SSSI. Insect colonisation of newly created bare ground areas. Survey 2007, Year 4 of 5*. Unpublished report to Hampshire County Council.

Pinchen, B. J. and Ward, L. K. (2002). The history, ecology and conservation of the New Forest cicada in Britain. *British Wildlife*, 13, 258–266.

Pöyry, J., Luoto, M., Paukkunen, J., Pykälä, J., Raatikainen, K. and Kuussaari, M. (2006). Different responses of plants and herbivore insects to a gradient of vegetation height: an indicator of the vertebrate grazing intensity and successional age. *Oikos*, 115, 401–412.

Putman, R. J. (1986). Grazing in temperate ecosystems. *Large herbivores and the ecology of the New Forest*. Croom Helm, London.

Ragge, D. (1965). *Grasshoppers, crickets and cockroaches of the British Isles*. Wayside and Woodland Series. F. Warne, London.

Robb, C. (ed.). (2001). *Findings of the 1998 national stag beetle survey*. People's Trust for Endangered Species, London.

Sparks, T. H., Greatorex-Davies, J. N., Mountford, J. O., Hall, M. L. and Marrs, R. H. (1996). The effects of shade on the plant communities of rides in plantation woodland and implications for butterfly conservation. *Forest Ecology and Management*, 80, 197–207.

Speight, M. C. D. (1989). *Saproxylic invertebrates and their conservation*. Nature and Environment Series No. 42. Council of Europe, Strasbourg.

Stewart, A. J. A. (2001). The impact of deer on lowland woodland invertebrates: a review of the evidence and priorities for future research. *Forestry*, 74, 259–270.

Tubbs, C. R. (1997). The ecology of pastoralism in the New Forest. *British Wildlife*, 9, 7–16.

Tubbs, C. R. (1986). *The New Forest*. New Naturalist Series 73. Collins, London.

Ward, L. K. (1990). Management of grassland scrub mosaics. In Hillier, S. H., Wells D. and Walton, D. W. H. (eds.) *Calcareous grasslands, ecology and conservation*, pp. 134–139. Bluntisham Books, Bluntisham.

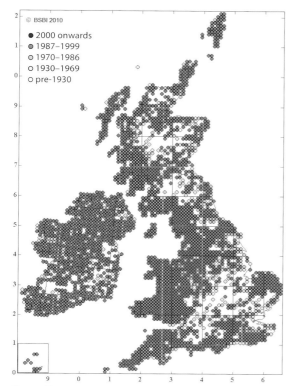

Figure 40
Distribution of marsh pennywort *Hydrocotyle vulgaris* in the UK.

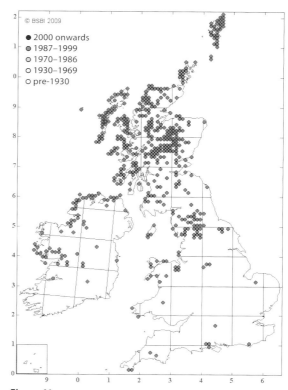

Figure 41
Distribution of field gentian *Gentianella campestris* in the UK.

Surveys carried out across the country by Plantlife International, and in Hampshire by the BSBI, New Forest Study Group and Hampshire Flora Group suggest that the New Forest is now a stronghold for this species in southern Britain, with populations typically one or two orders of magnitude greater than those found elsewhere. Yet this conspicuous and attractive species went largely unremarked here until very recently, and was not noted by the earlier workers on the flora at all.

Environmental characteristics

Appendix 1 gives British Red List species found in the Forest. Appendix 2 details the nationally and regionally significant species (those whose loss from the Forest would have an impact on the status of the plant nationally or internationally), and Appendix 4 gives those undergoing lowland decline; we refer here to these latter two lists collectively as the 'New Forest Notables'.

Each of these lists has been annotated with the Broad Habitat denotations of the habitats where it is known to occur, drawn from Hill *et al.* (2004) and supplemented by the authors' personal knowledge. Ellenberg indicator values for two of the most critical environmental demands (light and nitrogen) have

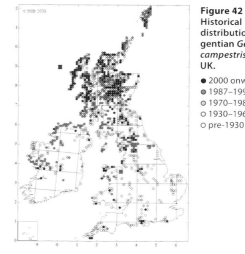

Figure 42
Historical distribution of field gentian *Gentianella campestris* in the UK.

- 2000 onwards
- 1987–1999
- 1970–1986
- 1930–1969
- pre-1930

also been added from the same source, where the scoring system is explained. A further analysis based on the growth height values and life forms given there would be interesting, and might be expected to reinforce the importance of grazing pressures in the Forest, but has not been carried out for the present chapter.

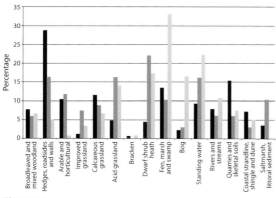

Figure 43
The habitat preferences of the Red List plants and Notables associated with the New Forest.

■ National
■ NF Red List
□ NF Notables

Figure 43 summarises the habitat preferences of the Red List plants and Notables against those of all British taxa. (As species can appear in more than one habitat, the total representation of one of these sets can exceed 100% in total). It is not surprising that acid grassland, heath and bog plants figure so prominently. However all mire and freshwater habitats are heavily represented. The low-intensity land use benefits the entire catchment and drainage; systems, rather than individual habitats within them, deserve to be the subject of conservation. There is nothing remarkable about the representation of woodland species, but coastal and arable plants are notably well-featured, especially on the Red List. Although the representation of calcareous grassland species is lower than the national lists, some people may still be surprised to see how high it is. Calcareous mire species also make up a significant proportion of those appearing under 'Fen, marsh and swamp'. The Tertiary geology of the Forest includes marly limestones, and such terrain has been much prone to agricultural improvements elsewhere in southern England in the past. But the presence of calcicoles also has to do with human activity, as we discuss in a later section.

Figure 44 shows the characterisation of our three groups of species in terms of nitrogen demand. While the national group shows a fairly even spread of taxa across the spectrum, recent works such as Braithwaite *et al.* (2006) give us an inkling of the degree to which species with high nitrogen requirements are in the ascendancy in present-day Britain. Local assessments of cover and biomass would, we are convinced, provide a picture that is even more stark. The New Forest Notables, however, show a very strong bias to low nitrogen demand. The subsidiary bump in the middle of the graph can mostly be attributed to coastal species and those of the middle and lower river systems.

Figure 45 shows a profile for light demand. All groups show a bias towards light-loving plants; as the more open and illuminated habitats tend to be more species-rich in temperate regions, this is to be expected. What is striking is the very small proportion of our Notables set that is tolerant of the higher levels of shading, and the very high proportion demanding high illumination.

These illustrations suggest why the New Forest, which must have been a somewhat special place for our flora for centuries, has become dramatically more so over the last two hundred years. Not only have the habitats supporting its most distinctive members been largely eradicated over the lowlands by building, enclosure, drainage, ploughing and fertilisation; such fragmented areas as remain have often degraded through lack of grazing, enrichment from contingent land and waterways, and the many other exigencies to which small areas of conservation value are continually exposed. In the 1810s, at the time when the Old Series Ordnance Survey maps for Hampshire were being published, a botanically minded curate could have walked the seven miles of Tertiary strata from Otterbourne to Southampton almost entirely on unenclosed land, largely grazed in common, with only the mildest of detours. The only remnant of this that survives, albeit in a much modified state and an urban setting, is Southampton Common itself.

In summary, the New Forest holds an important group of higher plants of Atlantic and Mediterranean–Atlantic distribution. These are distribution patterns for which Britain plays a significant role in biodiversity

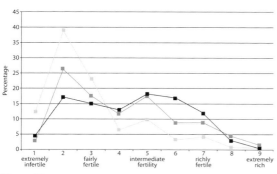

Figure 44
Nitrogen requirement of Red List plants and Notables associated with the New Forest.

□ NF Notables
■ National
■ NF Red List

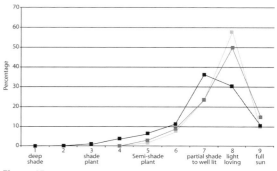

Figure 45
Light requirement of Red List plants and Notables associated with the New Forest.

□ NF Notables
■ National
■ NF Red List

conservation. It also serves as an outpost for Boreal and Boreal–Montane species, in which role it stands as a "relic of a relic" with respect to the former more widespread occurrence of these plants in the lowlands. It is a repository of the declining plants of stressed environments: low in nutrient input, heavily grazed, sporadically burnt, highly illuminated, and low in biomass, but rich in species diversity. It is not just a focus of the always rare, but is a last resort of the formerly common. In this role it assumes importance within the whole of northern Europe, where similar low-input or slow-input pastoral regimes have vanished just as in Britain; and where many species such as small fleabane *Pulicaria vulgaris*, even where they had a wider distribution and once occurred more abundantly on the Continent, are now close to terminal decline.

Our knowledge of the flora

It is not easy to undertake archival research on the Forest's flora and vegetation; much of the knowledge came late. John Goodyer, who held a steward's post at Holbury, supplied a few records in the 17th century, and there were more in Camden's *Britannia* in 1695. Eighteenth-century records came from the herbarium of Dean Garnier and the *Hampshire Repository* of 1799, and the scenic qualities of the Forest were clearly being appreciated by 1791 when Gilpin published his *Remarks on Forest Scenery*; but records remained sparse up to 1830. The 8th and last edition of Hooker and Arnott's *British Flora* in 1860 included just five localities that can be identified to the New Forest, and these include two of the most recent discoveries. By contrast, south-east Hampshire has nearly twice that number, and a single site in neighbouring Sussex (Amberley Wild Brooks) has almost as many. One can speculate that until the last great wave of enclosures, many now valued Forest species went unremarked in the published literature because they would have been of wide occurrence.

Much of the Forest can hardly have been easy of access in earlier centuries, and where early records can be localised at all, they tend to align with a couple of main thoroughfares. There will have been few livings able to sustain our wandering curate with an eye for nature; William Gilpin's Boldre was an obvious exception. The civil parish of Denny Lodge remains one of the least populated in all of England, upland regions included. The coming of the railway in 1847 made the Forest much more accessible from afar, its choice of route simultaneously damaging, and laying open to view, some of the finest lowland valley-mire systems on the Forest and in Europe. Papers on the plant life of the Forest began to appear in numbers in the national journals from the 1850s. Wise's *The New Forest: its History and Scenery*, first published in 1863, had a significant natural history content for the general reader. It is striking how many of the records from the latter half of the 19th century cluster around the railway stations and their closest neighbouring villages.

The 19th century efforts to record the Forest flora in detail, starting with Bromfield, supported by meticulous observers such as the Groves brothers, Trimen and Dyer, and occasionally pronounced on by the great and good of the national botanical scene, culminated in the first edition of Frederick Townsend's *Flora of Hampshire* in 1884. Here for the first time the occurrence, and a view on the abundance, of many New Forest species was documented in an accessible document. Townsend also took an interest in many critical taxa. His account of the Hampshire *Euphrasia* (eyebright) species, which appeared in the 1904 edition of the *Flora*, still makes useful reading.

Marshall was a major contributor at the end of the 19th century, although his contribution is somewhat obscured by being largely sunk within this second edition of the *Flora*. Work by various people, including members of the Hampshire Field Club, continued through the early part of the 20th century, and Rayner's *Supplement* to the *Flora* appeared in 1930. There are archives remaining to be mined from this period; but in general, while knowledge of the Forest was deepening, there was no concerted move towards a comprehensive, systematic, detailed record of the Forest's flora and vegetation.

The initiative for this had to wait until the 1950s, when the idea of a new *Flora of Hampshire* was first mooted. The initial endeavours of Alick Westrup were taken up by others, most notably by Paul Bowman who became one of the three authors of the new *Flora of Hampshire* that eventually appeared in 1996. It is hard to overstate his contribution to our current knowledge of the distribution of New Forest plants; for the more notable taxa, behind every dot on a tetrad map or terse account in the *Flora* there lie precise location details, dates spanning over 40 years, and a brief description of the habitat and population size, meticulously written up in longhand on foolscap sheets. It would be unfair not to pay tribute also to the cohort of botanists, amateur and professional, who supported him in this task either by joining the *Flora* recording and other, national, mapping projects sponsored by the BSBI, or by conducting surveys for individual species. Many of these workers are still, blessedly, alive and active.

Work on the Forest flora since that time has concentrated on computerising the records, with a view to making them more accessible and more amenable to analysis, and on recording individual populations in detail. The advent of hand-held GPS has made it easier to pinpoint populations, allowing better monitoring over time.

Table 18 gives the earliest recorded dates of several Forest notables. Given our preceding remarks it will not be surprising that some had to wait until the mid-19th century to be discovered; but the rate at which further species, by no means all critical or inconspicuous, continued to be found in the next century is striking. A few of these, such as coral-necklace *Illecebrum verticillatum*, are now thought to be recent introductions (Pearman 2008), but this is extremely improbable for most.

Table 18
The earliest recorded dates of selected New Forest notable plant species.

Species	Earliest recorded date
Narrow-leaved lungwort *Pulmonaria longifolia*	1620
Brown beak-sedge *Rhynchospora fusca*	1713
Marsh gentian *Gentiana pneumonanthe*	1836
Marsh clubmoss *Lycopodiella inundata*	1840s
Hampshire-purslane *Ludwigia palustris*	1843
Wild gladiolus *Gladiolus illyricus*	1856
Angular Solomon's-seal *Polygonatum odoratum*	1892
Slender marsh-bedstraw *Galium constrictum*	1924
Small adder's-tongue *Ophioglossum azoricum*	1984
Hay-scented buckler-fern *Dryopteris aemula*	1987

Even more striking is the small number of sites from which many plants were known. For the Forest's most emblematic plant, wild gladiolus *Gladiolus illyricus*, seven sites had been recorded by 1900. From the more readily available documents, we have been unable to find evidence that this had increased to more than nine sites by 1950. It is hard to escape the conclusion that most botanists were content to follow well-trodden paths. Yet the efforts of a very small number of people were able to increase this total to 60 sites by 2000; the overwhelming majority of these were added in the 1950s and 1960s. Bastard balm *Melittis melissophyllum* is an equally showy plant of woodland; in 1950 its total of two known sites in 1900 had been doubled to four, yet by 2000 this had been almost doubled again despite the fact that the plant was almost certainly going into decline by then.

This little history should serve to remind us that if we want to make inferences about 'ideal' conservation practice for New Forest plants based on historical evidence, we have amazingly little to go on. We have a good understanding of the larger and longer-lived organisms – trees – and of the general vegetation communities; these are well-summarised in Tubbs (1968) and Tubbs (2001). We also understand trends in the more distant past through peat bog sampling. But for the majority of individual species, there is no detailed evidence base for the effects of human activity in the last few centuries. Nor has there been much experimental work, unless one counts the 'negative experiments' of the Forestry Commission in the 1960s and 1970s in draining bogs and destroying ancient woodland.

This is not to say that conservation activists should be paralysed by indecision. It is quite well understood how many plant communities will respond to positive intervention when their habitats have become degraded, and this has been largely borne out by a number of bold initiatives taken in the last few years. But it should serve as a warning against attempts to 'micro-manage' for the benefit of this or that

individual species, when those attempts are based largely on supposition.

To summarise our current knowledge: barring a few gaps and excepting some critical groups, we have a very good idea now of where our notable Forest species are to be found, and how they fit into a national picture. We have a reasonable picture of population sizes for some species, with some idea of how they have changed or fluctuated over the past few decades. Something is known of the autecology of a few species in the Forest setting, yet there are many unanswered questions surrounding even such a flagship conservation target as wild gladiolus.

Introductions and exotic plants

Without doubt the most important introductions to the Forest, and the most drastic in their effect, have been of planted trees. Although early plantations were generally of oak *Quercus* spp., conifers have played an increasingly important part until in recent times they predominate. Planting of Scots pine *Pinus sylvestris* appears to have started, at least on any significant scale, as late as the 1820s; the Deer Removal Act of 1851 facilitated the more widespread planting of conifers. This subjected tracts of heathland to enclosure, and to aggressive natural invasion, which has remained a conservation challenge ever since. Scots pine is widespread as a native outside Britain and the provenance of early plantings is obscure, but from the 1920s the Forestry Commission was provenance testing and running selective breeding programmes on a number of species, Scots pine included.

Other coniferous species gained in importance, pre-eminently black pine *Pinus nigra* of which the Corsican pine *P. nigra* ssp. *laricio*, with a better growth form for straight clean timber, is favoured. Weymouth pine *Pinus strobus* was flirted with in the 19th century (along with other pines) but found to suffer from blister rust; its collapsing remains are still visible in a few places. Douglas fir *Pseudotsuga menziesii*, larches *Larix decidua*, *L. kaempferi* and their hybrid *L.* × *marschlinsii*, Norway spruce *Picea abies* and western hemlock *Tsuga heterophylla* all have commercially important stands. This last can show aggressive regeneration inside plantations, but not outside.

Further enclosure, and coniferisation of existing Inclosures, continued until the mid-20th century, and was finally formally halted in 1971. Since then, although replanting with conifers continues in some areas, there has been thinning from mixed stands, and more recently a programme to restore the Verderer's Inclosures to the heath from which they were so recently carved. This has had some spectacular successes in re-establishing heath and mire, for instance at Longdown and Fawley Inclosure.

The forestry practices attendant on new plantations and planting up of ancient woodland have undoubtedly done enormous damage. Most obviously they have swallowed up tracts of the vegetation that gives the New Forest its distinctiveness. Biologically this is probably less significant, though, than the management practices and laissez-faire attitude to grazing within the Inclosures during the second half of the 20th century, which led to catastrophic declines in many species groups; invertebrates were particularly affected (see Chapter 7) but flowering plants also suffered. Ferns may be one of the few vascular plant groups that have benefited from plantation, and even there the picture is not straightforward.

On the other hand, some of the older plantings have now become valued landscape features, and no doubt a public outcry would arise if they were to be done away with completely. They have also brought in new communities of some organisms, notably fungi; see, for instance, Ferris *et al.* (2000) and Chapter 10.

Invasive ericaceous (heath) species have been less of a problem in the New Forest than in some other parts of Britain, but rhododendron *Rhododendron ponticum* is widespread and has been the target of clearance programmes. Unfortunately the enclosed lands within the Forest provide an ever-present reservoir for recolonisation. Anyone doubting the power of this species to obliterate native communities should view the enclosed private woodlands within the National Park around Redlynch, along the northern border with Wiltshire. The shrubby species *Gaultheria shallon* has so far been more of a problem on the Avon Valley heathlands beyond the Forest boundaries. There are several other species that have been introduced onto the Forest, including American cranberry *Vaccinium macrocarpon*, blueberry *Vaccinium corymbosum* and Dorset heath *Erica ciliaris* (which might be native as well as introduced). These all have very small populations and are objects of curiosity to botanists rather than concern.

The Forest's ponds and waterways contain some of its most distinctive and prized plant species and communities, yet these have to contend with a veritable botanical garden of deliberately or inadvertently introduced aquatics. The species of most conservation concern at present is New Zealand pigmyweed *Crassula helmsii*. This aquarist's oxygenating plant appears to have arrived in the Forest in the mid-1970s, since when it has spread to all parts. Figure 46 shows its known distribution across all of South Hampshire before 1987, and at the present day. Although its rate of spread is impressive, what is even more remarkable is that not a single site has been lost since the early records – a highly unusual situation for newly invasive species.

Primarily a plant of ponds and pond margins, its habitat tolerances are in fact quite broad; it can be dredged in a vegetative state from deeper water at Hatchet Pond, yet infests lightly poached damp grassland at North Gorley. At worst, it forms a smothering blanket that inhibits the growth of other plants, including many that are Forest notables. The threat it presents has been questioned; Lockton (BSBI 2007) says 'No evidence has yet emerged for it outcompeting rare native plants'. But whatever the eventual outcome may be on the broader landscape, evidence for its local effects in the Forest is not hard to

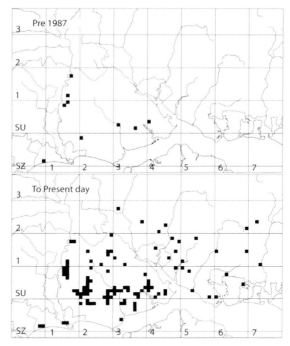

Figure 46
Distribution of New Zealand pigmyweed *Crassula helmsii* in the New Forest and South Hampshire.

find. For instance, the pond at Hilltop, near Beaulieu, became infested in 1983. Hampshire-purslane *Ludwigia palustris* ('fairly plentiful' in 1983) was last recorded there in 1986; slender marsh-bedstraw *Galium constrictum* (a 'dense patch' in 1983) in 1987. These are both nationally rare plants. Up until the present New Zealand pigmyweed continues to form a dense sward across the whole pond and its environs, and neither of the other species has re-established itself.

Since no effective method of control has been found where the solution is not more damaging than the problem, this is a phenomenon that will have to play itself out. The author's own informal observations suggest that of the more notable Forest species, shoreweed *Littorella uniflora* and lesser marshwort *Apium inundatum* seem best able to co-exist with it, while pillwort *Pilularia globulifera* and slender marsh-bedstraw seem least able to compete. This is a topic that deserves more rigorous study.

Similar concerns have been expressed nationally in the past over the waterweed species *Elodea canadensis* and *E. nuttallii*. The first of these has never been widespread in the Forest, seeming to prefer sites linked to larger and more eutrophic waterways in Hampshire. *E. nuttallii* does have quite a broad Forest distribution, but shows no rapid spread and appears on the whole to have reached a state of equilibrium.

The water-primrose species *Ludwigia grandiflora* and *L. peplis*, which are immensely invasive on the Continent and have spread rapidly northwards in our neighbours in recent decades, have mercifully not made dramatic incursions into Britain to date. So far *L. grandiflora* has been recorded in a pond on enclosed land in the Forest, and at a couple of sites 3 km beyond the National Park boundary. They are very beautiful plants but will rapidly engulf a pond, and if they became commercially popular the risk of their being cast out into the wild would be high. The Environment Agency is taking steps to eradicate all populations in the wild and prevent the plants becoming available for sale, with the backing of DEFRA and the Royal Horticultural Society. Although these species are commonest on relatively eutrophic sites, their patent ability to colonise heathland watercourses in the Landes in south-west France should give us pause for thought.

Most of the other ornamental exotic species on the Forest, of which there are many, occupy relatively little ground and out-compete native plants either not at all, or on a very local scale. The conservationist objection to them is therefore largely aesthetic or ethical rather than scientific in basis. Given that the Forest is not a wilderness, do we nevertheless value it more for its wild qualities or as an extension of a suburban garden? Ponds and ditches to the south and west of Brockenhurst and Burley give the impression that a fanatic iris-fancier has been at work, as several carry stands of non-native *Iris*, involving at least three species. These grate on the sensibilities of most expert botanists, but the public at large would not even register them as exceptional; and as far as the author knows, no attempt has been made to eradicate them. Other plants of similar standing include the potentially invasive pickerel-weed *Pontederia cordata*; fringed water-lily *Nymphoides peltata* (native elsewhere in Britain); and coloured garden forms of water-lily that are usually named *Nymphaea marliacea*.

There are interesting 'grey areas' in the spectrum of introductions, some of which excite ambivalence, if not a touch of gentle hypocrisy, in the botanists who observe them; the authors make no claim to be free of such. Of several plantings of exotic carnivorous plants onto Forest mires, only one has been successful (from the point of view of the plant); the pitcher-plant *Sarracenia purpurea*, which is well established over quite a large tract of one bog. It would be hard to claim that it out-competes the native vegetation, but it has been accused of eating rare dragonflies. The author and Dr Richard Gornall spent a sunny afternoon in a profoundly unscientific exercise of tearing pitchers open to find what they contained. Most remains were digested to a point where they were unrecognisable, at least to non-entomologists. Those that could be identified consisted mostly of beetles and flies, the wasp beetle *Clytus arietis* being the most spectacular. No Odonata remains were found. Most botanists would probably deplore this introduction publicly, but most have also been down to admire it.

Many will also have visited the Setley colony of white forget-me-not *Plagiobothrys scouleri*, a North American species, and felt very little need to condemn it. This is perhaps because it is a delicate species that seems to fit in well with the native vegetation it

inhabits, and so does not commit errors of conduct or taste. Pre-eminent in this group must be coral-necklace. While considered native in south-west Britain, it is thought of as a fairly recent arrival in the Forest (see Pearman 2008). It is now widespread and apparently still spreading, and has won an appreciative following as a Forest notable and 'honorary native'.

And so we come to 'cryptic introductions': that is, those species that have a native range nearby, that occur in situations where their status as long-standing natives is called into doubt, but whose arrival remains a matter of supposition. The former military camp between Pigbush and Beaulieu Road station introduced a lot of lime into the roadside soils and gave us at least one undoubted exotic plant, the mouse-ear hawkweed *Pilosella × floribunda*; but what are we to make of the calcicolous plants such as autumn gentian *Gentianella amarella* that also occur there? The three native sweet-briars (*Rosa rubiginosa, R. micrantha* and *R. agrestis*) are thought of primarily as chalk downland plants. They all occur on the Forest and may well be anciently native; yet it is remarkable how many of their sites relate to past disturbance and introduced lime in one form or another. They warn us not to be too doctrinaire in our thinking about 'aliens', and lead us on to a wider issue of Forest land use.

Cautionary tales

Figure 47 gives our assessment of the areas of the Forest that show particularly high vascular plant diversity. These are not, by and large, the least disturbed and most 'natural' areas. Figure 48 shows a further evaluation of these sites according to the degree of human disturbance and modification they have undergone. The 'yellowfield' sites are those where a significant part of the site has been influenced by direct human intervention, for example large-scale peat digging, the liming and reseeding of grassland, and sporadic conversion to arable. 'Brownfield' sites include large-scale gravel workings, marl-pit systems, aerodromes, encampments and bombing ranges. Large brownfield sites are easy to recognise. With more research, no doubt other 'green' sites could be turned 'yellow'. But in addition, many small loci of valued diversity are 'brown' (for example, car park margins and modified road embankments).

The diversity we refer to here is not an incursion of adventitious or 'weedy' species. These certainly crop up, and there are also curiosities such as the endemic downland early gentian *Gentianella anglica,* introduced to a wartime bombing range and still flourishing on its archipelago of dumped chalk. But it includes many flagship Forest species and first-rate habitat indicators. Examples are the endemic eyebright *Euphrasia anglica,* often at its most abundant on previously fertilised grass-heath and on grassland re-established over old military sites, and the Atlantic fern, small adder's-tongue *Ophioglossum azoricum,* found in grass-heath of fairly high base status, but pre-eminently around old marlpits and on World War 2 aerodromes. Many of the lime-

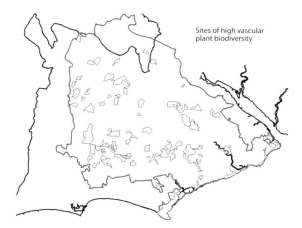

Figure 47
Areas of the New Forest with particularly high vascular plant diversity.

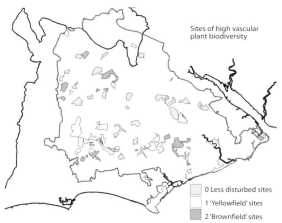

Figure 48
Areas of the New Forest with particularly high vascular plant diversity, according to the degree of human disturbance and modification they have undergone.

loving species and plants of open ground, which might otherwise have a restricted population in the Forest, occur abundantly in such places.

High species richness exists on these sites because of the past disturbance, not in spite of it. There is a difference from incursions such as modern forestry or mire drainage, which have been largely destructive of diversity. This is not to argue for a continued programme of airfield building over the Forest! However, this reminds us that the Forest is not a pristine wilderness, but has a long history of exploitation, which has served to enrich the environment at times as much as to degrade it. Its effects have not been malign because these activities have taken place on a local scale in a big, flourishing, biologically diverse setting. Time has acted not only to restore the initial damage but to exploit new niche

opportunities created. This should be borne in mind when projects to 'restore' the landscape to some assumed pristine state are being considered.

Our final story concerns a single species. Figure 49 shows the New Forest distribution of small fleabane *Pulicaria vulgaris*, which represents almost all of its present-day occurrence in Britain. This annual species is betraying its scientific name by declining rapidly over most of its range in Europe. Our plants thus represent a major conservation opportunity and responsibility. The map shows all historical records and population sizes are not distinguished, but for most of the time an individual site will maintain scores or hundreds of plants (Figure 49).

Populations of small fleabane have been recorded at intervals of a few years over the last 20 years or so, and this effort has captured a succession of population explosions in the period, which are mapped on Figure 50. As one might expect for an annual plant, maintenance of populations and renewal of the seed

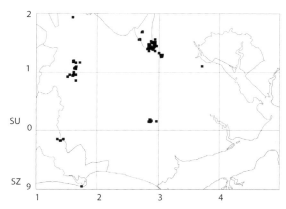

Figure 49
Distribution of small fleabane *Pulicaria vulgaris* in the New Forest.

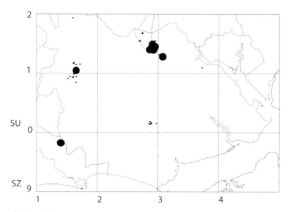

Figure 50
Major population surges of small fleabane *Pulicaria vulgaris* in the New Forest, 1990–2006.

bank depend on disturbance, and this has come in some unlooked-for ways.

For a number of years the biggest and best population occurred on a Forest trackway along which the neighbouring farmer, who also ran a haulage business, despatched his lorries to reach the nearby main road network. Since he has been prevented from following this reprehensible practice, the fleabane population has gone into a slow but steady decline.

However, this is as nothing compared to the commoner who put winter feed out on one of the National Trust commons, attracting a huge congregation of animals and creating a spectacular muddy morass. No doubt he had his knuckles rapped by the powers that be. But the effect was to bring up an estimated half a million plants of small fleabane the following year – probably more than anyone has seen anywhere else in recent decades. In contrast, a once famous site in the southern Forest was outside a commoner's cottage where old photographs show a happy assembly of geese and livestock churning up the muddy ground. Now the cottage is owned by non-commoning incomers, the scruffy patches have gone, and so has the fleabane, to be replaced by a smooth and untroubling greensward.

Conclusion

Although we like to celebrate our native wildlife – and so we should – most people now alive will have no conception of the huge impoverishment of the lowland landscape that has occurred over the past two centuries and still continues in recent decades, despite the attention now paid to conservation. The New Forest, even though it too has had its vicissitudes, stands not only as an extraordinary place in its own right, but also as a reminder of what used to be and might perhaps be again in the wider world. Conservation initiatives notwithstanding, it has achieved this status not by being a nature reserve but by its role as a living, working landscape with a diversity of use and more than a few conflicts of interest. It is sufficiently big and robust to sustain the occasional abuse, though when these reach a scale that only a government department can perpetrate the consequences can be dire enough. The best way to perpetuate its plant life, and much other biodiversity besides, is sympathetic and practical support for those people, practices and systems that have sustained it for so long.

References

Braithwaite, M. E., Ellis, R. W. and Preston, C. D. (2006). *Change in the British Flora 1987–2004*. Botanical Society of the British Isles, London.

BSBI (2007). *Crassula helmsii*. Botanical Society of the British Isles website. http://www.bsbi.org.uk/

Cheffing, C. M. and Farrell, L (eds.) (2005). The Vascular Plant Red Data List for Great Britain, *Species Status* 7, 1–116, Joint Nature Conservation Committee, Peterborough.

Dahl, E. (1998). *The Phytogeography of Northern Europe*. Cambridge University Press, Cambridge.

Ferris, R., Peace, A. J. and Newton, A. C. (2000). Macrofungal communities of lowland Scots pine (*Pinus sylvestris* L.) and Norway spruce (*Picea abies* (L.) Karsten.) plantations in England: relationships with site factors and stand structure. *Forest Ecology and Management*, 131, 255–267.

Ferrez, Y. and Prost, J-F. (2001). *Atlas des plantes rares ou protegées de Franche-Comté*. Société d'horticulture du Doubs et des amis du jardin botanique, Besançon. Naturalia Publications, Turriers.

Halliday, G. (1997). *A Flora of Cumbria*. University of Lancaster, Lancaster.

Hill, M. O., Preston, C. D. and Roy, D. B. (2004). *Plantatt: Attributes of British and Irish Plants*. Centre for Ecology and Hydrology, Monks Wood, UK.

Olivier, L., Galland, J-P. and Maurin, H. (1995). *Livre Rouge de la Flore Menacée de France, Tome 1 : Espèces Prioritaires*. Institut d'Ecologie et de Gestion de la Biodiversité, Service Du Patrimoine Naturel, *Collection Patrimoines Naturels*, Volume 20, Paris.

Page, C. N. (2006). Fern range determination within the Atlantic Arc by an environment of complex and interacting factors. In *Botanical Links in the Atlantic Arc*, eds. Leach, S. J., Page, C. N., Peytoureau Y. and Sanford, M. N., pp. 59–64. Botanical Society of the British Isles, London.

Pearman, D. A. (2008). The status of coral-necklace *Illecebrum verticillatum* L. (Caryophyllaceae) in Great Britain. *Watsonia*, 27, 143–148.

Preston, C. D., Pearman, D. A. and Dines, T. D. (2002). *New Atlas of the British and Irish Flora*. Oxford University Press, Oxford.

Tela Botanica (2008). Web site http://www.tela-botanica.org/page:chorologie. Association Tela Botanica, Institut de Botanique, Montpellier.

Tubbs, C. R. (1968). *The New Forest: an ecological history*. David and Charles, Newton Abbot.

Tubbs, C. R. (2001). *The New Forest. History, ecology and conservation*. New Forest Ninth Centenary Trust, Lyndhurst.

Appendix 1
New Forest Red List taxa (excluding extinct and impermanent).

Species	British status	1	2	3	4	5	6	7	8	9	10	11	12	13	14	15	16	17	18	19	21	N	L
Anacamptis morio Green-winged orchid	NT						X	X														3	8
Anagallis minima Chaffweed	NT								X													3	8
Anthemis cotula Stinking chamomile	VU			X																		6	7
Baldellia ranunculoides Lesser water-plantain	NT												X	X								2	8
Blysmus compressus Flat-sedge	VU											X										3	8
Bromus secalinus Rye brome	VU			X																		4	6
Bupleurum tenuissimum Slender hare's-ear	VU		X		X																	4	9
Carex divisa Divided sedge	VU				X																	6	8
Chamaemelum nobile Chamomile	VU							X														5	8
Chenopodium bonus-henricus Good-King-Henry	VU		X																			8	8
Chenopodium murale Nettle-leaved goosefoot	VU			X																		7	8
Chrysanthemum segetum Corn marigold	VU			X																		5	7
Cicendia filiformis Yellow centaury	VU										X											2	9
Cuscuta epithymum Dodder	VU										X											2	7
Cynoglossum officinale Hound's-tongue	NT						X													X		6	8
Cyperus fuscus Brown galingale	VU													X								4	9
Cyperus longus Galingale	NT											X		X								5	8
Drosera anglica Great sundew	NT											X	X									1	8
Equisetum x bowmanii Bowman's horsetail	VU	X		X																		5	5
Eriophorum gracile Slender cottongrass	NT											X										2	8
Euphorbia exigua Dwarf spurge	NT			X																		5	6
Euphrasia anglica	EN										X					X						3	7
Euphrasia arctica subsp. *borealis*	DD					X						X										4	7
Euphrasia confusa	DD							X	X							X						2	8
Euphrasia micrantha	DD								X		X											2	7
Euphrasia tetraquetra	DD					X					X											3	8
Fallopia dumetorum Copse bindweed	VU	X		X																		7	6
Filago vulgaris Common cudweed	NT		X																			4	7
Galeopsis angustifolia Red hemp-nettle	CR			X												X						4	8
Genista anglica Petty whin	NT										X											2	8
Gentianella campestris Field gentian	VU						X															3	8
Gnaphalium sylvaticum Heath cudweed	EN		X								X											3	7
Hypochaeris glabra Smooth cat's-ear	VU							X														2	8
Illecebrum verticillatum Coral-necklace	VU		X											X								2	8
Leersia oryzoides Cut-grass	EN													X								7	8
Lotus angustissimus Slender bird's-foot-trefoil	NT								X													3	8
Lycopodiella inundata Marsh clubmoss	EN										X	X										1	9
Melittis melissophyllum Bastard balm	VU	X		X																		5	5
Mentha pulegium Pennyroyal	EN				X									X								7	8
Misopates orontium Weasel's snout	VU			X																		6	7
Myosurus minimus Mousetail	VU			X																		5	8
Oenanthe fistulosa Tubular water-dropwort	VU											X										6	7
Orobanche rapum-genistae Greater broomrape	NT										X											2	7
Persicaria minor Small water-pepper	VU													X	X							8	7

Species	British status	1	2	3	4	5	6	7	8	9	10	11	12	13	14	15	16	17	18	19	21	N	L
Persicaria mitis Tasteless water-pepper	VU													X	X							9	7
Pilularia globulifera Pillwort	NT													X								2	8
Platanthera bifolia Lesser butterfly-orchid	VU	X									X											2	6
Puccinellia fasciculata Borrer's saltmarsh-grass	VU			X																	X	7	8
Pulicaria vulgaris Small fleabane	CR							X														7	9
Radiola linoides Allseed	NT										X											2	8
Ranunculus tripartitus Three-lobed crowfoot	EN													X								3	9
Rosa agrestis Small-leaved sweet-briar	NT							X														3	8
Ruppia cirrhosa Spiral tassel-weed	NT																				X	5	7
Salicornia nitens Shiny glasswort	DD																				X	6	9
Salicornia obscura Glaucous glasswort	DD																				X	6	9
Salsola kali ssp. *kali* Prickly saltwort	VU																			X		8	9
Scleranthus annuus Annual knawel	EN							X	X								X					4	7
Silene gallica Small-flowered catchfly	EN			X	X																	5	7
Silene nutans Nottingham catchfly	NT																X					4	8
Spartina maritima Small cord-grass	EN																				X	5	9
Spergula arvensis Corn spurrey	VU				X																	5	7
Spiranthes spiralis Autumn lady's-tresses	NT							X														3	8
Stachys arvensis Field woundwort	NT			X	X																	5	8
Stellaria palustris Marsh stitchwort	VU											X										4	7
Teesdalia nudicaulis Shepherd's cress	NT							X														2	8
Torilis arvensis Spreading hedge-parsley	EN			X																		4	8
Utricularia intermedia Intermediate bladderwort	DD													X								2	8
Viola canina Heath dog-violet	NT							X	X													2	8
Viola lactea Pale dog-violet	VU								X													2	7
Wahlenbergia hederacea Ivy-leaved bellflower	NT											X			X							3	6
Zostera marina Common eelgrass	NT																				X	6	6
Zostera noltei Dwarf eelgrass	VU																				X	5	8

73 taxa

Key to British Red List status
CR = Critically Endanged; E = Endangered; V = Vulnerable; NT = Near Threatened; DD = Data Deficient

Key to Broad Habitat Classifications relevant to Hampshire
1   Broadleaved and mixed woodland
2   Coniferous woodland
3   Hedges, roadsides, walls
4   Arable and horticultural
5   Improved grassland
6   Neutral grassland
7   Calcareous grassland
8   Acid grassland
9   Bracken
10 Dwarf shrub heath
11 Fen, marsh and swamp
12 Bog
13 Standing water
14 Rivers and streams
16 Quarries and skeletal soils
17 Built-up areas and gardens
18 Supralittoral rock
19 Coastal strandline, shingle, dune
21 Saltmarsh, littoral sediment

Key to Ellenberg Nitrogen Values (N)
1   Extremely infertile
2   ↓
3   Fairly infertile
4   ↓
5   Intermediate fertility
6   ↓
7   Richly fertile
8   ↓
9   Extremely rich

Key to Ellenberg Light Values (L)
1   Deep shade
2   ↓
3   Shade plant
4   ↓
5   Semi-shade plant
6   ↓
7   Partial shade to well lit
8   Light-loving
9   Full sun

Appendix 2
Other nationally rare and scarce New Forest taxa.

Species	British status
Alopecurus bulbosus Bulbous foxtail	Scarce
Althea officinalis Marsh mallow	Scarce
Atriplex longipes Long-stalked orache	Scarce
Briza minor Lesser Quaking-grass	Scarce
Carex montana Soft-leaved sedge	Scarce
Carex punctata Dotted sedge	Scarce
Deschampsia setacea Bog hair-grass	Scarce
Elatine hexandra Six-stamened waterwort	Scarce
Eleocharis parvula Dwarf spike-rush	Rare
Euphorbia portlandica Portland spurge	Scarce
Galium constrictum Slender marsh-bedstraw	Scarce
Gastridium ventricosum Nit-grass	Scarce
Gentiana pneumonathe Marsh gentian	Scarce
Geranium purpureum ssp. *forsteri* Little-Robin	Scarce
Gladiolus illyricus Wild gladiolus	Rare
Inula crithmoides Golden samphire	Scarce
Lathyrus japonicus Sea pea	Scarce
Leucojum aestivum ssp. *aestivum* Summer snowflake	Scarce
Limonium humile Lax-flowered sea-lavender	Scarce
Limosella aquatica Mudwort	Scarce
Lotus subbiflorus Hairy bird's-foot-trefoil	Scarce
Ludwigia palustris Hampshire-purslane	Rare
Luronium natans Floating water-plantain	Scarce
Marrubium vulgare White horehound	Scarce
Medicago polymorpha Toothed medick	Scarce
Montia fontana ssp. *amporitana* Blinks	Scarce
Ophioglossum azoricum Small adder's-tongue	Scarce
Parapholis incurva Curved hard-grass	Scarce
Poa bulbosa Bulbous meadow-grass	Scarce
Polygonatum odoratum Angular solomon's-seal	Scarce
Polypogon monspeliensis Annual beard-grass	Scarce
Puccinellia rupestris Stiff saltmarsh-grass	Scarce
Pulmonaria longifolia Narrow-leaved lungwort	Scarce
Ranunculus × *novae-forestae* New Forest water-crowfoot	Rare
Rhynchospora fusca Brown beak-sedge	Scarce
Salicornia pusilla One-flowered glasswort	Scarce
Sarcocornia perennis Perennial glasswort	Scarce
Sonchus palustris Marsh sow-thistle	Scarce
Thelypteris palustris Marsh fern	Scarce
Trifolium glomeratum Clustered clover	Scarce
Trifolium suffocatum Suffocated clover	Scarce
Vulpia ciliata ssp. *ambigua* Bearded fescue	Scarce
Vulpia fasciculata Dune fescue	Scarce
43 taxa	

Appendix 3
New Forest 'regionally significant' taxa.

Species	British status	Europe	1	2	3	4	5	6	7	8	9	10	11	12	13	14	15	16	17	18	19	21	N	L
Callitriche brutia Pedunculate water-starwort															X								5	8
Carex montana Soft-leaved sedge						X		X															1	7
Chamaemelum nobile Chamomile	VU																							
Cicendia filiformis Yellow centaury	VU										X												2	9
Crassula tillaea Mossy stonecrop					X																		2	8
Cyperus fuscus Brown galingale	VU													X									4	9
Deschampsia setacea Bog hair-grass		X																						
Eleocharis parvula Dwarf spike-rush																					X		5	6
Equisetum × *bowmanii* Bowman's horsetail	VU	X	X	X	X																		5	6
Eriophorum gracile Slender cottongrass	NT	X											X										2	8
Euphrasia anglica	EN	X																						
Galium constrictum Slender marsh-bedstraw														X									2	8

Species	British status	Europe	1	2	3	4	5	6	7	8	9	10	11	12	13	14	15	16	17	18	19	21	N	L
Gentiana pneumonanthe Marsh gentian		X																						
Geranium purpureum ssp. *forsteri* Little-Robin																					X		3	9
Gladiolus illyricus Wild gladiolus		(X)								X	X												3	5
Illecebrum verticillatum Coral-necklace	VU				X									X									2	8
Lobelia urens Heath lobelia	VU									X		X											2	8
Ludwigia palustris Hampshire-purslane															X								4	8
Lycopodiella inundata Marsh clubmoss	EN																							
Mentha pulegium Pennyroyal	EN																							
Ophioglossum azoricum Small adder's-tongue		X								X													2	8
Pilularia globulifera Pillwort	NT	X																						
Polypogon monspeliensis Annual beard-grass								X															6	8
Pulicaria vulgaris Small fleabane	CR	X																						
Pulmonaria longifolia Narrow-leaved lungwort			X		X																		5	6
Ranunculus × *novae-forestae* New Forest water-crowfoot		X													X	X							6	7
Rhynchospora fusca Brown beak-sedge														X									1	9
Trifolium glomeratum Clustered clover										X													2	9
Ulex minor Dwarf gorse																								
Viola lactea Pale dog-violet	VU	X																						
30 taxa overall	13 taxa	10–11 taxa																						

Key to British Red List status
CR = Critically Endanged; E = Endangered; V = Vulnerable; NT = Near Threatened; DD = Data Deficient

Key to Broad Habitat Classifications relevant to Hampshire
1   Broadleaved and mixed woodland
2   Coniferous woodland
3   Hedges, roadsides, walls
4   Arable and horticultural
5   Improved grassland
6   Neutral grassland
7   Calcareous grassland
8   Acid grassland
9   Bracken
10   Dwarf shrub heath
11   Fen, marsh and swamp
12   Bog
13   Standing water
14   Rivers and streams
16   Quarries and skeletal soils
17   Built-up areas and gardens
18   Supralittoral rock
19   Coastal strandline, shingle, dune
21   Saltmarsh, littoral sediment

Key to Ellenberg Nitrogen Values (N)
1   Extremely infertile
2   ↓
3   Fairly infertile
4   ↓
5   Intermediate fertility
6   ↓
7   Richly fertile
8   ↓
9   Extremely rich

Key to Ellenberg Light Values (L)
1   Deep shade
2   ↓
3   Shade plant
4   ↓
5   Semi-shade plant
6   ↓
7   Partial shade to well lit
8   Light-loving
9   Full sun

Appendix 4
New Forest northern (N)/western (W) 'outpost' taxa.

Species	British provenance		Species	British provenance	
Agrostis curtisii Bristle bent	W		*Lotus subbiflorus* Hairy bird's-foot-trefoil	W	
Botrychium lunaria Moonwort		N	*Melittis melissophyllum* Bastard balm	W	
Carex curta White sedge		N	*Montia fontana* ssp. *amporitana* Blinks	W	
Carex lasiocarpa Slender sedge		N	*Myrica gale* Bog myrtle		N
Carex limosa Bog sedge		N	*Myriophyllum alterniflorum* Alternate water-milfoil	W	
Carex punctata Dotted sedge	W		*Ophioglossum azoricum* Small adder's-tongue	W	
Carum verticillatum Whorled caraway	W		*Osmunda regalis* Royal fern	W	
Cicendia filiformis Yellow centaury	W		*Parentucellia viscosa* Yellow bartsia	W	
Deschampsia setacea Bog hair-grass	W	N	*Phegopteris connectilis* Beech fern		N
Drosera anglica Long-leaved sundew		N	*Pinguicula lusitanica* Pale butterwort	W	
Drosera intermedia Oblong-leaved sundew	W		*Pinguicula vulgaris* Common butterwort		N
Dryopteris aemula Hay-scented buckler-fern	W		*Polypodium cambricum* Southern polypody	W	
Eleocharis quinqueflora Few-flowered spike-rush		N	*Ranunculus omiophyllus* Round-leaved crowfoot	W	
Erica ciliaris Dorset heath	W		*Rhynchospora alba* White beak-sedge	W	
Eriophorum latifolium Broad-leaved cottongrass		N	*Rhynchospora fusca* Brown beak-sedge	W	
Eriophorum vaginatum Hare's-tail cottongrass		N	*Sagina subulata* Heath pearlwort	W	
Euphrasia confusa	W	N	*Schoenus nigricans* Black bog-rush	W	N
Euphrasia micrantha	W	N	*Sparganium angustifolium* Floating bur-reed	N	
Euphrasia tetraquetra	W		*Sparganium natans* Least bur-reed	N	
Gentianella campestris Field gentian		N	*Trichophorum cespitosum* Deergrass	N	
Gymnadenia borealis Heath fragrant-orchid	W	N	*Umbilicus rupestris* Navelwort	W	
Hammarbya paludosa Bog orchid		N	*Utricularia intermedia* Intermediate bladderwort		N
Hypericum elodes Marsh St John's-wort	W		*Utricularia minor* Lesser bladderwort		N
Isolepis cernua Slender club-rush	W		*Viola lactea* Pale dog-violet	W	
Juncus foliosus Leafy rush	W		*Wahlenbergia hederacea* Ivy-leaved bellflower	W	
Lobelia urens Heath lobelia	W		52 taxa	34	23
Lotus angustissimus Slender bird's-foot-trefoil	W				

Appendix 5
Taxa significantly declining elsewhere in the lowland zone.

Species	Broad Habitats																			N	L
	1	2	3	4	5	6	7	8	9	10	11	12	13	14	15	16	17	18	19 21		
Aira caryophyllea Silver hair-grass							8 X								15 X					2	8
Anacamptis morio Green-winged orchid				5 X	6 X															3	8
Anagallis minima Chaffweed							8 X													3	8
Anagallis tenella Bog pimpernel									10 X											3	8
Apium inundatum Lesser marshwort									10 X	12 X										4	7
Baldellia ranunculoides Lesser water-plantain									11 X	12 X										2	8
Bidens cernua Nodding bur-marigold									11 X	12 X										7	8
Bidens tripartita Trifid bur-marigold									10 X	12 X										7	8
Botrychium lunaria Moonwort						7 X									16 X					2	8
Calamagrostis canescens Purple small-reed									10 X											5	7
Carex curta White sedge									10 X											2	8
Carex echinata Star sedge									9 X	10 X	11 X									2	8
Carex hostiana Tawny sedge									10 X											2	8
Carex lasiocarpa Slender sedge									10 X											3	8
Carex pulicaris Flea sedge									10 X					15 X						2	8
Carex rostrata Bottle sedge									10 X											2	8

Species	1	2	3	4	5	6	7	8	9	10	11	12	13	14	15	16	17	18	19	21	N	L
Carex vesicaria Bladder sedge											X										4	8
Carex viridula ssp. *viridula* Small-fruited yellow-sedge											X								X		3	8
Catabrosa aquatica Whorl-grass													X	X							7	6
Chamaemelum nobile Chamomile							X														5	8
Cirsium dissectum Meadow thistle											X										2	8
Convallaria majalis Lily-of-the-valley		X					X														5	5
Cuscuta epithymum Dodder									X												2	7
Dactylorhiza incarnata Early marsh-orchid											X										2	8
Dactylorhiza maculata Heath spotted-orchid												X									2	7
Deschampsia setacea Bog hair-grass												X	X								1	8
Drosera anglica Great sundew											X	X									1	8
Drosera intermedia Oblong-leaved sundew												X		X							1	8
Drosera rotundifolia Round-leaved sundew												X									1	8
Elatine hexandra Six-stamened waterwort													X								4	7
Eleocharis acicularis Needle spike-rush													X	X							5	7
Eleocharis multicaulis Many-stalked spike-rush											X	X	X								1	8
Eleocharis quinqueflora Few-flowered spike-rush											X										2	9
Eleogiton fluitans Floating club-rush											X										2	8
Epilobium palustre Marsh willowherb											X		X								3	7
Epipactis palustris Marsh helleborine											X										3	8
Eriophorum angustifolium Common cottongrass												X									1	8
Eriophorum latifolium Broad-leaved cottongrass											X										2	9
Eriophorum vaginatum Hare's-tail cottongrass												X									1	8
Euphrasia anglica									X							X					3	7
Euphrasia micrantha								X	X												2	7
Filago minima Small cudweed																X					2	8
Filago vulgaris Common cudweed			X																		4	7
Gastridium ventricosum Nit-grass				X		X															2	9
Genista anglica Petty whin									X												2	8
Gentiana pneumonanthe Marsh gentian								X	X												1	8
Gentianella campestris Field gentian							X														3	8
Glyceria declinata Small sweet-grass													X	X							6	7
Hammarbya paludosa Bog orchid											X										1	9
Hydrocotyle vulgaris Marsh pennywort											X										3	8
Hypericum elodes Marsh St John's-wort											X										2	8
Hypochaeris glabra Smooth cat's-ear							X														2	8
Juncus squarrosus Heath rush							X			X											2	7
Limosella aquatica Mudwort													X								5	8
Littorella uniflora Shoreweed												X	X								3	8
Lycopodiella inundata Marsh clubmoss										X	X										1	9
Mentha pulegium Pennyroyal					X						X										7	8
Moenchia erecta Upright chickweed							X														3	9
Montia fontana ssp. *amporitana* Blinks											X										3	7
Myrica gale Bog myrtle												X									2	8
Myriophyllum alterniflorum Alternate water-milfoil													X	X							3	7
Nardus stricta Mat-grass							X														2	7
Narthecium ossifragum Bog asphodel												X									1	8
Oenanthe fistulosa Tubular water-dropwort											X										6	7
Oreopteris limbosperma Lemon-scented fern	X															X					3	6
Orobanche rapum-genistae Greater broomrape							X														2	7
Pedicularis palustris Marsh lousewort											X										2	8

Species	Broad Habitats																				N	L
	1	2	3	4	5	6	7	8	9	10	11	12	13	14	15	16	17	18	19	21		
Pedicularis sylvatica Lousewort										X		X		X							2	8
Persicaria minor Small water-pepper												X	X								8	7
Persicaria mitis Tasteless water-pepper												X	X								9	7
Pilularia globulifera Pillwort													X								2	8
Pinguicula vulgaris Common butterwort											X	X									2	8
Platanthera bifolia Lesser butterfly-orchid	X										X										2	6
Polygala serpyllifolia Heath milkwort								X		X		X									2	8
Potamogeton alpinus Red pondweed													X								5	7
Potentilla palustris Marsh cinquefoil											X										3	8
Pulicaria vulgaris Small fleabane						X															7	9
Radiola linoides Allseed											X										2	8
Ranunculus parviflorus Small-flowered buttercup				X																	5	7
Rhynchospora alba White beak-sedge												X									1	8
Rosa agrestis Small-leaved sweet-briar							X														3	8
Rosa pimpinellifolia Burnet rose											X					X		X			3	8
Rosa sherardii Sherard's downy-rose	X	X														X					4	6
Sagina nodosa Knotted pearlwort											X							X			3	8
Sagina subulata Heath pearlwort								X		X											4	8
Salix aurita Eared willow	X															X					3	7
Salix repens Creeping willow											X							X			3	8
Schoenus nigricans Black bog-rush											X										2	8
Serratula tinctoria Saw-wort							X														2	7
Sparganium natans Least bur-reed													X								3	7
Spiranthes spiralis Autumn lady's-tresses							X														3	8
Thelypteris palustris Marsh fern	X										X										5	6
Trichophorum cespitosum Deergrass										X		X									1	8
Ulex minor Dwarf gorse											X										2	8
Utricularia minor Lesser bladderwort											X	X									2	8
Valeriana dioica Marsh valerian											X										3	8
Veronica scutellata Marsh speedwell											X		X								3	8
Viola canina Heath dog-violet								X		X											2	8
Viola lactea Pale dog-violet											X										2	7
Viola palustris Marsh violet											X			X							2	7
Wahlenbergia hederacea Ivy-leaved bellflower											X			X							3	6

101 taxa

Key to Broad Habitat Classifications relevant to Hampshire
1 Broadleaved and mixed woodland
2 Coniferous woodland
3 Hedges, roadsides, walls
4 Arable and horticultural
5 Improved grassland
6 Neutral grassland
7 Calcareous grassland
8 Acid grassland
9 Bracken
10 Dwarf shrub heath
11 Fen, marsh and swamp
12 Bog
13 Standing water
14 Rivers and streams
16 Quarries and skeletal soils
17 Built-up areas and gardens
18 Supralittoral rock
19 Coastal strandline, shingle, dune
21 Saltmarsh, littoral sediment

Key to Ellenberg Nitrogen Values (N)
1 Extremely infertile
2 ↓
3 Fairly infertile
4 ↓
5 Intermediate fertility
6 ↓
7 Richly fertile
8 ↓
9 Extremely rich

Key to Ellenberg Light Values (L)
1 Deep shade
2 ↓
3 Shade plant
4 ↓
5 Semi-shade plant
6 ↓
7 Partial shade to well lit
8 Light-loving
9 Full sun

9 Lichens

Neil A. Sanderson

This chapter is dedicated to the memory of Dr Francis Rose, who loved these woods and their lichens, and without whom this work would not have been possible.

Introduction

The New Forest is famed as one the foremost sites for lichens in Europe. The most prominent lichen-rich habitats are found within the old growth pasture woodlands on open Forest common lands, locally known as the "Ancient and Ornamental Woods". They are described by Rose (1992a) as having, in lowland temperate Europe, the "largest epiphytic lichen flora known from any comparable area" and were assessed by Fletcher *et al.* (1982) as being the best example in Europe of a lichen-rich pasture woodland in a moderately oceanic climate. Rose (1992a) has argued that the epiphytic flora of the New Forest is likely to be closer to that of the original 'wildwood' than both the floras of more disturbed woodlands and those of less heavily grazed non-intervention woods. As such, the woods are not just important for biodiversity conservation, but as a possible model for wildwood epiphytic lichen ecology.

This chapter concentrates on reviewing the survey and research carried out on the internationally important epiphytic lichen floras. The progress in the survey of the lichen flora of the woods is described. The conservation value of the Forest, individual woods and habitats are also assessed, and the landscape ecology of the lichen recolonisation response to gross disturbance is described with reference to chronosequences. This latter work has important implications on the timescale and practicality of habitat restoration for lichen-rich old-growth woodland. The ecology of the lichen communities in relation to woodland structure, history, grazing and holly invasion is explored, and the implications for conserving the lichen floras are examined. The current state of knowledge on the impact of air pollution and of recreation are also briefly described.

Other lichen-rich habitats are less well known but are described for completeness. The heathlands are far less rich in terms of overall numbers of species than the old-growth woodlands, but have been assessed as the best example in Europe of lichen-rich heath of the heather *Calluna vulgaris* – dwarf gorse *Ulex minor* type (Fletcher *et al.* 1984). The lichen flora and impacts of management are described. Other habitats of interest for lichens within the National Park are also covered as far as current knowledge allows. These included woodland streams, coastal habitats, churchyards and young-growth woodlands.

Epiphytic lichen survey

Review of survey history

Lichenologists have recorded lichens from the New Forest since the 19th century, but with a long hiatus in the early 20th century. In the 19th century important collections were made by pioneer lichenologists especially Sir J. Lyell, who collected extensively between 1808 and 1818, and Rev. J. M. Crombie, who was responsible for the discovery of many of the rarer species in the area during the second half of the 19th century (Rose and James 1974).

Modern recording of the lichen flora of the New Forest started in 1967 led by Dr F. Rose (Rose and James 1974). Since 1967 a large mass of site-based records have been made for the New Forest woods, along with more generalised recording of the heathlands. A summary of the progress since 1974 in compiling a database and on research in the lichen ecology was made by Sanderson (1998) and heathland lichen ecology was summarised by Sanderson (1996a). Since then, further work has been carried out, and this chapter summarises the situation at present.

Between 1967 and 1974 Rose and James (1974) recorded 256 taxa from 40 woods on recording cards maintained by Dr Francis Rose. This survey was continued by Dr Rose, with 312 taxa recorded by 1992 (Rose 1992a). In the 1990s the recording card based system was converted into a computer database maintained by the author (Sanderson 1998) and called the New Forest Epiphytic Lichen Database. This is now held on a File Maker Pro database on an Apple Mac computer and holds records from 109 woods from which 12,164 individual records have been made of 430 taxa. The database is not a conventional biodiversity recording database, as it is based on site recording cards, not individual records; i.e. there is only one entry for one taxon per wood, even if the taxon has been recorded more than once. This is because the database was primarily intended to easily elucidate site factors in the conservation interest and ecology of the New Forest epiphytic lichen flora. Conventional species based records are sent on to the British Lichen Society databases, from where they will eventually be made available to the NBN.

Sites in database

A key feature of the database is strict definition of the sites recorded by land use history. There is a careful separation between little-managed woods on the Open Forest and areas modified by either 18th century or 19th century silvicultural practices (Sanderson 1998). The defined areas are intended to cover no more than 100 ha (1 km²) of woodland. The 109 sites on the database are listed in Appendix 2. The coverage is based on the core of the woodland of the Open Forest along with adjacent sites such as parklands with frequent old trees, and more disturbed woodlands within statutory Inclosures (areas of common land enclosed under the New Forest Acts for the sole purpose of growing timber). Also included within the database are three woods in the Langley Wood area, a separate smaller group of woodlands, which lie beyond the New Forest core but are included as they are within the New Forest SAC and the National Park. The database is intended to cover all old-growth stands (little-disturbed native woodlands with a stand age of over 200 years; Alexander *et al.* 2002) within the core woodlands (Figure 51) and a selection of more disturbed stands.

Three stand age categories are distinguished for sites on the database:

- *Ancient old-growth*: little-disturbed Ancient and Ornamental Woods or Parklands with abundant veteran trees, with no significant break in the continuity of old trees during the last 300 years. These include the typical pasture woodlands of the Open Forest and all known sites are included. Seventy sites on database.
- *Recent old-growth*: mainly covers woodlands that were clear-felled in the 18th century but since started reverting to little-disturbed woodlands with a stand age of between 200–300 years old. Classic

examples are the 18th century statutory Inclosures now open to forest grazing such as Ocknell Inclosure, which have became structurally almost indistinguishable from the undisturbed Ancient and Ornamental Woods. All such sites are included. Also included are some rather disturbed woods that still have a few veteran trees, which may be older than 300 years old. Fifteen sites on database.

- *Young-growth*: sites clear-felled in the 19th century, with dominant stand ages of between 100 to 200 years old. This mainly includes a sample of 19th century oak plantations within the statutory Inclosures. Twenty-four sites on database.

The 85 old-growth sites are clustered in 17 separate meta-sites (Figure 51).

Species recorded on database

All epiphytic (growing on trees) lichen and related fungi recorded from the defined sites have been entered into the database. A few young-growth sites have only been surveyed for species of interest but all other sites have been the focus of full surveys. Species growing on the soil of windblown root plates are included but terricolous unconnected with trees are not.

Figure 51
Distribution of old-growth stands in the New Forest showing meta-sites, including sites within the New Forest Epiphytic Lichen Database. Adapted from Sanderson (2007a).

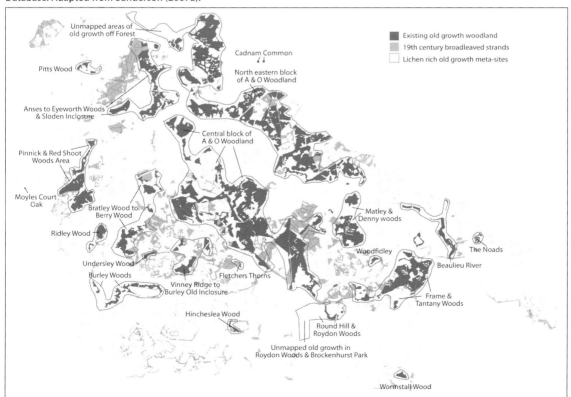

Lichens and related fungi are defined as whatever lichenologists can identify, and include classic lichens (fungi with symbiotic algae), some non-lichenised species that grow with, and resemble lichens and fungal parasites of lichens (lichenicolous fungi). In addition epiphytic fungi not normally recorded by lichenologists, but identified on passing, are added to the database, so the records are not lost. Since 1967 a total of 430 taxa have been added to the database, of which 11 are of epiphytic fungi not normally recorded by lichenologists. Of the remaining 419 taxa, 370 are lichens, 20 ecologically or taxonomically related fungi growing in lichen communities and 29 are parasitic fungi of lichens.

Species conservation status

In the database, data attached to the species records include Red Data Book (RDB) status, rarity (Nationally Rare (NR) and Nationally Scarce (NS)) and International Responsibility (IR) species status (Woods and Coppins 2003). Also indicated are those lichens that are used as old-growth woodland indicator lichens in the New Index of Ecological Continuity (NIEC) (Rose 1992a, Coppins and Coppins 2002). This index reflects high conservation quality in epiphytic lichen floras. High scores of over 20 or more species characteristic of undisturbed old-growth woodlands of nationally significance (Hodgetts 1992) and exceptional sites of international importance can be expected to score over 30 (the maximum score is 70). Also added were custom-made indices of species associated with ancient oaks, old beech stands and clean air.

Appendix 1 lists all species recorded with a national conservation status (RDB, NR, NS and IR). For convenience all NR, NS or IR species not listed in the RDB are referred to as Notable (Nb) species in this paper. Also listed in Appendix 1 are the NIEC indicator species that are not RDB or Notable species. The new Priority Biodiversity Action Plan (BAP) species (Biodiversity Reporting and Information Group 2007) are also given in Appendix 1.

Survey effort

The bulk of the survey effort that has produced this database has been carried out on a voluntary basis. This survey work was carried out by Francis Rose, Neil Sanderson and many other members of the British Lichen Society. As new species are constantly being described, no site can ever be completely surveyed, and an informal rota of revisits is made to all the old-growth sites. In addition to voluntary survey, the Hampshire Wildlife Trust funded a project to organise and report of the results of the database (Sanderson 1998).

Some funded site surveys have been also carried out on the sites covered by the New Forest Epiphytic Lichen Database:

- A lichen survey of Langley Wood NNR, Wiltshire for English Nature (Sanderson 1994c).
- A lichen survey of Brockenhurst Park for the Countryside Commission Sanderson *et al.* (1994).

- A survey of epiphytic lichens in surviving and developing old-growth stands and a sample of 19th century oak plantations within the New Forest Inclosures for Hampshire Wildlife Trust (Sanderson 1996b).
- Lichen surveys of several woods in or near Forest campsites as part of the preparation for a planning application for Terrence O'Rourke (Edwards 2001).
- A survey of epiphytic lichens of Whiteparish Common for English Nature (Sanderson 2003a).
- A survey of epiphytic lichens at Round Hill, close to Round Hill Campsite as part of the preparation for a planning application for Terrence O'Rourke (Sanderson 2003b).
- A survey of epiphytic lichens at Hollands Wood Campsite as part of the preparation for a planning application for Terrence O'Rourke (Sanderson 2004b).
- A survey of epiphytic lichens of Loosehanger Copse for English Nature (Sanderson 2004a).

Epiphytic lichen monitoring

Several monitoring schemes have been carried out on lichens within the Forest. In the 1980s, several small fixed quadrats were located over *Lobaria* species as part of a national project to monitor the effect of acid rain on lichens (Looney and James 1990). There has been no re-monitoring since then. Similar small fixed quadrats were located on some trees in Langley Wood NNR (Sanderson 1994c), for reserve monitoring purposes, but have never been re-examined. Monitoring with small fixed quadrats has proved problematic; losses from quadrats often appear the result of natural dynamics and colonisation is not measured, so the information derived does not give a comprehensive picture of population dynamics.

Other monitoring has tried to be more extensive but less detailed so that an indication of population dynamics can be gained. Single species monitoring has occurred for the Schedule 8 species *Megalaria laureri* (*Catillaria laureri*) and *Parmelinopsis minarum* (*Parmelia minarum*) in 1994, with re-monitoring in 1999 (Sanderson 1994a, 1994b and 1999), which recorded all known trees, and photographed parts of each colony. Species dossiers, consisting of all known data plus field surveys, compiled for the BAP species *Bacidia incompta* (Edwards 2002) and *Enterographa sorediata* (Sanderson 2002) provide baseline data for possible future monitoring of these species.

Detailed baseline monitoring plots covering all species of interest have also been set up in several areas of the Forest. In 1996 Cox and Rose (1996) recorded epiphytic lichens within plots in some areas of New Forest woodland heavily used for recreation, including Hollands Wood campsite. In 1997 within South Bentley Inclosure, in a recent old-growth stand of oak sown in 1700, all trees with species of interest were tagged and the lichen species of conservation interest recorded (Sanderson 1997a).

In 2000 five fixed plots of about 15 ha were set up and randomly sampled to produce data on the numbers of trees occupied per ha by lichen species of conservation interest (Sanderson 2001). The baseline plots were made in three 19th century oak plantations, two intended to be left to develop into pasture woodland, one which is to remain managed for timber production. Two others were made in Ancient and Ornamental woods, both ancient old-growth stands. One has remained densely wooded for centuries, while the second had been opened up by selective felling in the 18th century but had subsequently largely infilled in the 19th century.

Research on conservation, ecology and management of lichens

In addition to simple survey and baseline data, several reports and papers have described the conservation value of the New Forest epiphytic lichen flora and drawn conclusions on the ecology and management requirements of this flora. These include Rose (1993), Rose and James (1974), Sanderson (1991, 1994a, 1994b, 1994c, 1996b, 1997a, 1997b, 1998, 1999, 2001, 2002, 2007a, 2007b and in prep). More general papers on pasture woodland management have also drawn heavily on research results and observations resulting the ongoing survey of the New Forest epiphytic lichen flora (Chatters and Sanderson 1994, Sanderson 1996c, Sanderson and Wolseley 2001). The results of this work are summarised below.

Conservation value

Flora

Since 1967 a total of 421 taxa have been added to the New Forest Epiphytic Database, of which two species *Caloplaca flavorubescens* (EN) and *Lecania chlorotiza* (NT) have only been recorded from the Langley Wood area north of the New Forest woods and not from the core woods of the New Forest. The total has increased from 256 taxa in 1974 (Rose and James 1974), 312 taxa in 1992 (Rose 1992a) and 345 taxa in 1998 (Sanderson 1998). The species added since 1974 have included species not seen since the 19th century in the New Forest or Britain e.g. *Arthonia zwackhii, Bacidia subturgidula* and *Enterographa elaborata*, new species to Britain e.g. *Calicium hyperelloides* or new to science e.g. *Enterographa sorediata* and *Ramonia nigra*.

Numbers of taxa recorded from individual sites range from over 200 in the richest pasture woodlands in areas of about 1 km^2, with a maximum of 254 from Mark Ash Wood, to less than 100 from disturbed or small sites. Twenty-one other woods have species densities of higher than 150 species km^{-2} and the flora is variably rich throughout the pasture woodlands. The richest woods in the New Forest are among the richest woods in Europe for epiphytic lichens. No woods in the lowlands of continental western Europe approach this diversity and woods with over 150 species km^{-2} are virtually unknown elsewhere (Rose 1988, 1990, 1992a).

The flora of the New Forest is noted for numerous species that have a significant proportion of their known populations in Britain or Europe. These are listed in Appendix 1. Some Red Data Book species such as *Agonimia octospora, Pertusaria velata* and *Porina hibernica* are locally frequent within the Forest but very rare beyond. Others such as *Ramonia nigra* and *Bacidia subturgidula* are rare within the Forest but are very rare beyond. *Bacidia subturgidula* is an extreme example, only four records have ever been made; it was collected twice in the 19th century and is currently known from dry lignum on two hollies at Queen's Bower and Mark Ash Wood.

Biogeography

The lichen flora of the New Forest is essentially southern oceanic and there are few continental species. Many oceanic species reach their eastern limits in the Forest, however it lacks species of hyperoceanic woodland. Many of the latter are large leafy species, which are commoner in the west of Britain, but the flora of crust-forming lichens includes numerous southern oceanic and veteran tree specialist species that are less frequent in the west. In the west competition from mosses is more severe, reducing the diversity of niches available to crust-forming species.

Rare species

The epiphytic lichen flora of the New Forest is of outstanding international importance. The recent publication of a full conservation evaluation of lichens (Wood and Coppins 2003) now allows the rare and threatened species recorded from the Forest since 1967 to be listed (Appendix 1). This assessment excluded less well-known genera of parasitic fungi of lichens.

A total of 64 Red Data Book (RDB) species have been recorded from the main New Forest woodlands since 1967. These are broken down by threat categories below (Table 19).

Many of the Near Threatened species are only accorded this status as they have strong populations within the New Forest. Without these populations they would have been classified as threatened. Two additional RDB species have been recorded from the separate woodland complex at Langley Woods.

In addition, simple definitions of geographic rarity are covered by the National Rare and National Scarce categories, with 34 and 89 species recorded respectively (two additional National Scarce have only been

Table 19
Red Data Book lichen species recorded from the New Forest Woodlands.

Red Data Book category	Number of species
Critically Endangered	3
Endangered	3
Vulnerable	11
Near Threatened	39
Data Deficient	7

recorded from the Langley Wood area). Finally a category of International Responsibility was introduced by Wood and Coppins (2003) for species thought to have 10% or more of their European or World population in Britain. A total of 55 of these species have been recorded with the New Forest woods, with one more recorded from Langley Wood. These totals are among the highest recorded from any woodland complex in Britain, including the richest woods in the west of Scotland.

As well as all the RDB species, the Nationally Rare, Nationally Scarce and International Responsibility species include 78 species of conservation interest, which are not included within the RDB (Notable species). The new list of BAP species includes 30 New Forest lichen species (Biodiversity Reporting and Information Group 2007).

New Index of Ecological Continuity

The NIEC index of old growth woodland indicator lichens (Rose 1992a, Coppins and Coppins 2002) is intended to reflect habitat quality associated with old-growth conditions within ancient woodland. This is a separate concept from vascular plant ancient woodland indicators, which are species associated with continuity of woodland sites, rather than continuity of old trees. A site of national (SSSI) quality for woodland lichens would be expected to score at least 20 on the index (Hodgetts 1992). Since 1967 the whole New Forest complex has had 67 species on the index recorded and scores 61. Within the New Forest woods, the New Forest Epiphytic Lichen Database includes 67 individual woods scoring over 20 in the index (Appendix 2). The highest score currently, is for Frame Wood, scoring 50, with Busketts Wood 48, Bramshaw Wood 48, Mark Ash Wood 47 and Hollands Wood 47 close behind. These are woods are among the most important individual woods in lowland Europe for epiphytic lichens. The break down of numbers of woods by NIEC score above 20 is given on Table 20.

The total of 48 woods scoring 30 or more in the NIEC indicator list is likely to represent more than half of such woods in England. In Appendix 2, the woods on the New Forest Epiphytic Lichen Database are listed in order of their NIEC index scores added to the number of non-index bonus species (i.e. all other species of conservation interest).

Forest-level trends and extinctions

The richness of the New Forest epiphytic lichen flora, and the extent of lichen rich habitat, means that

Table 20
Number of woods scoring 20 or over with the New Index of Ecological Continuity.

Range	Number of woods
40–50	16
30–39	32
20–29	21

Table 21
Apparent losses of lichen species from the New Forest.

Large leafy species recorded in the 19th century and not seen since
Collema fasiculata *
Lobaria scrobiculata *
Meneggazzia terebrata
Pannaria rubiginosa *
Pseudocyphellaria aurata
Large leafy species probably lost since 1967
Degelia plumbea *
Nephroma laevigata *
Pannaria sampaiana *
Parmeliella testacea *
Large highly threatened species 1967–2007
Lobaria amplissima +
Pannaria conoplea *
Pannaria mediterranea *
Sticta limbata

* Alga partner blue-green algae
+ Blue-green algae in secondary structures

detailed monitoring is not easy; after 40 years investigation of the lichen flora is still at the exploration stage. The majority of uncommon species appear to be holding their own. A few species, however, are clearly declining and some extinctions appear to have occurred. Several species have not been refound since the 19th century, although since 1997 two species then thought extinct (Sanderson 1998) have been refound, showing extinction can never be certain. A total of 13 species were recorded from the New Forest woods in the 19th century and have not yet been refound (Appendix 1). Of these, most are crust-forming species that could still be overlooked but five are more obvious leafy species. The latter are much easier to locate, and observed loses are much more likely to be real than for small crust-forming species. In addition, four leafy species recorded since 1967 appear to have been lost and a further four are declining and rare (Table 21).

All of these species are known to be highly pollution sensitive. Of the 13 leafy species lost or threatened since the 19th century, 10 (i.e. 77%) have blue-green algae (Cyanobacteria) symbiotic partners present. This is a far higher proportion than the proportion (4.6%) of blue-green-algae-containing lichens (20) in the total recorded New Forest flora, and probably reflects the exceptionally high sensitivity of blue green algae partners to low level SO_2 pollution or acid rain (Richardson and Cameron 2004). It must be noted, however, that the main observed recent cause of loss of individual colonies is the death of trees and not simply the death of the lichen colonies, and there is no indication of acidification from the composition of the associated species. The current threat appears to be associated with difficulties in colonising rather than direct poisoning of the mature thalli. These could either be related to continuing effects of low-level pollution or to reduced viability of the small surviving populations. This trend can also be seen for the same species in Dorset and Wiltshire and, for the most sensitive species, further west into Devon and Cornwall. Further work would be required to identify exactly what is causing these declines but it appears that a small proportion of the flora, which includes some of the most spectacular species, require pristine air conditions to survive.

Habitats and communities

Nature of the flora
The flora is essentially a woodland one and is rich in species that thrive in partial shade and low nutrient conditions and which are rare or absent in more open and nutrient-enriched parkland-like habitat. Conversely, species of old trees in sunny nutrient-rich conditions, as found in typical old parklands, are not prominent.

Tree species
The dominant oak and beech provide the main substrates for the majority of the uncommon species recorded within the woodlands. Some specialist species are completely confined to the dry bark of ancient oaks and others to the smooth bark of beech, often where flushed by rain tracks. Most species are found on both oak and beech, although some show preferences for one or the other tree species.

There appear to be slight differences between the lichen assemblages on the two oak species, with base-rich bark often more frequent on sessile oak than on pedunculate oak, but more work is needed to confirm this suggestion. Collectively the two oak species are certainly the richest tree species within the New Forest woodlands. The specialists of ancient dry oak bark show a distribution pattern, which is related the presence of large populations of veteran oaks and hence to continuity of oak generations. This may reflect the felling intensity of oak during the 17th and 18th centuries (Sanderson 1998). Some very rich woods, such as Mark Ash Wood, are poor in these species, and may have been over-exploited for oak in the early modern period.

The richness of the beech trees in the New Forest is a unique feature in Britain. Other old growth beech forests within the native range of beech are all badly polluted and now have impoverished epiphyte floras. Beech has been widely introduced to north and west of Britain, where it thrives, suggesting its native range was not constrained by climatic factors (Peterken 1993). Here, however, even where veteran trees now occur, they never support the diversity of lichens of the New Forest beech (F. Rose, pers. comm.). As well as lacking the specialist species, many more generalist old woodland species often do not colonise readily even when present on native trees. The beech specialists include a group of species that were once common on old elm trees but have been lost owing to elm disease

in the rest of Britain (including *Collema fragrans* and *Bacidia incompta*), and a group that are confined to beech in Britain ('beech specialist species') (*Catillaria laureri, Enterographa elaborata* and *Pyrenula nitida*). The latter are confined to two distinct areas west of Lyndhurst (Mark Ash Wood to Lyndhurst Hill and Highland Water Inclosure to Gritnam) and east and north of Lyndhurst (Mallard Wood to Sunny Bushes). The distributions of these species are believed to correspond to the ancient core of beech colonisation in the Forest before the expansion of this tree species in the last 400 years (Sanderson 1999, Richard Reeves, pers. comm.).

Ash trees can be locally important, especially where old pollards are frequent, as by the Highland Water south of the A31 (SU2410), supporting a flora similar to that of oak but with a few specialists, including *Collema subflaccidum* and *Wadeana dendrographa*. Holly supports a specialist flora unique in England, including species with disjunct distributions (e.g. *Mycoporum lacteum*) mainly recorded from Ireland and Scotland beyond the New Forest. Old hazel, were it occurs, also supports a number of specialist smooth bark species. Although hazel is now scarce in the Forest, where it occurs the bushes are often old and uncoppiced, and are far richer in specialist species than the abundant coppiced hazel in enclosed coppices. The specialist species are generally rare in the lowlands and the hazel flora of the New Forest pasture woodlands is of regional significance.

Other species of tree and shrub are much less important for lichens but sheltered old birch in glades, base-rich maple and old blackthorn scrub can be of high interest locally. Minor species such as wild service trees (Chatters *et al.* 1999) are rarely of note but are generally richer in lichens than the same species beyond the Forest. Exotic trees such as sweet chestnut, sycamore, Turkey oak and pine are generally very species poor.

Pine occasionally has been colonised by species such as *Imshaugia aleurites*, which are typical northern pinewood species. They, however, have survived on lignum or on acid bark of native species in southern woods with a high continuity of dead wood, and then colonised the introduced pine. An unusual exception is the recent discovery of *Calicium parvum* on a pine in Wood Crates. This is the first record for England for a species of sheltered well-lit pine previously only known from north-east Scotland.

Epiphytic communities
Lichens of conservation interest are concentrated in distinctive habitats that are summarised below, while the main habitat preferences of each species are indicated in Appendix 1. Lichen species typically have very tight niches, more resembling invertebrates than plants, and often occur at very low densities. A single species-rich tree can have up to 30 to 40 species in the first 2 m of the trunk arranged in several very different communities. The variety of communities on one trunk can be equivalent to entire landscapes if compared to terrestrial plant communities.

Significant factors determining the species composition of epiphytic communities are:

- *Water supply*; ranges from overhanging areas receiving water only as dew, through shedding sites that readily wet in rain then dry out rapidly, to rain tracks that remain wet long after rain.
- *Acidity*; ranges from strongly acidic (about 4.5 pH) through intermediate bark to base rich condition (up to 6.0 pH). Very variable, even on the same species of tree, although birch and alder are rarely anything but acid, maple and ash are rarely acid, while old oak and beech can span the whole range.
- *Exposure to sunshine*; many species of conservation interest are woodland species that avoid long exposure to strong summer sunlight.
- *Shelter from drying winds*; more sheltered sites maintain humid conditions for longer.
- *Rate of tree growth*; old trees expand slowly producing a more stable bark habitat, encouraging the colonisation of slow growing species, as opposed to fast growing pioneer species found on fast growing young trees.
- *Nutrient availability*; generally low in the New Forest but wound tracks can have elevated nutrient availabilities, which can also be somewhat higher in areas with heavy grazing or exposure to external pollution.

The main habitats of conservation interest are summarised below, with the phytosociological classification following James *et al.* (1977). Characteristic species are listed in Appendix 1. The publication of the full conservation evaluation of lichens (Woods and Coppins 2003) allows the comparison of the conservation significance of the main habitats.

- *Base Rich Bark* (*Lobarion*): found on old trees in places weakly flushed by base-rich water. Ancient woodland lichens are a constant feature and the community is confined to veteran trees. Most frequent on oak and beech but also found on ash and maple. It is the richest community in the New Forest for species of conservation interest. The leafy lichen component is not as rich as in hyperoceanic stands of the community in western areas, but the diversity of crust-forming species is exceptionally high, with species such as *Porina hibernica* and *Porina rosei* more abundant than in any other British site.
- *Mature Mesic Bark* (*Pertusarietum amarae and Parmelietum revolutae*): found on mature less acidic bark on wet but shedding bark of mature and veteran trees. In sheltered woodland conditions, crust-forming species dominate (*Pertusarietum amarae*), whereas in more open conditions leafy species become abundant (*Parmelietum revolutae*). The basic communities are composed of widespread lichen species, especially *Pertusaria* and *Parmelia sensu lato* in shaded and well-lit situations respectively. In old-growth stands, ancient woodland species can occur and be locally prominent. The community is richest on beech but

good examples are also found on oak and ash. Individual stands of this community are rarely as rich as the Base Rich or Acid Bark habitats but collectively the Mature Mesic Bark habitat is the second richest in lichens of conservation interest. Characteristic species include most of Britain's population of *Pertusaria velata* and significant occurrences of the parasites *Arthonia zwackhii* and *Melaspilea lentiginosa*.

- *Acid Bark* (*Parmelion laevigatae*): found on mature strongly acidic bark on wet but shedding bark of mature and veteran trees. Mainly on oak, beech, holly and alder. The examples in the New Forest represent a mildly oceanic version of the described hyperoceanic association *Parmelietum laevigatae*. A provisional description as the *Cladonia-Thelotrema* community is given by Sanderson (1994a). Ancient woodland species and species rare in the lowlands are always present. Individual stands are usually richer than the Mesic Bark community, but overall the flora is not quite as rich in species of interest. Significant species include *Parmelinopsis minarum*, *Arthonia invadens*, *Micarea pycnidiophora* and *Parmelinopsis horrescens*.
- *Dry Lignum* (*Calicietum abietini*): a very specialised habitat of dry wood on vertical surfaces of exposed lignum on live trees, standing dead trees or rapidly rain-shedding sections of very large fallen logs. Characterised by pinhead lichens and fungi in genera such as *Calicium*, *Chaenotheca* and *Chaenothecopsis*. The habitat is best developed in more continental conditions, but the New Forest assemblage is still among the best in lowland England and the habitat contributes significantly to the diversity of lichens in the New Forest.
- *Ancient Dry Bark* (*Lecanactidetum premneae and Calicietum abietini*): this community is largely confined to the dry craggy bark of ancient oaks and well developed examples are restricted to woods with stand continuity predating the 18th century (ancient old-growth woodland). Leaning trees and deformed trunks are the main habitat and although it does occur on pollards too, this is a minority habitat (Sanderson 2002). The lichens mainly receive their water from dew and the community is southern oceanic in distribution. It supports several very specialist species (*Lecanographa amylacea*, *Blarneya hibernica*, *Enterographa sorediata*, *Opegrapha prosodea* and *Lecanographa lyncea*) and is exceptionally rare in Europe outside of southern Britain and Ireland. The Forest contains a significant proportion of the world resource of this community. In very dry bark the community passes into the more continental *Calicietum abietini*, which is also found on dry lignum.
- *Smooth Bark* (*Graphidion*: *Graphidetum scriptae and Arthpyrenietum punctiformis*): found on the smooth bark of thin barked shrubs within woodlands. The basic community is composed of widespread species, especially on young vigorous trees or bushes. However on ancient hazels and holly, and

slow growing suppressed young trees, ancient woodland and uncommon species can occur. Well-developed examples occur widely on holly in woodland with a stand continuity predating the 19th century (old-growth woodland) support several rare specialists, including *Arthonia astroidestera*, over 90% of the British population of *Mycoporum lacteum* and most of the lowland English population of *Arthonia ilicina*. These holly communities are scarcely developed in southern Britain outside the New Forest. Rich hazel communities with specialist species (including *Arthothelium ruanum* and *Eopyrenula grandicula*) are rare in southern England owing to coppicing, but do occur in sites such as Ivy Wood where long uncut hazel occurs, unlike rich hollies. These are not restricted to old growth woodlands, but appear to require about 75–100 years to colonise. The rarest non-holly species is *Phaeographis lyellii* recorded from hawthorn, beech, hazel and hornbeam in the Forest.

- *Wound Tracks* (*Gyalectinetum carneoluteae*): wound tracks occur where sap or exudates from rot holes flows down trunks. Lichens typically colonise wound tracks when the flow is reducing. Lichen-rich wound tracks occur mainly on beech but also occur on holly, ash and maple, including inside hollow trees. The habitat is nutrient rich and extreme, with only a limited number of specialist lichens occurring. These include some widespread ruderal species but they also include a number of now very rare and threatened species. Often these threatened species were once widespread on old hedgerow and parkland elms, but these trees have now been lost to disease. Important species include five threatened species: *Ramonia nigra*, *Collema fragrans*, *Bacidia circumspecta*, *Bacidia incompta* and *Cryptolechia carneolutea*. The habitat supports more Threatened species than any other habitat analysed.

- *Parkland Trees* (*Pertusarietum amarae*, *Parmelietum revolutae* and *Physcietum ascendentis*): a small group of species are characteristic of old mesic to base-rich well-lit trees in pasture and woodland edge situations. Nutrient availabilities are typically higher than within the woodlands. The uncommon species present include *Rinodina colobinoides*, *Anaptychia ciliaris*, *Lecanora quercicola* and *Lecanora sublivescens*. This is a rather rare element in the New Forest lichen flora, and is better developed in parklands in other areas of lowland England and Wales.

- *Branch and Sheltered Mid-trunk Habitats* (*Usneetum articulato-floridae var ceratinae*): branches and twigs support mainly common and rapidly colonising species but sheltered areas can support rarer species and especially pollution-sensitive species. Of these *Usnea ceratina* is particularly abundant on sheltered mid-trunks and *Usnea articulata* is very local. *Usnea florida* is a species that appears to be holding its own in the Forest, but is declining in the west country in the face of increased ammonia pollution (Benfield 1994).

- *Rain Tracks* (*Pyrenuletum nitidae*): a local but important community that occurs on strongly flushed areas of bark on old twisted, forked or occasionally pollarded ancient beeches. It includes some of the rarest lichen species in Britain including *Enterographa elaborata* (only in the Forest on three trees), *Megalaria laureri* (only in the Forest on fewer than 30 trees) and *Pyrenula nitida* (locally widespread in the New Forest, but only three known sites beyond the Forest). The community may have a strong relationship with wound tracks, with new colonisation occurring were wound tracks heal and open up new habitat for these species (Sanderson 2007b). Once formed, rain track communities appear to remain as fixed mosaics with no further opportunities for colonisation (Sanderson 1999). This community is still confined to the area occupied by beech in 1565 (Sanderson 1999).

- *Damp Lignum* (*Cladonietum coniocraeae*): a widespread community on damper dead wood and stumps with *Cladonia* species dominant along with crust-forming *Trapeliopsis* species. It occurs on stumps and is frequent well beyond the old-growth stands. This community is not usually of great conservation interests for lichens, presumably because damp lignum is not a rare or declining habitat; there are plenty of stumps in managed woods. The habitat does, however, support a large population ancient woodland species *Cladonia parasitica* in the New Forest. Very rarely *Cladonia incrassata* occurs in this habitat but this is more frequent in the heathlands.

- *Dry Bark* (*Lecanactidetum abietinae* and *Calicium hyperelli*): dry bark on mature trees is a species-poor habitat, both for overall numbers and for species of conservation interest. An exception is the widespread occurrence of *Schismatomma niveum* on the dry sides of oak and beech, and the very rare occurrence of the threatened northern continental species *Schismatomma graphidoides*.

- *Conifer*: the native gymnosperm yew *Taxus baccata* supports only a limited lichen flora on bark, but exposed lignum can support Dry Lignum habitats (*Calicietum abietini*) of interest and this community can also be found on the introduced Scots pine. These are considered in the Dry Lignum habitat described above. Only two species, however, are confined to introduced conifer species: the under-recorded ephemeral *Absconditella pauxilla* and the pinhead *Calicium parvum*. The latter is an unexpected record of a species otherwise known in the UK only from native pinewoods in NE Scotland. It has however also turned up in the Forêt de Fontainebleau in northern France (Rose 1990), where pine is also introduced, and is likely to be an example of long distance dispersal. It was recorded on pine in a humid glade in beech – oak pasture woodland, a habitat more similar to native pinewood than most occurrence of pine in the New Forest. Finally *Lecidea doliiformis*, which occurs on old acid oaks, has found a widespread secondary habitat on the bark of 19th century Douglas fir and occasionally old Scots pine.

Table 22
Numbers of lichen species of conservation interest recorded from different habitats in the New Forest (for details of habitats and abbreviations, see text).

Habitat	Threatened RDB	NT and DD	Nb	Other NIEC	Total
Base rich bark	2	15	15	15	47
Mesic bark	2	7	10	9	28
Acid bark	2	3	14	5	24
Dry lignum	1	3	11	2	17
Ancient dry bark	1	4	6	4	15
Smooth bark	0	3	8	3	14
Wound tracks	3	1	9	0	13
Park	2	5	1	0	8
Rain tracks	5	0	2	0	7
Branch	0	3	1	2	6
Damp lignum	0	0	3	1	4
Dry bark	1	0	2	0	3
Conifer	0	1	2	0	3

To summarise, the numbers of lichen species of conservation interest recorded from the main habitats of interest are presented on Table 22, in declining order of overall species numbers. Overall, it is clear that the richness of the woodland lichen flora depends on the presence of a wide range of habitats on the trees and dead wood and is not dependent on simply the presence of the base-rich bark community, although this is the richest community. Individual species make use of specific niches on tree bark or wood, many of which (e.g. rain and wound tracks) are scarce or absent in intensively managed woods, because 'poorly grown' (i.e. niche-rich) trees are removed during management operations.

Landscape ecology

Epiphytic lichen data
The extensive, and relatively comprehensive, series of data from defined sites of known stand age permits an analysis of the response of old-growth lichen communities to disturbance. Such analysis is comparatively easier for lichens than for other old-growth-dependant groups.

Stand continuity and lichen diversity
Stand continuity and lichen diversity within the New Forest
A study of a chronosequence of broadleaved stands within the New Forest statutory and freehold Inclosures (Sanderson 1996b and in prep.) of 92 species of lichens that are generally confined to little-disturbed woodlands in England, found the following:
- Six species were found to have widely colonised the 19th century young-growth woods and were common in old-growth woods.
- A further 14 species were present in the 19th century stands but at lower frequencies than found in the old-growth woods.

- Six species were also found to be restricted in the Inclosures to Ivy Wood, where they were associated with old hazel and maple in riparian wood.
- Forty-five species were recorded equally from both the 18th century plantations and in undisturbed pasture woodlands.
- Twenty-one were confined to, or much more frequent in, the pre-enclosure pasture woodlands.

All communities were found to have strongly colonised the 18th century woods, except for assemblages of lichens on ancient dry bark on ancient oaks (*Lecanactidetum premneae*) and wound and rain track assemblages of broken beeches (*Pyrenuletum nitidae* and *Gyalectinetum carneoluteae*). Within the whole flora there are over 100 old-growth dependant species in the New Forest, as opposed to five old-growth dependant epiphytic bryophytes.

In summary it appears that given the relative lack of fragmentation of woodlands that still exists in the New Forest, all but one of the epiphytic lichen communities of the old-growth woodlands can colonise adjacent new stands within 200 to 300 years. The ancient dry barked community, however, requires over 300 years to fully re-establish itself. An old-growth stand at Pigbush, on farmland thought to be abandoned as a result of the Black Death 600 years ago (Richard Reeves, pers. comm.), had a fully developed ancient dry barked community.

Stand continuity and lichen diversity in nearby woods
Sanderson (1998) reviewed the lichen flora of areas adjacent to the core woods of the New Forest, and noted that:
- Isolated woods, situated more than about 1 km from old woods, similar in stand age to the 18th century Inclosures (e.g. Ridley Wood and Langley Wood), are considerably poorer in lichens of conservation interest than 18th century stands close to ancient old-growth stands.
- At Roydon Wood there was widespread colonisation by lichen species characteristic of grazed high forest on to old trees that have been absorbed into recent pasture woodland with the last 150 years in the south of Brockenhurst Park. Previously these were formerly exposed ex-hedgerow trees in a 18th century park created by removing the hedges. These lichen species were absent from veteran trees in the northern part of the Park that has remained as farmland. The site is adjacent to undisturbed ancient old-growth pasture woodland. This suggests that many old-growth dependant lichens can colonise faster than the trees mature, and that it is the slow development of suitable niches that controls the rate of recovery from clear felling.

These observations suggest that fragmentation of over 1 km had a negative effect on the recovery of the lichen flora. In contrast, in developing stands close to existing lichen-rich woodland, the rate of recovery was governed by the time taken for suitable niches to develop on the trees.

Colonisation of individual trees

Within the woods, the lichen species restricted to old-growth woodland are mainly found on oak and beech of over 2 m in girth, but are not especially restricted to very ancient trees (Sanderson 1994a, 1994b, 1997a). The ancient dry barked community tends to be more frequently found on larger trees than the other communities, but can still be found on trees as small as 1.9 m in girth (e.g. *Lecanactis lyncea* in Frame Wood). The smallest trees colonised tend to be suppressed trees or naturally damaged trees. The invariable presence of ancient trees within lichen-rich stands is a characteristic indicating stand continuity, but is not the result of the restriction of lichens to really ancient trees. This fact means that other than in a few old beech stands and small fragmented woods, there are few obvious problems with tree generation gaps in the New Forest for lichens. Large woods are likely to have little problem with beech and there is no significant generation gap in oak anywhere in the New Forest for lichens.

Historic woodland management

Impacts of early modern woodland management
The existing structure and species composition of the pasture woodlands is largely a product of the past interaction of grazing and tree felling (Tubbs 2001, see also Chapter 13). Although much emphasis is often put on the impact of grazing, the combination of felling and grazing may actually have had more impact on the current species composition than grazing alone. Under current conditions of grazing and no cutting, the sensitive hazel is slowly reinvading from adjacent hedges, as have non-native limes (Sanderson 1996c). Other minor species, such as wild service, have also been recorded as increasing within the Forest pasture woodlands (Chatters *et al.* 1999). Ash is extensively regenerating in some riverine woodlands (Bakker *et al.* 2004). The Forest appears to be recovering tree species diversity under current quite high grazing pressures, but equally appears to have lost diversity in the early modern period when grazing and cutting co-existed (Chatters *et al.* 1999).

The lichen flora of the pasture woodlands appears to have survived this period of high exploitation surprisingly well, although local impacts of over exploitation of oak can be detected (Sanderson 1998), and clearly hazel specialist species have been severely restricted in distribution.

Tree felling and coppicing
Recent documentary research is giving a clearer picture of the degree and type of exploitation that the unenclosed pasture woodlands were subjected to in the early modern period. This exploitation included both cutting timber for the navy (Stagg 1989) and cutting underwood to produce charcoal for export to Cornwall for metal smelting (Roberts 2002). Several unpublished pollen analysis indicate that small-leaved lime appears to have been very locally abundant right into the 18th century (Tubbs 2001 and C. Chatters, pers. comm.), and hazel also steadily declined, to

become rare about this time. It is probable that the 17th and 18th century timber and underwood exploitation, especially the charcoaling, compromised the browsing resistance of species such as hazel, which is much more resistant to browsing if left uncut.

Pollarding
In addition to the sale and theft of timber and coppice wood, extensive pollarding was carried out by the Forest keepers to produce fodder for deer and this may have been a key factor in conserving old-growth characteristics and the associated veteran tree flora and fauna. A great deal of documentary information on the keeper's activities has now been published (Stagg 1983, Reeves 2006). Only ash was recorded as being cut in summer and stored as leaf hay. Other species were cut in winter in hard weather to feed directly to deer, either as bark for oak and beech or as bark and leaves in the case of holly, with the resultant left over wood belonging to the keepers as a perk (Reeves 2006). Cutting of species other than ash began at St Andrew's Tide (30 November), with thorn cut in spring. In the 17th century keepers were regularly fined for cutting pollards without regard to feeding the deer (Stagg 1983, Reeves 2006); they appear to have been cutting on a longer cycle than desirable for feeding deer, thus proving themselves with more wood. A 17th century document specifically blames browsing (pollarding) by the keepers for converting thriving and useful trees to spoiled and decayed dotards (senescent ancient trees) (Reeves 2006).

Dead wood
Dead wood was also heavily exploited, with fallen wood apparently rapidly removed. Reeves (2006) gives many 17th century references to the removal of breaknecks (trees with snapped trunks) and morefalls (up rooted trees). The pressure on the fallen wood resource is illustrated by frequent references to morewood (roots) being dug up to get at the firewood. In contrast there were clearly many dotards (senescent ancient trees) and stubs (standing dead trees), even if the references are to the felling of these. Stubs stood long enough to be recorded as whitecoats (dead trees with no bark). In 1677 a stub was reported as stolen from Godshill Wood that had been dead for 30 years or more. The picture is of heavily exploited old-growth woodland that did, however, maintain old-growth characteristics.

Tree regeneration
Reeves (2006) also contains references to 17th century exploitation, damaging 'Vera style' regeneration protected by thorns (Vera 2000; see also Chapter 13), such as:

"*Cutting down thorns and covert by the keepers is a destruction to the preservation of young trees.*"

"*Digging of mores of trees (stump and roots) after trees are felled is destructive to any young trees that grow out of (i.e. coppice growth) and about the roots (i.e. protected saplings) of such mores.*"

"*Pigs without rings root out bushes that would preserve young trees*".

As a result, the early modern woodland may have been more sensitive to grazing pressures influencing regeneration rates than are the modern pasture woodlands. This could explain the difference in view between Peterken and Tubbs (1965) and Morgan (1987a, 1987b, 1991) concerning the regeneration history of the Forest and modern regeneration patterns (see also Chapter 13).

Modern changes

Since the beginning of the 19th century the exploitation of the pasture woodlands has steadily declined, first with the cessation of the felling of timber in between 1800 and 1850 to the present decade, when the removal of dead wood all but came to an end.

Pollarding ceased in 1851, when the deer forest was abolished by the Deer Removal Act and the duties of the keepers to feed the deer were removed. By this time, timber exploitation had ceased within the remaining Open Forest allowing the recovery of near natural woodland structures. Under this act an attempt was made to remove the deer and numbers were reduced to very low numbers. This reduction in grazing pressure and the cessation of holly cutting led to a surge in holly cover within the woods, with many dense holly stands post-dating 1851 (Tubbs 2001). This spread was noticed at the time, and Pasmore (1976) records that the first complaint about the spread of pine on the heaths in 1904 by the Commoner's League and the New Forest Association also contained a complaint about the 'injury done to the old ornamental woods by the dense undergrowth of holly'. This spread of holly is now a significant issue in lichen conservation within the pasture woodlands.

Current factors affecting lichen diversity

Woodland structure and lichens
Structure of the New Forest woodlands
During the monitoring of 19th century oak stands within Inclosures and oak-dominated stands within Ancient and Ornamental woods carried out by Sanderson (2001), structural data were collected along with lichen data. There was a strong contrast between the managed Inclosure oak woods, where structural patterns were very even across stands, and the Ancient and Ornamental woods. In the latter, every sample plot of 20 × 20 m appeared to be unique. There is also strong patterning in tree density within the Ancient and Ornamental woods, with a glade and grove pattern apparently repeating at scales from 20 × 20 m through to 1 km × 1 km. This pattering has every appearance of being fundamental to maintaining lichen diversity, by providing great variation in light availability and in tree architecture, but much more work could be done on this issue.

The existing highly patterned structure has been largely regulated by grazing impacts and appears to at least partly match the theory of Vera (2000) on the functioning of grazed woodlands (see Chapter 13). The reality, however, is probably more complex than

this, with areas of core grazed high forest and permanent glades surviving long periods, as well as other areas cycling between high forest and glade as Vera described.

Recent surveys have highlighted a role of extensive canopy collapse within originally dark cores of beech high forest stands in producing very high quality habitats for some very rare lichens (Sanderson 2007b). It appears especially fundamental for wound and rain track specialists of beech trees and is also highly beneficial to dry lignum specialists. The threatened BAP species *Enterographa elaborata*, *Collema fragrans*, *Bacidia circumspecta* and *Bacidia incompta* are all strongly associated with areas of beech canopy collapse.

Although there have been conflicting studies of the Forest regeneration history at a Forest-wide level (Peterken and Tubbs 1965, Morgan, 1987a, 1987b, 1991; see Chapter 13), there appears to have been no detailed analysis of pattern and woodland history at the stand level with the pasture woodlands. This could be a very interesting study in relation to old-growth biodiversity conservation.

Light, shelter, grazing and holly
Several studies of individual species across the Forest (Sanderson 1994a, 1994b and 1999) and of the flora of one stand (Sanderson 1997a) have recorded estimated light and shelter levels. These found a variation in the tolerance of different lichen species but made the following general conclusions for the New Forest:
- Lichen floras tend to be most diverse where the lower trunks of the trees are most sheltered from drying winds, allowing the air to remain more humid for longer.
- Lichen floras were richest on trees with good indirect light but diversity dropped off rapidly with exposure to summer sun, but tailed off more gradually with increased shade.
- Dense shrub layers of holly are a serious threat to rich and diverse lichen communities on old trees.

The consequence of increasing holly cover was demonstrated by Sanderson (1996b) at Woodfidley Inclosure. Here an old-growth beech stand dating from 1700 was partly fenced in the early 1960s, with about 4 ha enclosed and left completely ungrazed while about 3 ha remained open to heavy deer grazing and light pony grazing. Inside the Inclosure, holly and beech had regenerated profusely, producing a nearly impenetrable shrub layer, whereas the grazed stand had remained open and well lit. Within the grazing exclosure, species diversity was much lower, with only 46% the number of species of lichen and bryophyte found in the lowest 2 m of the trunks. The losses were especially severe for more uncommon species with 18 NIEC old-growth indicator lichens recorded within the grazed are, a but none within the grazing exclosure. Similar results have been reported from Exmoor, where rapid expansion of the shrub layer in response to reduced grazing pressure has caused significant declines in epiphytic lichen communities over a short period (Coppins and Coppins 1998). At Woodfidley the removal of grazing also similarly depressed the terricolous vegetation, with 40% fewer species in the grazing exclosure.

Holly has clearly increased greatly in cover since 1851 but shrub holly can also undergo local recession owing to winter browsing of stems. Recession appears much more uncommon than spread at present. Since 1989 holly coppice and pollarding has been extensively revived both to conserve epiphytic and terricolous floras within the woodlands and to provide winter feed to ponies and deer (Sanderson 1991, Sanderson 1997b, Wright and Westerhoff 2001).

External factors affecting lichen diversity
Pollution
Many lichen species are very sensitive to sulphur dioxide (SO_2) pollution (dry deposition), which acts as a direct toxin. Levels of this pollutant have been low over much of the Forest, even during the height of sulphur dioxide pollution in the mid 20th century, but were certainly elevated over pristine conditions and were locally significant. Obviously depressed numbers of slow-colonising sensitive species are present in a few exposed woods in the south-west (and the Bournemouth conurbation), e.g. Ridley Wood and Berry Wood, and in the south-east (close to industrial pollution sources on the Waterside), e.g. the Noads and the east of Denny Wood (Sanderson 1998). The effect, however, is complex; the latter two contain sheltered little-polluted areas rich in lichens and the nearby Frame Wood complex is one of the least affected woodlands in the Forest. A few very sensitive species, especially those with blue green algae partners, have been affected by the low levels of pollution that occur throughout the Forest and species such as *Pannaria conoplea*, *Sticta limbata* and *Nephroma laevigata* are not thriving or have become extinct. Levels of sulphur dioxide have declined nationally and Dr Francis Rose noted that the SO_2 pollution-tolerant lichen *Lecanora conizaeoides*, which was formerly prominent on twigs on wood edges in the New Forest in the 1960s, had entirely disappeared from twigs by the late 1990s.

There is no evidence of differential loss of species requiring base-rich bark as opposed to those requiring acidic bark, which would indicate that there is, or has ever been, an acid rain (wet deposition) problem in the Forest sufficient to negatively effect epiphytic lichen floras. Recent examinations of lichen twig floras using the method described by Wolesey *et al.* (2006) indicate that the epiphytic lichen flora shows no signs of a response to nitrogen deposition as ammonia, the main form of nitrogen deposition known to affect epiphytes. Trees very close to busy roads (i.e. less than 4 or 5 m) are affected by road dust and show a loss of sensitive species and the appearance of nitrogen-loving species (Sanderson 1996d), but there is no obvious effect to be seen further from roads, although detailed studies have not been carried out. Trees in a caravan site in an old-growth woodland show signs of acidification, which may result from car exhausts (Edwards 2001, Sanderson 2004b).

Recreation and health and safety
Lichen communities on trees are largely unaffected by recreation within in most woods but there have been very rare instances of illegal fires built against trees with rare species (Francis Rose, pers. comm.). More significant are localised problems with recreation infrastructure built close to veteran trees, in particular car parks and campsites. In the past, heavy-handed tree surgery for health and safety reasons by car parks and roads killed many veteran trees. Now more sensitive safety assessments and tree surgery is generally carried out in such situations (Hayward 1996).

A few caravan sites are placed in or beside Ancient and Ornamental woods. These are clearly problematic; intensive people and vehicle access and veteran trees do not mix well, and this has lead to unfavourable condition assessments for some sites (Wright and Westerhoff 2001). The lichen flora of Hollands Wood campsite has been intensively studied (Cox and Rose 1996, Edwards 2001, Sanderson 2004b). In the most heavily used areas, the safety felling of veteran trees has led to the loss of much of the conservation interest. In areas with surviving veteran trees, internationally important communities survived, but there was a differential loss of dead wood species from the felling of standing dead trees and of species of base rich bark. The latter was a marked effect and could be due to acidification from car exhaust gasses.

Implications for woodland lichen conservation

Lichen conservation in the Ancient and Ornamental Woodlands
The following conclusions are drawn from the above survey and research:
- Direct conservation measures are not practical or significant, the number of rare species and trees of interest is too high for significant individual conservation measures. An added factor is the inability to cultivate many of these lichen species, or to even translocate the majority of the crust-forming species. Actions to conserve lichens will need to be carried out at the habitat level.
- The woods are near-natural: the minimum amount of management required to maintain the biodiversity should be carried out.
- Maintain variable levels of grazing that allow low-level or periodic tree regeneration, thus both maintaining the woods and variable levels of light and exposure.
- The spread of holly, and hence increased shade, in the last 150 years is the most significant internal issue.
- Externally attaining very low levels of sulphur and nitrogen pollution is more significant than all but the more extreme anthropogenic global warming projections. The flora is predominantly a southern Atlantic one and few species are at the southern edge of their distributions.

Specific issues

Holly management

Current holly management for lichen conservation is described by Sanderson (1991, 1997b). Areas where dense holly was potentially threatening lichen diversity within the woods were mapped in a general way by Sanderson (1997b). Forest Enterprise had since directed cutting to these areas. This has proved remarkably effective as cutting has several times revealed unknown trees supporting RDB lichens previously obscured and threatened by dense holly. Directing cutting precisely around known trees would have not achieved this.

The cutting procedure recommended in areas cut to open up dense holly, dominated by small diameter holly, is as follows (Sanderson 1997b): the holly is cut in blocks between 30 to 100 m across within woods, with dense holly left as shelter on the edges. The smallest diameter holly (<10 cm diameter) is coppiced, as is all but the largest holly close to mature trees. A scatter of holly over 10 cm diameter is pollarded and all larger holly (>15 cm diameter) pollarded. Ideally green branches should be left below the cut. Old pollards, especially those over 0.3 m diameter should only be cut if green branches can be left below the cuts.

The condition assessments introduced by English Nature (now Natural England) requires less than 50% of woodland units to have dense holly shrub layers (Wright and Westerhoff 2001; see Chapter 12). Many woods are still in unfavourable condition owing to high holly cover, but because of the introduction of the extensive holly cutting programme, most of these are in Unfavourable Recovering condition (see Chapter 12).

Tree pollarding

Pollarding trees is an important cultural tradition within the New Forest woodlands. In biodiversity conservation terms, however, natural damage to trees and partial competition with other trees in unevenly stocked grazed woodlands seems to generate specialist niches just as well as pollarding. No rare species of lichen is restricted to pollards. For this reason, although cutting new pollards is considered important to maintain the cultural tradition, it is not considered important for biodiversity conservation (Wright and Westerhoff 2001). Most Forest woods lack large generation gaps that could justify attempting to revive lapsed pollards to extend their lives, especially as out of cycle re-cutting of pollards often results in a high percentage of tree death.

Fragmentation

The low density of occurrence of many of the most threatened lichens in the New Forest indicates that they require very large areas of old-growth woodland for long-term survival. Although there are large areas of surviving old-growth woodland within the New Forest, there has been substantial fragmentation of the old-growth woods that existed at the beginning of the 18th century. This fragmentation has been assessed by Sanderson (2007a).

The earliest fragmentation caused by 18th fellings is now being healed by the old-growth stands developing from abandoned 18th century plantations. The demonstrated ability of old growth lichen floras to recolonise such woodlands, suggests that there is the potential to counteract fragmentation, especially if 18th or 19th century oak plantations are available for reversion to pasture woodland. The presence of these older plantations makes counteracting fragmentation within 100 to 200 years a practical proposition.

Forest Enterprise is committed, through its Forest Design Plan, to reverting large areas of 18th and 19th century plantations to old-growth woodlands, mainly as unenclosed pasture woodlands. These will increase the connectivity between many formerly fragmented pasture woodlands. Sanderson (2007a) found, however, that there were still significant important stands of surviving old-growth woodland, which will still be left isolated on existing plans. This is especially so west of Mark Ash Wood. The New Forest Association has suggested that a radical rewilding project is required in the block of Inclosures between Mark Ash Wood and Burley (Reeves *et al.* 2006). If carried out, this would convert the current solid mass of enclosed woodland dominated by plantation to a mosaic of smaller enclosed ungrazed broadleaved woodland set in a matrix of heathland, ancient relic old-growth and old-growth developing from former 19th century oak plantations.

Relationship with browsing and grazing pressure

The New Forest pasture woodlands are now very unusual in a lowland context in having extensive stock and deer grazing within unenclosed woodlands. A common response from commentators is concern that the woodland habitats are being "overgrazed" (e.g. see Chapter 7). The features for which these woods are being overgrazed is often not explicitly stated (Chatter and Sanderson 1994). In the case of the internationally important epiphytic lichen flora it is difficult to substantiate the suggestion that the woods are currently being overgrazed, or ever have been. The converse is the case; the lichen flora of the New Forest appears to be thriving under current conditions, while under-grazing is a frequently cited problem for lichen conservation in other lowland, and increasingly upland old-growth woodlands (Rose 1992a, Coppins and Coppins 1998, Sanderson and Wolseley 2001). Were woods being lost to total regeneration failure, this certainly would be an issue for lichen conservation, but this has not happened to any significant scale to date. Localised temporary regeneration failure in fact appears essential to maintain high lichen diversity.

Epiphytic lichen floras clearly cannot be used to set the upper levels of grazing pressure as they are highly grazing tolerant. They probably do need to be accounted for in setting lower limits to gazing pressure, as rich epiphytic lichen floras are strongly grazing dependent. As grazed woodland is an integral part of the internationally important cultural landscape of the New Forest commons, low stocking levels are not a pressing short-term issue. They may become significant if the socio-economic system of commoning fails in the longer term. Beyond the Forest there are critical lessons to be learned for conserving old-growth and pasture woodland biodiversity, which do not appear to be widely appreciated. Essentially, for rich epiphytic floras to survive within woodlands, free regeneration of trees must be partly suppressed to prevent dense growth shading out rich sheltered lower trunk communities.

Other forest habitats

Heathland
Lichen flora
The other significant habitat for lichens within the New Forest National Park is the heathlands. This habitat includes both *Calluna*-dominated dwarf shrub heath and associated acid grasslands. These habitats have not been systematically surveyed, but to date at least 82 lichen taxa have been recorded recently from the Open Forest's heaths and grasslands, of which 45 have not been recorded from the woodlands. The ecology and conservation management of heathland lichen habitats in the New Forest has been summarised by Sanderson (1996e). Within the heathlands there are two habitats with significant lichen floras: open patches of compact humus within low productivity heather heaths with little grass component, and short open dry acid grassland. Flints within both habitats add to the species diversity. The flora includes 30 taxa of *Cladonia*. Compared to the woods, the heathlands are not nearly as rich in rare species, but include a few rare species such as the nationally scarce *Cladonia incrassata* on sandy banks in the heaths and *Cladonia cariosa*, *Peltigera neckeri* and *Leptogium palmatum* in the grasslands. This reflects the main significance of the New Forest heathland lichen flora; it supports populations of species that are still widespread in the uplands but are in decline outside of the New Forest in the lowlands (Rose 1992b, Sanderson 1995). Especially significant are species such as *Cladonia arbuscula*, now extinct in the heaths of West Sussex (Rose 1992b), and *Cladonia strepsilis* and *Pycnothelia papillaria*, which are now rare and declining in most lowland heathland areas.

The lichen rich heaths have *Cladonia* species prominent, with more than 10 species typically present in the best sites. *Cladonia portentosa* is ubiquitous but species characteristic of richer sites include *Cladonia arbuscula*, *Cladonia ciliata*, *Cladonia gracilis*, *Cladonia uncialis* ssp. *biuncialis*, *Cetraria aculeata*, *Cetraria muricata*, *Dibaeis baeomyces*, *Micarea lignaria* var. *lignaria* and *Pycnothelia papillaria* on soil and *Micarea erratica*, *Porpidia crustulata* and *Porpidia soredizodes* on flints.

In contrast, grasslands with a high lichen cover normally only have a few *Cladonia* species and a small number of associated species including *Peltigera canina*. Exceptions are the heathland "brown field" sites where acid grassland has developed on the sites of ripped up World War II military installations. These grade towards calcicolous grasslands and have distinctive assemblages including species characteristic of less acid conditions, such as *Agonimia gelatinosa* (NS), *Agonimia tristicula*,

Bacidia bagliettoana, *Cladonia cariosa* (NS), *Cladonia foliacea*, *Diploschistes muscorum*, *Leptogium intermedium* (NS), *Leptogium schraderi*, *Leptogium tenuissimum* (NS), *Peltigera neckeri* (NS) and *Peltigera rufescens*.

A significant rediscovery made in 2007 is the Near Threatened *Leptogium palmatum* (NS). A single collection was made of this species in the 1930s (Rose and James 1974), which is otherwise a specialist species of winter damp sandy tracks in the upland fringes, with its headquarters in mid-Wales and Dartmoor. It was found in two sites in the Open Forest, growing in gaps in mats of robust mosses on the edges of trampled areas within parched acid grasslands. These and a third site, just outside of the National Park, are the only know extant lowland sites for this species.

Only two rare species with old records have not been refound: *Cladonia zopfii* (NS), a northern species, and the Near Threatened *Rinodina aspersa* (NR), a species of flints in the south.

Ecology
Lichen-rich acid grassland sites appear mainly to depend on heavy grazing to maintain open conditions, but the richest sites show an obvious association with past soil disruption. The latter sites are also rich in uncommon vascular plants (see Chapter 8). The future conservation of such habitats raises interesting questions of how to maintain the periodic large scale disruption characteristic of heathland cultural landscapes in the past, in a controlled and protected future.

The rich heaths are more complex and observations on their ecology have been summarised by Sanderson (1996e). Diverse lichen communities are found in two situations:

- Heather stands so heavily grazed that the heather is reduced to a prostrate creeping growth form. Pony and cattle grazing does not kill heather and it can survive in this condition for decades. Most large areas of prostrate heather in the Forest have been in this condition for living memory. Such heaths are kept permanently in the pioneer stage and are very important for species that depend on this stage of heather regrowth such as woodlark. These stands also have much bare ground that remains open for decades; ideal conditions for lichens. The richest and largest lichen rich heaths of the New Forest are all in this type of habitat.
- Small areas of lichen-rich heath do occur locally in less heavily grazed heaths that develop through the normal cycle from pioneer to senescent heather stands. These are managed by grazing and a controlled burning on a roughly 25-year cycle.

Two factors appear to link most lichen-rich heaths:
- low soil productivity, which prevents a significant grass sward forming;
- long-lasting gaps in the heather canopies that allow light demanding lichens to survive.

In more lightly grazed stands, rich lichen floras develop where gaps are maintained in the heather canopies in spite of normal heather regrowth. The use of cool controlled burns appears very important; lichen regeneration is rapid, presumably from surviving propagules. The thalli of most species do not survive burns, but abundant regrowth of new squamules from bare humus occurs in the second spring after a burn. *Cladonia strepsilis* thalli can actually directly survive and regrow. The burns also clear away competing late-succession mosses, which mowing does not. In contrast, after hot wild fires lichen regeneration appears to occur by colonisation from beyond the burnt area and has been shown to take about 13 years (Coppins and Shimwell 1971).

In the first summer after a spring fire both *Calluna* and *Erica* species regenerate, the *Calluna*, at least, mostly as coppice regrowth from existing root stocks. Any grass and the *Calluna* are grazed heavily in the first few years but the *Erica* species are not. Heather regeneration is patchy, with many small bare patches that are the locus of the lichen regeneration. The lichens appear to take about five seasons to fully develop and achieve high ground cover. During this period, however, the gaps can be lost to heather seedlings. *Calluna* flowers in the second summer after the burn, and in the third spring masses of *Calluna* seedlings can be found. Mostly, these will die off, but in a wet summer the gaps could be lost to regeneration from seed. New gaps in the heather cover are also created in the pioneer phase by the parasitic plant dodder *Cuscuta epithymum*. This frequently kills off patches of *Calluna* at this stage.

If the gaps remain open until the *Cladonia* dominates, then further seedling establishment does not occur, possibly owing to an the allelopathic effect on *Calluna* seeds from chemicals produced by the *Cladonia* (Hobbs 1985). From this stage on, only the shade of the growing heather bushes can destroy the lichen-dominated patches. If the ageing of the heather is slowed by grazing, then the gaps will survive longer and the lichen flora become better developed, but all such lichen-rich stands will eventually be shaded out. The occurrence of lichen rich heathland beyond the heavily grazed prostrate heaths is therefore a relatively temporary phenomenon. Lichen-rich patches develop where the effects of burning, grazing and weather combine to allow the survival of canopy gaps in the heather for a decade or more, but most patches are probably lost after about twenty years or so. Recent observations suggest that controlled burns on overgrown impoverished formerly rich lichen heaths can rejuvenate new lichen-rich stands in the same site. Most of the above observations have been confirmed by more detailed experimental observations in eastern America (Johansson and Reich 2005). Lichen-rich heaths are best regarded as late-succession fire-dependent features. They even reappear in time after hot wildfires, recovery just takes longer. For example, the sites of 1976 wild fires were the main lichen-rich areas in the unmanaged Dorset Heath in the 1990s (Davey 1994, B. Edwards, pers. comm.). The common misapprehension that lichen-rich heaths are fire-sensitive features is a serious threat to their continued survival in heathlands outside of the New Forest.

The long length of the burning rotation in comparison to upland gorse moors is probably significant; these are burned on a roughly 10 year or so cycle and here the regular fire impoverishes the lichen flora (B. Coppins, pers. comm.). Colonisation similar to that occurring after hot fires can be seen in old mineral sites on acidic substrates. Gravel pits abandoned back to heathland can also be colonised by rich lichen floras within about 10 years. This has occurred at Fields Heath, near Fawley, within the National Park. Currently the richest such site locally is in the Blashford gravel pit complex, just outside of the National Park, where 63 lichen taxa have been recorded (including 18 concrete weeds and normally epiphytic species), of which 23 were *Cladonia* species, in an area abandoned in 1992.

Woodland streams
Aquatic lichen communities
Acid watercourses with abundant stable rock outcrops support rich lichen assemblages, including uncommon specialist species (Gilbert and Giavarini 1997). Rich examples of this habitat are confined to the uplands in Britain, but the New Forest does support outlying examples of this habitat, which is otherwise very rare in the lowlands. The New Forest examples, however, are very attenuated and consist of a handful of species that are widespread in the uplands but rare in the lowlands, with *Verrucaria hydrela* common, *Verrucaria aquatilis* and *Porina chlorotica* frequent and *Micarea bauschiana*, *Verrucaria rheitrophila* (NS) and *Verrucaria margacea* rare (Gilbert and Giavarini 1997, Sandell and Rose 1996). However, Gilbert and Giavarini (1997) encountered two taxa that they were unable to name, so there may be rare specialist species present.

Aquatic lichen habitats
Aquatic lichens require stable rock surfaces, free of silt deposits, which remain moist or humid through out the year. These conditions are not common in New Forest streams (see Chapter 15). They can be found in shoals of flint pebbles in the beds of small head woodland water streams, where flows of sufficient force to move the flints are rare. Further downstream, the habitat is confined to flints embedded in the banks of the wooded middle reaches of Forest rivers. An extension of the former habitat is found where flints occur in shaded flushes along spring lines, although only *Verrucaria hydrela* occurs in this habitat. Lower reaches of rivers are too silty, even if fixed flints occur in the banks. Tree cover is a common factor of all sites; flints of open heathland streams dry out too much in summer and this lichen habitat is strongly associated with ancient woodland in the New Forest. The richest sites recorded by Gilbert and Giavarini (1997), on the Dockens Water, Shepherds Gutter and the Highland Water headwaters, were all associated with ancient pasture woodlands. Wooded flushes with flints supporting only *Verrucaria hydrela*, however, have been noted in Roydon Wood in overstood coppice.

Woodland terricolous habitats
The ground flora of the woodlands is very poor in lichen species but two obscure crust-forming species

have been recorded on disturbed ground of tracks and boundary banks: the nationally scarce *Thelocarpon lichenicola* and one of the few lowland records of the common upland lichen *Trapeliopsis gelatinosa*. Also the nationally scarce fungal parasite of liverworts *Mniacea jungermanniae* (recorded by lichenologists but not strictly a lichenicolous species) is local but widespread.

Lichen habitats beyond the forest core

Introduction
Beyond pasture woodlands and heaths the National Park the countryside and villages contain typical lowland lichen habitats and, as a result, ordinary and unexceptional lichen floras, but with some rare or threatened species occurring occasionally. The lichen-rich habitats that do occur, however, have been rather neglected for survey, owing to the attractions of the New Forest.

Coastal habitats
At a county level the most significant habitats outside of the Forest core are coastal, where rich lichen communities are associated with undisturbed shingle beeches. Hurst Spit uniquely includes stable intertidal pebbles on the lee side of the spit. This provides a habitat for maritime rock-growing species that are common on the west coast but are rare in the south-east, with *Lecanora actophila*, *Verrucaria maura* and *Verrucaria mucosa* recorded along with the coastal *Lecania hutchinsiae* (NS) (Sandell and Rose 1996). Other shingle beeches support non-maritime flint and acid grassland floras that require greater study, but include some local species, such as the only natural stone occurrence in Hampshire of the county-rare *Aspicilia caesiocinerea* on flint at Keyhaven. Marine sediment at Tom Tidlers Ground at Fawley power station, dumped in the 1960s, also supports a lichen rich acid grassland on shingle, with the county-rare *Cladonia scrabriuscula*, which is not yet recorded from the Open Forest.

The built environment
Stone buildings have introduced a wide range of rock types, in an area where there is no natural rock other than flint pebbles. These provide niches for several hundred lichen species that would otherwise be absent. The richest sites for this anthropogenic lichen flora are medieval churches and churchyards in rural settings. These have a long continuity of habitat, the greatest variety of rock type and are in the clean environments. Much informal survey work of churchyard lichens has been carried by members of the BLS, especially by Dr Francis Rose but also by Ken Sandell. The results are unpublished and the following was extracted from the papers of the late Dr Francis Rose.

Many churches within the National Park are of 19th century buildings, which are of no particular interest, but the few medieval buildings are much richer. Old Brockenhurst Church is among the richest churchyards in Hampshire, with 103 species recorded. This is partly because of the presence of numerous veteran oak and an ancient yew. These support a significant assemblage of Ancient Dry Bark community species, including the Near Threatened *Opegrapha prosodea*. Dr Rose considered that this was probably the richest churchyard for epiphytic lichen interest in Britain. The trees are contiguous with Brockenhurst Park, itself part of the New Forest meta-site. The rock flora of the churchyard is also rich and with 80 species recorded, it is the richest churchyard in the National Park, but has no rare species. (The richest churches in the county have over 90 lichen species recorded from rock). The other significant old building complex is the remains of Beaulieu Abbey from which 75 species have been recorded. The old precinct walls are especially rich and include *Caloplaca cirrochroa*, a widespread species on natural hard limestone outcrops in the north and west, which is rare in the lowlands and confined to stonework of medieval date. Also recorded from here is the Nationally Scarce parasitic fungus *Toninia episema* on *Aspicilia calcarea*. Both of these species have their only Hampshire sites at Beaulieu. Other significant churches are Minstead Church with 67 species and Bramshaw Church with 60 species, including one of only two records of *Protoblastenia calva* from the county and the nationally scarce *Hymenelia prevostii*.

Trees and woodlands
Beyond the pasture woodlands of the New Forest SAC, the adjacent parks and the Langley Wood complex covered above, there are there are scattered sites of at least county significance for their epiphytic interest. Again this habitat has been neglected compared to the much richer core New Forest woodlands. Before the advent of Dutch elm disease there was a significant flora of elm specialist lichens on the hedgerow elms in the enclosed land south of the New Forest commons. This has now been completely lost, with the total loss of veteran elms. Other habitats of interest are neglected coppices that have been invaded by the more mobile ancient woodland species and veteran boundary oaks. The former habitat normally harbours an attenuated version of the New Forest pasture woodland flora, but the richest example recorded, Sims Wood, on the banks of the Beaulieu estuary, has 12 NIEC indicator species. The mainly northern lichen *Pertusaria pupillaris* has its only known south Hampshire site on an old wild service-tree here.

The veteran boundary trees support the internationally rare Ancient Dry Bark community *Lecanactidetum premneae*. As the core New Forest is the single most important site in the world for this species assemblage, these are more significant. The current incomplete knowledge suggests that there are two significant areas:

- A scatter of rich veteran old trees extends down the Lymington River valley from Roydon Wood (part of the core New Forest woodlands) and then east along the coastal plain, intermittently to the Beaulieu estuary. This includes two known important concentrations of veteran oaks: field oaks on the National Park boundary at Ampress, and the landscape park of Pylwell Park, both with the Near Threatened *Opegrapha prosodea*. This species has stronger populations in this area than within the core New Forest woodlands.

- A thinner scatter of veteran oaks along lanes on the west side of the Forest on the terraces of the River Avon. This area includes the impressive Moyles Court oak north of Ringwood, and extends as far south as Burton, but many of the trees identified within this area are outside of the National Park.

There are many other landscape parks recorded on 19th century maps around the New Forest but apart from New Park, Brockenhurst Park and Pyewell Park, these appear to be 19th century in origin and have no significant populations of veteran trees.

References

Alexander, K. N. A., Smith, M., Stiven, R. and Sanderson, N. A. (2002). *Defining 'Old Growth' in the UK Context*. English Nature research Reports No 494. English Nature, Peterborough.

Bakker, E. S., Olff. H., Vanderberghe, C., Maeyer, K. De, Smit, R., Gleichman, J. M., and Vera, F. W. M. (2004). Ecological anachronisms in the recruitment of temperate light-demanding tree species in wooded pastures. *Journal of Applied Ecology*, 41, 571–582.

Benfield, B. (1994). Impact of agriculture on epiphytic lichens at Plymtree, East Devon. *The Lichenologist*, 26, 91–94.

Biodiversity Reporting and Information Group (2007). *Report on the Species and Habitat Review*. Report to the UK Biodiversity Partnership. JNCC, Peterborough.

Chatters, C. and Sanderson, N. A. (1994). Grazing lowland pasture woodlands. *British Wildlife*, 6, 78–88.

Chatters, C., Sanderson, N. A. and Stern, R. C. (1999). Wild service trees in a New Forest wood pasture. *Proceedings of the Hampshire Field Club and Archaeological Society*, 54, 57–62.

Coppins, A. M. and Coppins, B. J. (1998). Lichen survey of Horner Woods NNR – 1998. Unpublished Report to the National Trust.

Coppins, A. M. and Coppins, B. J. (2002). Indices of Ecological Continuity for woodland epiphytic lichen habitats in the British Isles. British Lichen Society, London.

Coppins, B. J. and Shimwell, D. W. (1971). Variations in cryptogam complement and biomass in dry *Calluna* heaths of various ages. *Oikos*, 22, 204–209.

Cox, J. and Rose, F. (1996). *A preliminary assessment of proposed changes in camping and car parking provision in the New Forest*. An unpublished report to the New Forest Association and Hampshire Wildlife Trust.

Davey, S. (1994). *Dorset Lichen Survey: Contract No. 13/F2B/247*. An unpublished report to English Nature.

Edwards, B. (2001). *Relocation of New Forest campsites; lower plant assessment*. Dorset Environmental Records Centre, unpublished report for Terrence O'Rourke.

Edwards, B. (2002). *The past and present distribution of Bacidia incompta, Biatoridium monasteriense and Caloplaca luteoalba in England*. Plantlife, London.

Fletcher, A., Coppins, B. J., Hawksworth, D. L., James, P. W. and Rose, F. (1982). *Survey and assessment of epiphytic lichen habitats*. A report prepared by the Woodland Working Party of the British Lichen Society, for the Nature Conservancy Council [contract HF3/03/208].

Fletcher, A. (ed.) (1984). *Survey and assessment of lowland heathland lichen habitats*. [Report prepared by the Heathland Lichen Working Party of the British Lichen Society for the Nature Conservancy Council; Contract no.: HF 3/03/266]. 111 pp.

Gilbert, O. L. and Giavarini, V. J. (1997). The lichen vegetation of acid watercourses in England. *Lichenologist*, 29, 347–367.

Hayward, N. (1996). Conservation and safety: the beginnings of a veteran tree management strategy for the New Forest. In H. J. Read (ed.): *Pollard and Veteran Tree Management. II.* pp. 71–74. Corporation of London.

Hobbs, R. J. (1985). The persistence of *Cladonia* patches in closed heathland stands. *Lichenologist*, 17, 103–110.

Hodgetts, N. G. (1992) *Guidelines for selection of biological SSSIs: non-vascular plants*. JNCC, Peterborough.

James, P. W., Hawksworth, D. L. and Rose, F. (1977). Lichen communities in the British Isles: a preliminary conspectus. In M. Seaward (ed.), *Lichen ecology*, pp. 295–413. Academic Press, London.

Johansson, P. and Reich, P. B. (2005). Population size and fire intensity determine post-fire abundance in grassland lichens. *Applied Vegetation Science*, 8, 193–198.

Looney, J. H. H. and James, P. W. (1990). *The effects of acidification on lichens – Final report, 1989*. CSD Report 1057. Nature Conservancy Council, Peterborough.

Morgan, R. K. (1987a). Composition, structure and regeneration characteristics of open woodlands of the New Forest, Hampshire. *Journal of Biogeography*, 14, 423–438.

Morgan, R. K. (1987b). An evaluation of the impact of anthropogenic pressures on woodland regeneration in the New Forest, Hampshire. *Journal of Biogeography*, 14, 439–450.

Morgan, R. K. (1991). The role of protective understorey in the regeneration system of a heavily browsed woodland. *Vegetatio*, 92, 119–132.

Pasmore, A. (1976). *Verderers of the New Forest. A History of the New Forest 1877–1977*. Pioneer Publications Ltd., Beaulieu.

Peterken G. F. (1993). *Woodland conservation and management. Second edition*. Chapman and Hall, London and New York.

Peterken, G. F. and Tubbs, C. R. (1965). Woodland regeneration in the New Forest, Hampshire, since 1650. *Journal of Applied Ecology*, 2, 159–170.

Reeves, R. P. (2006). *Use and abuse of a forest resource: New Forest documents 1632–1700*. New Forest Ninth Centenary Trust, Lyndhurst.

Reeves, R. P., Cox, J., Frost, P., Tubbs, J. M., Sanderson, N. A. and Humbert D. (2006). *The New Forest Design Plan: recovering lost landscapes*. New Forest Association, Lyndhurst.

Richardson, D. H. S. and Cameron, R. P. (2004). Cyanolichens: their response to pollution and possible management strategies for their conservation in northeastern North America. *Northeastern Naturalist*, 11, 1–22.

Roberts, P. (2002). *Minstead. Life in a 17th century New Forest Community*. Nova Foresta Publishing, Southampton.

Rose, F. (1988). Phytogeographical and ecological aspects of *Lobarion* communities in Europe. *Botanical Journal of the Linnean Society*, 69, 69–79.

Rose, F. (1990). The epiphytic (corticolous and lignicolous) lichen flora of the Forêt de Fontainebleau. *Bulletin Société Botanique de France*, 137, 197–209.

Rose, F. (1992a). Temperate forest management: its effects on bryophytes and lichen floras and habitats. In Bates, J. W. and Farmer, A. M. (eds.) *Bryophytes and lichens in a changing environment*, pp. 211–233. Oxford University Press, Oxford.

Rose, F. (1992b). *Report on the remaining heathlands of West Sussex 1991–1992*. West Sussex County Council.

Rose, F. (1993). Ancient British woodlands and their epiphytes. *British Wildlife*, 5, 3–93.

Rose, F. and James, P. W. (1974). Regional studies on the British lichen flora I. The corticolous and lichenicolous species of the New Forest, Hampshire. *Lichenologist*, 6, 1–72.

Sandell, K. A. and Rose, F. (1996). The lichen flora. In: *The flora of Hampshire* (ed. Brewis A., Bowman P. and Rose F.), pp. 306–324. Harley Books, Colchester, Essex.

Sanderson, N. A. (1991). Notes on holly cutting in the New Forest. In H. J. Read (ed.), *Pollard and veteran tree management*, pp. 53–55. Corporation of London.

Sanderson, N. A. (1994a). *An ecological survey of the lichens Catillaria laureri and Parmelia minarum in the New Forest, Hampshire*. An unpublished Botanical Survey and Assessment report to Hampshire Wildlife Trust.

Sanderson, N. A. (1994b). *An ecological survey of the lichens Catillaria laureri and Parmelia minarum in the New Forest, Hampshire. Second Report*. An unpublished Botanical Survey and Assessment report to Hampshire Wildlife Trust.

Sanderson, N. A. (1994c). *Lichen survey of Langley Wood NNR Wiltshire*. A unpublished Botanical Survey and Assessment report to English Nature.

Sanderson, N. A. (1995). *Ambersham and Heyshott Commons Lower Plant Survey*. An unpublished Botanical Survey and Assessment report to English Nature.

Sanderson, N. A. (1996a). *New Forest heathland management and lichens*. An unpublished Botanical Survey and Assessment report to the British Lichen Society.

Sanderson, N. A. (1996b). *Lichen conservation within the New Forest timber Inclosures*. An unpublished report to Hampshire Wildlife Trust.

Sanderson, N. A. (1996c). The role of grazing in the ecology of lowland pasture woodland with special reference to the New Forest. In H. J. Read (ed.) *Pollard and veteran tree management. II*, pp. 111–118. Corporation of London.

Sanderson, N. A. (1996d). *Lower Plant Survey of the southern verge of the A35 between Ashurst and Lyndhurst*. An unpublished report to Hampshire Wildlife Trust.

Sanderson, N. A. (1996e). *New Forest heathland management and lichens*. An unpublished Botanical Survey and Assessment report to the British Lichen Society.

Sanderson, N. A. (1997a). *A lichen survey of South Bentley Inclosure*. An unpublished Botanical Survey and Assessment report to the Forestry Commission.

Sanderson, N. A. (1997b). *A review of holly cutting in the New Forest*. An unpublished report to Hampshire Wildlife Trust.

Sanderson, N. A. (1998). *New Forest epiphytic lichen data base, volume 4. Part 3. Summary of results*. An unpublished report to Hampshire Wildlife Trust.

Sanderson, N. A. (1999). *New Forest Rare Lichen Monitoring Project*. (*Catillaria laureri, Parmelia minarum* and *Enterographa elaborata*). An unpublished report to Hampshire Wildlife Trust.

Sanderson, N. A. (2001). *Epiphytic lichen monitoring in the New Forest 2000. LIFE Job L33A2U*. An unpublished report by Botanical Survey and Assessment to Forest Enterprise.

Sanderson, N. A. (2002). *Species dossier for Enterographa sorediata*. An unpublished report by Botanical Survey and Assessment to English Nature.

Sanderson, N. A. (2003a). *Lichen survey of Whiteparish Common 2003*. An unpublished report by Botanical Survey and Assessment to English Nature.

Sanderson, N. A. (2003b). *Epiphyte survey of Round Hill, New Forest, Hampshire 2003*. An unpublished report by Botanical Survey and Assessment to Terrence O'Rouke.

Sanderson, N. A. (2004a). *Lichen survey of Loosehanger Copse, Wiltshire 2003*. An unpublished report by Botanical Survey and Assessment to English Nature.

Sanderson, N. A. (2004b). *Epiphyte Survey of Hollands Wood campsite, New Forest, Hampshire*. An unpublished report by Botanical Survey and Assessment to Terrence O'Rourke.

Sanderson, N. A. (2007a). *New Forest Inclosure habitats, habitat fragmentation and landscape history*. Hampshire & Isle of Wight Wildlife Trust, Botley.

Sanderson, N. A. (2007b). *Enterographa elaborata*: canopy collapse and lichen diversity in New Forest beech woods. *British Lichen Society Bulletin*, 100, 27–30.

Sanderson, N. A. (in prep). Recolonisation by epiphytic lichens after clear felling in the New Forest, Hampshire, UK. *Lichenologist*.

Sanderson, N. A., Bannister, N. and Colebourn P. C. (1994). *A restoration plan for Brockenhurst Park*. An unpublished report by Ecological Planning and Research to the Countryside Commission.

Sanderson, N. A. and Wolseley, P. (2001). Management of pasture woodlands for lichens. In A. Fletcher (ed.) *Habitat management for lichens*. pp. 05-1 – 05-25. British Lichen Society, London.

Smith, C. W., Aptroot, A., Coppins, B. J., Fletcher, A., Gilbert, O. L., James, P.W. & Wolseley. P. A. (2009) *The Lichens of Great Britain and Ireland*. London: British Lichen Society.

Stagg, D. J. (1983). *A calendar of New Forest documents. The Fifteenth to the Seventeenth Centuries*. Hampshire County Council, Winchester.

Stagg, D. J. (1989). Silvicultural inclosure in the New Forest to 1780. *Proceedings of the Hampshire Field Club and Archaeological Society*, 45, 135–145.

Tubbs, C. R. (2001). *The New Forest*. New Forest Centenary Trust, Lyndhurst.

Vera, F. W. M. (2000). *Grazing ecology and forest history*. CABI Publishing, Wallingford.

Wolesey, P. A., James, P. A., Theobald, M. R. and Sutton, M. A. (2006). Detecting changes in epiphytic lichen communities at sites effected by atmospheric ammonia from agricultural sources. *The Lichenologist*, 38, 161–176.

Wright, R. N. and Westerhoff, D. V. (2001). *New Forest SAC Management Plan*. English Nature, Lyndhurst.

Woods, R. G. and Coppins, B. J. (2003). *A conservation evaluation of lichens*. British Lichen Society, London.

Appendix 1
Lichen species of conservation concern occurring in the New Forest.
NIEC refers to the New Index of Ecological Continuity (see text). RDB refers to Red Data Book.

Species	Conservation status	NIEC	Habitat	Number of woods	Comment
Critically Endangered RDB species					
Bacidia subturgidula ***	EX NR BAP		Dry lignum	2	Very rare species of standing holly lignum
Enterographa elaborata **	CR NR BAP		Rain track	3	On three beech in rain tracks in ancient old growth
Ramonia nigra ***	CR NR IR BAP E		Base rich and wound track	9	Rare inside hollow beech, ash and holly and on oak bark in old growth
Total 3					
Endangered RDB species					
Caloplaca flavorubescens	EN NS BAP		Park	1	Recorded on an ash in Langley Wood
Collema fragrans **	EN NS IR BAP		Wound track	17	Occasional, sap runs and root knot holes on beech and ash old growth
Megalaria laurerii **	EN NR IR		Rain track	8	Rare sp. of beech rain tracks in ancient old growth
Strigula stigmatella var. *stigmatella*	EN NR BAP		Base rich	1	Recorded once on oak in Great Wood
Total 4					
Vulnerable RDB species					
Bacidia circumspecta *	VU NS BAP		Wound track	3	Rare in wound tracks on old beech
Bacidia incompta **	VU BAP		Wound track	37	Local in hollow holly and sap runs on beech in old growth, once ash
Buellia hyperbolica	VU NR BAP		Acid	2	Rare on old acidic ancient oak, Rowbarrow and Denny Wood
Cryptolechia carneolutea	VU NS IR BAP		Wound	6	Rare in rain tracks (six beech and one ash) in ancient old growth
Lecanographa amylacea *	VU NS IR BAP		Ancient dry	14	Occasional on dry bark on ancient oak in ancient old growth
Parmelinopsis minarum **	VU NR		Acid	14	Very local on acid beech in ancient old growth
Pertusaria pustulata	VU NR		Mesic	5	Rare but probably overlooked species of beech in ancient old growth
Pertusaria velata ***	VU NS IR BAP		Mesic	33	Widespread beech, rare oak and ash in old growth. Very rare in Europe
Pyrenula nitida **	VU NR BAP		Rain track	11	Very local but frequent on beech in ancient old growth
Rinodina colobinoides **	VU NR		Park	1	On an old field maple in pasture Brockenhurst Park
Schismatomma graphidoides *	VU NR BAP		Dry	1	Rare on ash and oak in Drivers Nursery
Total 11					
Near Threatened RDB species					
Agonimia octospora **	NT NS IR	1	Base rich	62	Widespread and frequent in old-growth woodlands
Anaptychia ciliaris	NT BAP		Park	2	Recorded from a wayside oak and a parkland oak
Arthonia astroidestera **	NT NS IR	1	Smooth	31	Widespread and occasional in ancient old growth on holly, rare beech
Arthonia invadens ***	NT NR IR BAP E		Acid	22	Rare parasite of *Schismatomma quercicola* in dense populations
Arthonia zwackhii	NT NR		Mesic	2	Rare two modern records, parasitic on *Phlyctis argena*
Blarneya hibernica	NT NR IR BAP		Ancient dry	2	Rare species of dry side ancient oaks, initially a parasite
Calicium parvum	NT NR		Conifer	1	Pine specialist, recorded once on pine in sheltered glade, Wood Crates
Caloplaca herbidella	NT NR		Base rich	2	Rare in ancient old-growth ash and oak
Chaenothecopsis caespitosa	NT NR		Dry lignum	0	Yew stump, SU2603
Collema occultatum	NT NS		Base rich	1	Recorded from field maple in Ivy Wood
Cyphelium tigillare	NT		Dry lignum	1	Seen once on lignum on fence post, not seen recently

Species	Conservation status	NIEC	Habitat	Number of woods	Comment
Near Threatened RDB species ... continued					
Enterographa sorediata ***	NT NR IR BAP E	1	Ancient dry	27	Occasional on dry bark on ancient oak in ancient old growth
Fuscopannaria sampaiana	NT NS BAP		Base rich	1	Recorded from one ash Lucas Castle, not seen recently
Gyalecta flotowii	NT NS		Wound track	1	Recorded once from Pinnick Wood on ash
Heterodermia japonica	NT NS	1	Branch	1	Rare recorded once from Busketts Wood, possibly overlooked as a twig species
Lecania chlorotiza	NT NS IR BAP		Base rich	1	On a base rich oak in Langley Wood
Lecanora horiza	NT NS		Park	7	Rare on well light trunks of old trees
Lecanora quercicola	NT NS IR BAP	1	Park	9	Rare on old well lit oak trunks in ancient old growth
Lecanora sublivescens	NT NS IR BAP	1	Park	1	Rare on old oak in Frame Wood in ancient old growth
Megalospora tuberculosa	NT NS IR BAP	1	Base rich	13	Rare on base rich trees in ancient old growth (possibly over recorded)
Melaspilea amota **	NT NR		Mesic	13	Recent recorded and overlooked species of older oaks
Melaspilea lentiginosa **	NT NR IR		Mesic	19	Rare parasite on *Phaeographis dendritica*, on beech
Micarea pycnidiophora **	NT NS IR	1	Acid	57	Widespread acid beech and holly plus oak and birch mainly in old growth
Mycoporum lacteum **	NT NR		Smooth	57	Widespread on old holly in old growth, rare oak, English HQ
Opegrapha prosodea	NT NS IR	1	Ancient dry	2	Rare on dry bark of ancient oak in ancient old growth and parkland
Parmeliella testacea	NT NS IR BAP		Base rich	1	Recorded from one ash Lucas Castle, not seen recently
Parmelinopsis horrescens	NT NS IR		Acid	12	Very locally frequent on acid bark in old growth
Parmotrema arnoldii	NT NS		Branch	4	Very rare on branches in sheltered sites in ancient old growth
Pertusaria coronata	NT NS		Unclear	2	Very rare recorded twice oak and ash
Phaeographis lyellii	NT NS IR		Smooth	14	Rare on smooth bark, mainly old beech and hawthorn
Phlyctis agelaea	NT NS		Mesic	1	Pollution sensitive species recorded once on field maple, Ivy Wood
Porina hibernica **	NT NR IR BAP	1	Base rich	47	Often frequent, if localised, old base rich oaks in old growth
Porina rosei **	NT NS IR		Base rich	51	More widespread than *P. hibernica* but not as frequent
Protoparmelia oleagina	NT NS		Dry lignum	2	Recorded once on lignum on fallen old oak, Jacks Wood
Ramonia chrysophaea **	NT NS IR BAP		Base rich	39	Occasional, base rich bare bark and lignum, on old trees
Ramonia dictyospora	NT NR IR BAP E		Unclear	3	Rarer than *R. chrysophaea*, possibly on more acid habitat?
Rinodina isidioides **	NT NS BAP	1	Base rich	20	Local in old-growth woods, mainly to north
Usnea articulata	NT IR BAP		Branch	10	Rare pollution-sensitive canopy species
Wadeana dendrographa	NT NS IR BAP	1	Base rich	15	Occasional old ash, rare oak in old growth
Wadeana minuta	NT NS IR BAP		Base rich	1	Rare recorded twice on oak in the Frame Wood area
Total 40					
Data Deficient RDB species					
Biatora britannica **	DD NR		Base rich	10	Local, sheltered base rich bark
Byssoloma leucoblepharum **	DD NR		Base rich	7	Very rare species in New Forest and Britain AOG on old oak in old growth

Species	Conservation status	NIEC	Habitat	Number of woods	Comment
Data Deficient RDB species ... continued					
Calicium hyperelloides **	DD NR		Mesic	1	Single record on old oak, very rare in Europe but a common tropical sp.
Cliostomum flavidulum **	DD NR		Mesic	44	Recent find, appears widespread on acid-mesic trunks
Lecanora barkmaneana	DD NR		Park	1	Not known on open forest, parkland oak tree in New Park
Opegrapha viridis	DD		Mesic	3	Rare on beech in ancient old growth
Opegrapha xerica	DD NS		Ancient dry	11	Local on dry bark on ancient oak in ancient old growth
Total 7					
Total RDB 65					
Non-threatened nationally rare species					
Absconditella lignicola	NR		Unclear	1	Ephemeral species found on grunge in crack on old oak trunk
Absconditella pauxilla	NR		Damp lignum	0	Ephemeral species found on conifer stump Appleslade Inclosure
Micarea viridileporosa	NR		Acid	5	Recently described sp of acid substrates, now NS likely to be common
Micarea xanthonica *	NR IR		Acid	3	Recently identified sp of oceanic woods, now NS likely to be uncommon
Pycnora sorophora *	NR		Dry lignum	2	A northern lignum specialist recorded rarely from oak and pine lignum
Thelocarpon strasseri	NR		Damp lignum	1	An ephemeral species seen once on beech lignum
Total 6					
Non-threatened nationally scarce species					
Absconditella delutula	NS		Unclear	2	Rarely recorded ephemeral of debris in rot holes
Agonimia allobata	NS	1	Base rich	20	Occasional in old-growth woodlands on base rich bark
Anisomeridium viridescens	NS IR		Smooth	4	On old hazel stems
Arthonia graphidicola *	NS IR		Mesic	3	Rare parasite of *Graphis scripta* on old beech
Arthonia leucopellaea *	NS		Acid	14	Local species of acid oak in old growth
Arthothelium ruanum	NS		Smooth	1	Hazel specialist Drivers Nursery only
Bacidia absistens	NS		Unclear	1	Record from pastures woodland Bakers Copse in Roydon Wood
Bacidia delicata	NS		Base rich	1	Field maple, Ivy Wood
Bacidia friesiana	NS		Wound track	1	Rare wound track on beech, Mark Ash Wood
Bactrospora corticola	NS		Dry	2	Rare on dry side old but not ancient oaks
Buellia erubescens	NS	1	Smooth and mesic	8	Rare in ancient old growth on beech and holly in ancient old growth
Caloplaca ferruginea	NS IR		Base rich	8	Rare in ancient old growth on base rich beech, ash and oak
Catillaria nigroclavata *	NS		Wound track and mesic	8	Recorded from aspen and elder and on rain tracks on beech
Celothelium ischnobelum	NS		Smooth	3	Rare on smooth bark of hazel and oak
Chaenotheca brachypoda	NS	0	Dry lignum and ancient dry	20	On beech and ash lignum in ancient old growth
Chaenotheca hispidula	NS	0	Dry lignum	19	Beech, ash, oak and alder lignum and dry bark on oak in old growth
Chaenotheca stemonea	NS	0	Ancient dry	3	Dry bark ancient oaks
Chaenothecopsis nigra *	NS		Dry lignum	19	Confined to oak, rarely beech, lignum on standing old or dead trees
Chaenothecopsis pusilla *	NS		Dry lignum	13	Confined to oak, rarely beech, lignum on standing old or dead trees

Species	Conservation status	NIEC	Habitat	Number of woods	Comment
Non-threatened nationally scarce species ... continued					
Cladonia incrassata	NS		Damp lignum	2	Oak lignum on damp lignum, more frequent on heaths
Eopyrenula grandicula	NS IR		Smooth	11	Specialist of old hazel stems
Fuscopannaria mediterranea	NS		Base rich	1	Single ancient oak, Shave Wood area
Gyalecta derivata	NS		Wound track	2	Rare on ash
Lecania cyrtellina	NS		Wound track	8	Wound tracks on beech and twice on field maple
Lecanora aitema	NS		Dry lignum	5	Probably under recorded on pine, yew and oak lignum
Lecanora albellula	NS		Dry lignum	7	Rare on beech and oak lignum in ancient old growth SW of Lyndhurst
Lecanora alboflavida *	NS	1	Acid	47	Widespread on acid bark in old growth rare in young growth
Lecanora argentata	NS		Mesic	8	Well lit trunks of old beech and ash
Lecanora compallens	NS		Dry lignum	7	Recently described, mainly lignum, outside Forest also polluted bark
Lecidea doliiformis	NS		Acid and conifer	25	Occasional on ancient oak lignum, acidifed bark and old conifers
Lepraria umbricola	NS		Acid	6	Acidic shaded bark on old oak
Leptogium subtile	NS		Wound track	1	Rare beech knot hole on root, Mallard Wood
Leptorhaphis maggiana	NS		Smooth	4	Young branches on old hazel bushes
Macentina stigonemoides	NS		Wound track	15	Over growing mosses on nutrient enriched bark, especially wound tracks
Melaspilea ochrothalamia	NS		Mesic	13	Under recorded on mature trees
Micarea coppinsii	NS		Acid	3	Under recorded, acid bark bog woodland
Micarea myriocarpa	NS			1	Pebbles in soil on root plate of fallen tree
Microcalicium ahlneri *	NS		Dry lignum	39	Widespread on dry oak lignum on standing trees
Mycocalicium subtile	NS		Dry lignum	10	Rare on standing oak and beech lignum in ancient old growth
Mycoglaena myricae *	NS		Myrica gale	16	Occasional on bog myrtle at the edge of woods, widespread in heaths
Ochrolechia microstictoides	NS		Acid and damp lignum	9	On old birch, especially bog woodland, also oak lignum
Opegrapha corticola	NS IR	1	Base rich	62	Common on old trees in ancient old growth rare in younger stands
Opegrapha fumosa *	NS IR		Acid	20	Abundant in the north of the Forest in old growth on acid bark
Phaeographis inusta	NS IR		Smooth	54	Widespread but occasional on smooth bark
Phaeophyscia endophoenicea	NS		Park	2	On several well lit oak Long Beech and beech branch at Busketts
Phyllopsora rosei *	NS	1	Base rich	24	Locally frequent in old growth on base rich bark
Porina borreri	NS		Wound and rain track	35	Occasional but widespread wound and rain tracks on beech in old growth
Porina coralloidea *	NS IR	1	Mesic and base rich	80	Old woodland species colonising 19th century Inclosures, mainly on oak
Ramonia interjecta	NS IR		Wound track	1	Wound track on beech, Gritnam Wood
Ropalospora viridis	NS		Acid	5	Rare on acid beech, once oak, in ancient old growth woodland
Thelocarpon lichenicola	NS			1	Sandy soil of upturned root-plate
Sphinctrina turbinata	NS		Mesic	13	Parasite on Pertusaria on trunks of old trees, occasional
Strangospora moriformis	NS		Dry lignum	1	On holly lignum
Strigula jamesii	NS		Wound and rain track	6	In rain tracks on holly and beech

Species	Conservation status	NIEC	Habitat	Number of woods	Comment
Non-threatened nationally scarce species ... continued					
Strigula phaea *	NS		Rain track	15	Mainly in rain tracks on beech and holly in old growth
Strigula taylorii	NS IR		Wound track	21	Under recorded in rain tracks on beech
Usnea wasmuthii	NS		Branch	1	Recorded once on beech branch, Undersley Wood, overlooked?
Total 57					
Non-threatened widespread species that are international responsibility species					
Arthonia ilicina *	IR	1	Smooth and mesic	37	Occasional in old growth on smooth bark on holly, beech and ash
Cresponea premnea **	IR	1	Ancient dry	68	Abundant mainly on old oaks in ancient old growth rare younger stands
Degelia plumbea	IR	1	Base rich	1	Single ash, Roydon Wood, now lost
Hypotrachyna sinuosa	IR		Acid	2	Very rare on sheltered acid bark
Hypotrachyna taylorensis	IR		Acid	2	A few trees in Anses Wood and South Bentley in old growth
Lecanactis subabietina	IR	1	Ancient dry	28	Occasional on dry bark on ancient oak in ancient dry bark
Lecanographa lyncea ***	IR	1	Ancient dry	47	Frequent on dry bark on ancient oak in ancient old growth
Lobaria amplissima	IR	1	Base rich	6	Ancient base rich trees, decline one extant tree
Lobaria pulmonaria	IR	1	Base rich	40	Still widespread on old trees but probably declining, rarely fertile
Lobaria virens *	IR	1	Base rich	26	Infrequent on old trees but often fertile
Nephroma laevigatum	IR	1	Base rich	1	Recorded from Vinney Ridge, probably extinct
Pannaria conoplea	IR	1	Base rich	10	Rare and declining species of base rich bark in ancient old growth
Rinodina roboris	IR		Mesic and base rich	68	Frequent well lit mature trees, especially oak, also on beech
Schismatomma cretaceum	IR		Ancient dry	61	Dry bark on old oak and occasional beech and ash in old growth
Schismatomma niveum **	IR	1	Acid, mesic and dry	103	Ubiquitous old woodland species on acid and mesic bark
Schismatomma quercicola **	IR E	1	Acid	103	Ubiquitous old woodland species on acid bark
Sticta limbata	IR	1	Base rich	12	Rare and declining sp of base rich bark in old growth
Total 17					
Total Notable 80					
Widely distributed and non-threatened NIEC ancient indicator lichens					
Anisomeridium ranunculosporum		1	Acid, smooth and mesic	105	Ubiquitous old woodland species
Arthonia vinosa		1	Mesic and base rich	100	Old woodland species widely colonising 19th century Inclosures
Bacidia biatorina		1	Mesic and base rich	78	Old woodland species widely colonising 19th century Inclosures
Catinaria atropurpurea		1	Base rich	74	Old woodland species colonising 19th century Inclosures
Cetrelia olivetorum		1	Acid	2	Recorded twice on acid beech in ancient old growth woodlands
Chaenotheca brunneola		1	Dry lignum and ancient dry	53	Lignum and dry bark on old trees, mainly old growth
Chaenotheca chrysocephala		0	Dry lignum and ancient dry	9	Rare dry bark on old oak and birch and beech lignum, old growth
Chaenotheca furfuracea		0	Ancient dry	3	Rare on dry bark
Chaenotheca trichialis		0	Ancient dry	14	Occasional on old oak and rare beech

Species	Conservation status	NIEC	Habitat	Number of woods	Comment
Widely distributed and non-threatened NIEC ancient indicator lichens ... continued					
Cladonia caespiticia		1	Acid	37	Local alder and other acid barked trees, soil on root plates, in old growth
Cladonia parasitica		1	Damp lignum	78	Oak lignum, more abundant in New Forest than elsewhere in UK
Collema subflaccidum		1	Base rich	4	Rare on ash in ancient old-growth woodland
Dimerella lutea		1	Base rich	56	Widespread but never frequent in old growth rare young growth
Lecanora jamesii		1	Mesic	49	Mainly on beech, but also willow, in old growth, rare young growth
Leptogium lichenoides		1	Base rich	27	Occasional on moss on oak, beech and ash in old growth
Leptogium teretiusculum		1	Base rich	16	Occasional on oak, ash and beech in old growth
Loxospora elatina		1	Acid	95	Old woodland species colonising 19th century Inclosures
Micarea cinerea		1	Acid	1	Recorded once on oak in Red Shoot Wood
Mycobilimbia epixanthoides		1	Base rich	20	Local old-growth woodland species on oak, beech and ash
Mycobilimbia pilularis		1	Base rich	33	Widespread old-growth sp. of shaded base rich bark
Mycoporum antecellens		1	Smooth and mesic	62	Old woodland species widely colonising 19th century Inclosures
Pachyphiale carneola		1	Base rich	99	Old woodland species widely colonising 19th century Inclosures
Parmotrema crinitum		1	Mesic and base rich	51	Fairly frequent on well lit trunks mainly in old growth
Peltigera horizontalis		1	Base rich	17	Local on sheltered base rich trees in old growth
Pertusaria multipuncta		1	Mesic	98	Ubiquitous old woodland species
Phaeographis dendritica		1	Mesic	88	Old woodland species colonising 19th century Inclosures
Punctelia reddenda		1	Mesic and base rich	69	Fairly frequent on well lit trunks mainly in old growth
Stenocybe septata		1	Smooth	103	Ubiquitous on holly and rare hazel, oak and wild service-tree
Strangospora ochrophora		1	Base rich	9	Occasional on base rich oak in old growth
Thelopsis rubella *		1	Base rich	71	Frequent in old-growth woods on base rich bark on old trees
Thelotrema lepadinum		1	Acid, smooth and mesic	107	Ubiquitous old woodland sp., population density up to over 400 trees/ha
Usnea ceratina		1	Branch	82	Old woodland sp of high well lit trunks and branches
Usnea florida	BAP	1	Branch	67	Locally frequent in sheltered canopy in woods with clean air
Total 33					
Recently confirmed and not used in the habitat analysis					
Bacidia assulata	NR DD		Wound track	1	Rain track on old beech in Mark Ash Wood
Strigula tagananae	NR DD BAP		Rain track	2	Rain tracks on old beeches in Busketts Wood area, new to England
Nationally under-recorded fungal parasites of lichens					
Abrothallus bertianus	NS			3	Parasitic on *Melanelia f. glabratula*, may be of conservation significance
Abrothallus microspermus	NS			23	Parasitic on *Flavoparmelia caperata*, a common species
Biatoropsis usnearum	NS			2	Parasitic on *Usnea cornuta*, probably rare in lowlands

Species	Conservation status	NIEC	Habitat	Number of woods	Comment
Nationally under-recorded fungal parasites of lichens ... continued					
Dactylospora parasitica	NS			23	Parasite on Pertusaria pertusa and hymenea, rare in lowlands
Epicladonia sandstedii	NR			2	Parasitic on Cladonia, rarely recorded
Epicladonia simplex	NR			1	Parasitic on Cladonia, new to Britain 1998
Homostegia piggotii	NS			14	Parasitic on Hypogymia phyosodes, rare in lowlands?
Intralichen christiansenii	NS			1	Parasitic fungus recorded Wood Crates 1998
Laeviomyces pertusariicola	NS			5	Parasitic on Pertusaria leioplaca, common species
Lichenoconium erodens	NS			2	A probably common parasitic fungus
Lichenoconium lecanorae	NS			1	A probably common parasitic fungus
Marchandiomyces corallinus	NS			11	A probably common parasitic fungus, attacks many species
Milospium graphideorum	NS			28	Parasite on L. lyncea and other spp. on old oaks, conservation significance
Plectocarpon lichenum	NS			1	Only lowland record of a Lobaria pulmonaria parasite
Pronectria anisospora	NR			2	Parasitic on Hypogymnia physodes, rarely recorded
Roselliniopsis sp.	NR			4	Parasitic on Pertusaria petusa on old beech, conservation significance, only collected from New Forest and Melbury Park
Skyttea nitschkei *	NS			66	Parasitic on Thelotrema lepadinum where population dense
Stigmidium microspilum	NS			7	Parasitic on Graphis scripta, common species
Taeniolina scripta	NR			7	Parasite on Pertusaria leioplaca and Thelotrema
Tremella pertusariae	NR			10	Parasitic on on Pertusaria hymenea, possibly uncommon species
Last records from the 19th century					
Arthonia anglica	EN BAP				Species of old hollies, currently only in a couple of sites in south-west
Arthopyrenia nitescens	NS				A strongly oceanic species of smooth bark
Calicium adspersum	CR BAP				An continental species of ancient oaks
Calicium lenticulare	NS				Oceanic species, found inside hollow oak on edge of range
Collema fasiculata	NS BAP				A highly pollution sensitive species
Graphina ruiziana	NS				A strongly oceanic species of smooth and acid bark
Lecania fuscella	EX				Extinct species in Britain
Lobaria scrobiculata	IR				A highly pollution sensitive species, lost from the lowlands
Meneggazzia terebrata	IR				A strongly oceanic species of acid bark species in Britain
Ochrolechia tartarea					An upland species, lost from all its few lowland sites
Pannaria rubiginosa	IR				A highly pollution sensitive species, lost from the lowlands
Pseudocyphellaria aurata	CR BAP				A highly pollution sensitive species
Sphinctrina tubiformis	DD NR				A parasite of Pertusaria leioplaca, currently only recorded from east Wales

Appendix 2

Important locations for lichen species in the New Forest. NIEC refers to the New Index of Ecological Continuity (see text).

Name	NIEC	Bonus spp	NIEC + B	Site Code	Grid Ref	Habitat	Status	NF Old Growth Meta Sites
Mark Ash Wood	47	46	93	NF02	SU 255075	Pasture woodland	SAC	Central Block
Busketts Wood	48	40	88	NF15	SU 307110	Pasture woodland	SAC	NE Block
Wood Crates	43	40	83	NF22	SU 270083	Pasture woodland	SAC	Central Block

Name	NIEC	Bonus spp	NIEC + B	Site Code	Grid Ref	Habitat	Status	NF Old Growth Meta Sites
Frame Wood	50	29	79	NF28A	SU 360035	Pasture woodland	SAC	Frame and Tantany Woods
Hollands Wood	47	29	76	NF18	SU 305050	Pasture woodland	SAC	Central Block
Bramshaw Wood	48	27	75	NF03	SU 260165	Pasture woodland	SAC	NE Block
Gritnam Wood	45	23	68	NF19B	SU 285065	Pasture woodland	SAC	Central Block
Red Shoot Wood	43	21	64	NF09	SU 188085	Pasture woodland	SAC	Pinnick and Red Shoot Woods Area
Shave Wood	40	23	63	NF14	SU 295122	Pasture woodland	SAC	NE Block
Emery Down	38	24	62	NF20	SU 280080	Pasture woodland	SAC	Central Block
Great Wood	45	16	61	NF08A	SU 255155	Pasture woodland	SAC	NE Block
Queen's Bower	42	19	61	NF36	SU 289043	Pasture woodland	SAC	Central Block
Stricknage Wood	44	16	60	NF11	SU 261125	Pasture woodland	SAC	NE Block
Bakers Copse	41	19	60	NF40A	SU 319017	Pasture woodland	SAC	Round Hill and Roydon Wood
Denny Wood	33	26	59	NF27	SU 357022	Pasture woodland	SAC	Matley and Denny Woods
Highland Water	40	18	58	NF38B	SU 254097	Pasture woodland	SAC	Central Block
Vinney Ridge	40	17	57	NF01	SU 257055	Pasture woodland	SAC	Vinney Ridge to Burley Old
Brinken Wood	40	16	56	NF19A	SU 282052	Pasture woodland	SAC	Central Block
Rushpole Wood	35	21	56	NF16	SU 310097	Pasture woodland	SAC	NE Block
South Ocknell Wood	44	11	55	NF37	SU 246106	Pasture woodland	SAC	Central Block
Ladycross area	39	15	54	NF51	SU 338030	Pasture woodland	SAC	Frame and Tantany Woods
Whitley Wood	38	15	53	NF17	SU 298055	Pasture woodland	SAC	Central Block
Knightwood Inclosure	36	16	52	NF30	SU 260066	Relic pasture woodland	SAC	Central Block
Sunny Bushes	36	15	51	NF08B	SU 261142	Pasture woodland	SAC	NE Block
Parkhill	35	16	51	NF57	SU 315065	Pasture woodland	SAC	Central Block
Ocknell Inclosure	33	17	50	NF34	SU 245115	18th century Inclosure/ pasture woodland	SAC	Central Block
Anses Wood	36	13	49	NF06	SU 230125	Pasture woodland	SAC	Anses to Eyeworth Woods
Coppice of Linwood	35	14	49	NF55A	SU 251135	18th century Inclosure/ pasture woodland	SAC	NE Block
Tantany Wood	31	18	49	NF28B	SU 365045	Pasture woodland	SAC	Frame and Tantany Woods
Canterton Glen	35	13	48	NF12	SU 273125	Pasture woodland	SAC	NE Block
Round Hill	31	17	48	NF71	SU 335016	Pasture woodland	SAC	Round Hill and Roydon Wood
Long Beech Inclosure	34	13	47	NF55B	SU 250143	18th century Inclosure/ pasture woodland	SAC	NE Block
Holidays Hill	32	15	47	NF21	SU 273070	Pasture woodland	SAC	Central Block
Bignell Wood	36	10	46	NF35	SU 280130	Pasture woodland	SAC	NE Block
Burley Old Inclosure	36	10	46	NF31	SU 248042	Pasture woodland	SAC	Vinney Ridge to Burley Old
Eyeworth Wood	36	10	46	NF04	SU 225150	Pasture woodland	SAC	Anses to Eyeworth Woods
Pinnick Wood	34	12	46	NF10	SU 192079	Pasture woodland	SAC	Pinnick and Red Shoot Woods Area
Ashurst Wood	34	11	45	NF47	SU 334093	Pasture woodland	SAC	NE Block
Undersley Wood	32	13	45	NF23	SU 230049	Pasture woodland	SAC	Undersley Wood
South Bentley	31	14	45	NF32	SU 234128	18th century Inclosure/ pasture woodland	SAC	Anses to Eyeworth Woods
Hincheslea Wood	33	10	43	NF49	SU 273007	Pasture woodland	SAC	Hincheslea Wood
Matley Wood	32	11	43	NF39	SU 334078	Pasture woodland	SAC	Matley and Denny Woods
Sloden Inclosure	36	6	42	NF33	SU 215126	18th century Inclosure/ pasture woodland	SAC	Anses To Eyeworth Woods
Jacks Wood	33	8	41	NF62	SU 312030	Pasture woodland	SAC	Round Hill and Roydon Wood
Mallard Wood	33	8	41	NF41	SU 320091	Pasture woodland	SAC	NE Block
Beaulieu River	30	11	41	NF48	SU 386050	Pasture woodland	SAC	Beaulieu River
Crows Nest Bottom	30	11	41	NF50	SU 241161	Pasture woodland	SAC	NE Block
Berry Wood	29	12	41	NF25	SU 215055	Pasture woodland	SAC	Bratley to Berry Woods
Lin Wood	30	9	39	NF05	SU 194094	Pasture woodland	SAC	Pinnick and Red Shoot Woods Area

Name	NIEC	Bonus spp	NIEC + B	Site Code	Grid Ref	Habitat	Status	NF Old Growth Meta Sites
Pitts Wood area	29	10	39	NF44	SU 198147	Pasture woodland	SAC	Pitts Wood
Rockram Wood	28	11	39	NF13	SU 293133	Pasture woodland	SAC	NE Block
Drivers Nursery	27	12	39	NF69	SU 287048	Riverine 19th century oak plantation	SAC	Adjacent to Central Block
Brockenhurst Park	29	8	37	NF40B	SU 310020	Landscape park, large population of old oak	none	Round Hill and Roydon Wood
Woodhouse Copse	29	8	37	NF40C	SU 310010	Pasture woodland	SAC	Round Hill and Roydon Wood
Bratley Wood	29	7	36	NF24	SU 230083	Pasture woodland	SAC	Bratley to Berry Woods
Mouse's Cupboard	23	11	34	NF87	SU 228062	Pasture woodland and relic pasture woodland	SAC	Bratley to Berry Woods
Wormstall Wood	27	6	33	NF43	SZ 360985	Pasture woodland	SAC	Wormstall Wood
Howen Bushes	26	7	33	NF07	SU 230145	Pasture woodland	SAC	Anses to Eyeworth Woods
Stonard Wood	25	8	33	NF38A	SU 295104	Pasture woodland	SAC	Central Block
Langley Wood	24	8	32	SW01	SU225205	Relic pasture woodland	SAC	Langley Wood Area
Ivy Wood	20	12	32	NF42	SU 316024	Riverine 19th century oak plantation	SAC	Adjacent to Round Hill and Roydon Wood
Burley Woods	22	9	31	NF67	SU 215030	Pasture woodland	SAC	Burley Woods
Cadnam Common	25	5	30	NF73	SU 290153	Pasture woodland, only small cores of old growth	SAC	Cadnam Common
Dames Slough Incosure	24	6	30	NF60	SU 246055	Pasture woodland	SAC	Vinney Ridge to Burley Old
Little Wood	23	7	30	NF28C	SU 357022	Relic pasture woodland	SAC	Frame and Tantany Woods
Ravensnest Inclosure	24	5	29	NF66	SU 255150	18th century Inclosure/ pasture woodland	SAC	NE Block
Fletchers Thorns Inclosure	22	6	28	NF63	SU 274044	Pasture woodland	SAC	Fletchers Thorns
Deazle Wood	19	9	28	NF92	SU269174	Pasture woodland	SAC	NE Block
Franchises Woods	23	4	27	NF59	SU 233168	Relic pasture woodland	SAC	NE Block
Loosehanger Copse	20	5	25	SW03	SU 215191	Old coppice with some veteran trees	SAC	Langley Wood Area
Avon Water	19	6	25	NF70	SZ 259994	Bog and riverine pasture woodland	SAC	Isolated from old growth
High Corner	18	6	24	NF61	SU 198107	Pasture woodland	SAC	Pinnick and Red Shoot Woods Area
Budgen Wood	17	7	24	NF93	SU264137	Pasture woodland	SAC	NE Block
Minstead Manor	19	4	23	NF56	SU 277107	Pasture woodland	SAC	Central Block
The Noads	18	5	23	NF58	SU 399057	Pasture woodland	SAC	The Noads
Burley Outer Rails	15	8	23	NF96	SU 235060	19th century oak plantation	SAC	Adjacent to Undersley Wood
Woodfidley	17	5	22	NF64	SU 345045	Pasture woodland	SAC	Woodfidley
Amberwood Inclosure	16	6	22	NF52	SU 213139	19th century oak plantation	SAC	Adjacent to Anses to Eyeworth Woods
Hanger Corner	16	6	22	NF91	SU 381078	Pasture woodland	SAC	Beaulieu River
Deerleap Inclosure	19	2	21	NF65A	SU 338092	Pasture woodland	SAC	NE Block
Park Ground Inclosure	17	4	21	NF68	SU 305065	19th century oak plantation	SAC	Adjacent to Central Block
Perrywood Inclosure	17	4	21	NF74	SU 325020	Relic pasture woodland, 19th century oak plantation	SAC	Round Hill and Roydon Wood
Ridley Wood	18	2	20	NF26	SU 202060	Pasture woodland	SAC	Ridley Wood
Busketts Lawn Inclosure	17	3	20	NF72	SU 320107	19th century oak plantation	SAC	Adjacent to NE Block
Beech Bed Inclosure	15	5	20	NF95	SU 230064	19th century oak plantation	SAC	Adjacent to Bratley to Berry Woods
Water Copse Inclosure	15	5	20	NF84	SU 295038	19th century oak plantation	SAC	Adjacent to Central Block

Name	NIEC	Bonus NIEC spp + B	Site Code	Grid Ref	Habitat	Status	NF Old Growth Meta Sites
North Oakley Inlosure	12	7	19	NF94	SU 237072	19th century oak plantation	SAC	Adjacent to Vinney Ridge to Burley Old
New Park	13	4	17	NF97	SU 296046	Deer park converted to farmland	SAC	Central Block
Brockishill Inclosure	15	1	16	NF46	SU 300113	19th century oak plantation	SAC	Adjacent to NE Block
Blackwater	13	3	16	NF89	SU260046	19th century oak plantation	SAC	Adjacent to Vinney Ridge to Burley Old
Bramshaw Inclosure	14	1	15	NF80	SU 255170	19th century oak plantation	SAC	Adjacent to NE Block
Burley New Inclosure	14		14	NF86	SU 235049	19th century oak plantation	SAC	Adjacent to Vinney Ridge to Burley Old
Moyles Court Oak	11	3	14	NF29	SU 163083	Ancient oak and younger trees	SAC	Moyles Court Oak
Red Rise	11	3	14	NF54	SU 245038	Pasture woodland	SAC	Central Block
Whiteparish Common	11	3	14	SW02	SU 254223	Relic pasture woodland	SAC	Langley Wood Area
Wooson's Hill Inclosure	13	0	13	NF82	SU 254072	19th century oak plantation	SAC	Adjacent to Central Block
Pondhead Inclosure	11	1	12	NF45	SU 310070	19th century oak plantation	SAC	Adjacent to Central Block
Ironshill Inclosure	10	1	11	NF53	SU 316099	19th century oak plantation	SAC	Adjacent to NE Block
Anderwood Inclosure	10		10	NF83	SU 250060	19th century oak plantation	SAC	Adjacent to Central Block
Bratley Inclosure	10		10	NF88	SU 225090	19th century oak plantation	SAC	Adjacent to Bratley to Berry Woods
Langley Hat	10		10	NF65B	SU 352096	Relic pasture woodland	SAC	NE Block
New Copse Inclosure	8		8	NF81	SU 325025	19th century oak plantation	SAC	Adjacent to Round Hill and Roydon Wood
Ober Corner	8		8	NF85	SU 284034	19th century oak plantation	SAC	Isolated from old growth
Churchplace Inclosure	7	1	8	NF77	SU 340010	19th century oak plantation	SAC	Adjacent to NE Block
Holmhill Inclosure	7	1	8	NF78	SU 255085	19th century oak plantation	SAC	Adjacent to Central Block
Slufters Inclosure	7		7	NF90	SU 223091	Relic pasture woodland	SAC	Bratley to Berry Woods
Stockley Inclosure	5	2	7	NF75	SU 345022	19th century oak plantation	SAC	Adjacent to Frame and Tantany Woods
North Bentley	4		4	NF79	SU 240134	18th century oak plantation	SAC	Anses to Eyeworth Woods
Godshill Wood	3		3	NF76	SU 175165	19th century oak plantation	SAC	Isolated from old growth

Post script

Since writing this account, exploration of the New Forest lichen flora has continued with a particularly important study of very old beech stands carried out (Sanderson 2009). There are now 449 taxa in The New Forest Epiphytic Lichen Database, an increase of 29 taxa. Of these, 14 are of epiphytic fungi not normally recorded by lichenologists. Of the remaining 435 taxa, 382 are lichens, 20 ecologically or taxonomically related fungi growing in lichen communities and 33 are parasitic fungi of lichens. Significant additions are *Anisomeridium robustum* NS,

Arthonia anombrophila NS IR, *Normandina acroglypta* NS, *Micarea alabastrites* IR, *Opegrapha thelotrematis* NS IR, *Psilolechia clavulifera* NS, *Scoliciosporum sarothamni* NS, *Usnea esperantiana* NT NR IR and *Xerotrema quercicola* NR. Sanderson (2009) confirmed the exceptional importance of old open beech stands and raised the known population of *Enterographa elaborata* CR NR BAP from three trees to 20, suggesting a small but viable population.

Sanderson, N. A. (2009). *A Species Dossier for* Enterographa elaborata *in Britain.* A report by Botanical Survey & Assessment to Natural England.

10 Fungi

Adrian C. Newton

Introduction

It is now recognised that fungi make up one of seven major kingdoms, with an estimated 1.5 million species occurring worldwide, around 12,000 of which occur in the British Isles (Spooner and Roberts 2005). This compares with a national total of around 2,000 species of vascular plant. Major groups of fungi include the Ascomycetes (cup fungi or discomycetes), Basidiomycetes (including most larger fungi), Glomeromycetes (endomycorrhiza-formers) and Zygomycetes (Spooner and Roberts 2005). The focus here is primarily on larger fungi (macrofungi); relatively little is known about microfungi, and it is likely that many species of the latter await discovery within the New Forest.

The most significant milestone in the history of mycology in the New Forest was undoubtedly the publication of the Mycota in 1996 (Dickson and Leonard 1996). This incorporated a collation of previous records, together with an assessment of herbarium accessions at the Royal Botanic Gardens, Kew, and records from previous forays organised by the British Mycological Society (BMS). These records were supplemented by the results of additional field surveys focusing on selected sites. Some 25,000 records were compiled, covering approximately 2,600 species.

During the past 10 years, fungal recording has intensified through the activities of the Hampshire Fungus Recording Group (HFRG) (http://www.hampshirefungi.org.uk/). Founded in 1988, the HFRG currently has around 30 members active in fungus recording throughout Hampshire, and holds an annual programme of 20–30 fungus forays, many of which are held in the New Forest. Records are made available to the BMS, which maintains a national database of fungal records (http://194.203.77.76/fieldmycology/FRDBI/FRDBI.asp). Knowledge of fungi in the New Forest has also benefited from a number of systematic surveys organised by the Hampshire Wildlife Trust, of which details are provided below. Special mention should also be made of individual mycologists who have collected intensively within the area over many years, including Gordon Dickson, Peter Orton, Alan Lucas and Martyn Ainsworth.

The particular aim of this chapter is to evaluate the importance of the New Forest as a habitat for fungi, and to highlight some of those species for which the New Forest is particularly important. Some information is also provided on current trends in the status and distribution of selected species, although it should be emphasised that such information is always highly tentative, because of the difficulties of providing robust monitoring information for fungi (Watling 2001). This overview is necessarily selective, because of the large number of species that occur in the area and

the poor state of knowledge of many fungal groups. The focus is primarily on species or groups that have attracted particular conservation attention in recent years, at the national or international scale. The fungal partners of lichens are not considered here (see Chapter 9).

It is only in the past two decades that fungi have become the focus of significant conservation interest. This growth in concern has largely been driven by reports of rapid declines in a number of species in continental Europe (Arnolds 1991), primarily as a result of the combined effects of habitat loss and aerial pollution (Jansen and Van Dobben 1987, Arnolds and De Vries 1993). While conservation practitioners and policy makers in the UK were perhaps rather slow to recognise the issue, the importance of conserving fungi is now widely appreciated, supported both by scientific symposia (Pegler *et al.* 1993, Moore *et al.* 2001) and by regular features in the mycological literature and articles in the popular press. The inclusion of fungi in the Biodiversity Action Plan process was a particularly important milestone, and has stimulated a substantial increase in systematic survey effort for selected taxa (Fleming 2001). A national conservation strategy for fungi has also recently been developed (Plantlife International 2008).

This chapter first provides a brief evaluation of importance of the New Forest as a locality for fungi, by comparing species richness estimates with those obtained for other areas. Selected species are then considered in greater detail, namely stipitate hydnoids, waxcap grassland fungi, *Poronia punctata*, beech deadwood fungi and *Hericium* spp. The potential impacts of fungal harvesting, and the conservation management of fungi, are then briefly considered.

Species richness of New Forest fungi: how does it compare?

Estimates of fungal species richness are available for selected areas in the UK, where records have been compiled and /or targeted survey work has been undertaken. Comparison of these estimates should be undertaken with caution, as they vary substantially in terms of survey effort and taxonomic scope. As noted by Watling (2001), knowledge of the British mycota has increased rapidly in recent decades, with around 700 species described or added to the national list over the past 40 years. Earlier accounts are therefore likely to provide lower estimates than those employing more recent taxonomic treatments. However, the data suggest that the number of fungal species recorded in the New Forest records favourably with some areas that are much larger in extent (Table 23). In contrast, some much smaller areas (such as Kew Gardens, Esher

Common and Slapton Ley) have provided species richness estimates that are roughly the same as, or even greater than, that of the New Forest. Significantly, each of these three areas has been intensively surveyed over many years by professional mycologists, with a wide range of taxonomic expertise. The figures in Table 23 therefore largely reflect survey effort and the expertise of the surveyors; many groups of fungi are difficult to identify, and require specialist knowledge that is difficult to acquire. The implication of these data is that many more species could potentially be added to the New Forest mycota, should the area be surveyed more intensively by experts in lesser-known groups.

Although a large number of fungal species have been recorded in the New Forest, and many others doubtless await discovery, it is not only the high species richness that is important, but the communities of fungi that occur in association with particular habitats. From a mycological perspective, it is the existence of an extensive area of long-established semi-natural woodland that affords the New Forest its particular value and interest. Other important habitat features include the relatively large number of ancient or 'veteran' trees, large volumes of coarse woody debris, and extensive areas of unimproved grassland. Although distinctive fungal communities are also likely to be associated with the heathland, mire and reedbed communities that are present in the area, these have received relatively little attention from mycologists to date.

The importance of the New Forest for fungi was recognised by a national assessment designed to identify Important Fungal Areas (Evans *et al.* 2001). The criteria for selection included: (A) that the site holds significant populations of rare fungal species that are of European or UK conservation concern, (B) that the site has an exceptionally rich and well-recorded mycota (i.e. >500 species), and (C) that the site is an outstanding example of a habitat type of known mycological importance. In this assessment, the New Forest qualified under all three of these criteria, and was described as 'of the highest importance for fungi, especially mycorrhizal fungi and fungi of over-mature trees and deadwood'. A number of 'hotspots' were identified within the New Forest as of particular importance, namely Churchplace Inclosure, Crockford Bridge marlpit, Denny Wood, Norley Copse, Gritnam Wood, Mark Ash Wood, Millyford Bridge, Nices Hill, Roydon Wood, Rufus Stone, Stubbs Wood, Whitley Wood, Wormstall Wood (and East End Pond), and Set Thorns Inclosure (Evans *et al.* 2001). The New Forest therefore accounts for 14 of these nationally important areas out of a total of 236 for the UK as a whole (i.e. 6%).

Table 23
Comparison of fungal species richness between different areas surveyed in the UK. Note that new species have continued to be discovered for the New Forest, subsequent to the publication of Dickson and Leonard (1996).

Area	Number of species (approx)	Notes	Source
Esher Common and Oxshott Heath, Surrey	3,300	Described as 'perhaps the most comprehensively inventoried area for fungi in the world' (380 ha)	Spooner and Roberts (2005)
Hebrides	2,905	More than 30 years' collecting by the author, covering a wide range of fungal groups, with a particular emphasis on microfungi	Dennis (1986)
Kew Gardens, Surrey	2,600	Includes survey of many fungal groups (132 ha)	Spooner and Roberts (2005)
Kindrogan, Perthshire	1,235	Intensive survey activity over many years, much undertaken in connection with a fungus identification course, focusing largely on macrofungi	Newton and Davy (1997)
New Forest	2,600	Ten years' intensive survey effort largely focused on macrofungi, coupled with compilation of earlier records spanning a wide range of fungal groups	Dickson and Leonard (1996)
Orkney	1,513	Compiled from eight years collecting macrofungi combined with prior records	Watling (1999)
South-east England	2,300	Compilation of many years' recording effort, including a wide range of fungal groups	Dennis (1995)
Shetland	984	Compiled from six years collecting macrofungi combined with prior records	Watling (1992)
Skye	831	Results of three-year survey of macrofungi plus earlier records including microfungi	Watling (1983)
Slapton Ley, Devon	2,400	Includes survey of many fungal groups (250 ha)	Spooner and Roberts (2005)
Warwickshire	2,486	More than 10 years' intensive systematic surveying covering a wide range of fungal groups	Clark (1980)
Yorkshire	3,400	Compilation of foray records spanning many decades and fungal groups	Bramley (1985)

Stipitate hydnoid fungi ('tooth fungi')

Stipitate hydnoid fungi are those with a toothed hymenophore (giving rise to the commonly used epithet, 'tooth fungi' or 'hedgehog fungi'). Those of conservation interest are all considered to be ectomycorrhizal associates of trees (Pegler *et al.* 1997). The Biodiversity Action Plan (BAP) for stipitate hydnoid fungi refers to 15 species in the genera *Bankera*, *Phellodon* (Bankeraceae), *Hydnellum* and *Sarcodon* (Thelephoraceae), all of which appear to display similar habitat requirements (UK Steering Group 1999). All species tended to be associated with particular microsites, namely riverbanks, mossy woodbanks, tracksides, railway cuttings, marl pits or other areas of exposed mineral soil (Marren 2000, Ewald 2001, Newton *et al.* 2002a,b). Managed semi-natural woodland, parkland and plantations all appear to provide suitable habitats. Marren and Dickson (2000) provide a useful introductory account of the group.

The BAP for this group of fungi was developed in response to reports of widespread declines in northern and central Europe. For example, in the Netherlands 13 species of hydnoid fungus have declined by at least 50%, and eight species have apparently become extinct in recent decades (Arnolds 1989), while in the Czech Republic, considerable declines have also been reported for virtually all the species in this group (Hrouda 1999). As an illustration of this concern, stipitate hydnoid fungi are now included in the Red Lists of a number of European countries, including the Netherlands, Poland, Germany and the UK (Lizon 1993, 1995), as well as in the provisional Red List for Europe (Ing 1993). Loss and degradation of habitat appear to be the main factors that have caused decline, although aerial pollution may also have contributed (Arnolds 1989).

Two main initiatives have been undertaken in England in response to the BAP: a desk study giving an overview of the status and distribution of stipitate hydnoid fungi, commissioned by English Nature and Plantlife (Marren 2000), and a survey of tooth fungi in the New Forest undertaken by Hampshire Wildlife Trust (Ewald 2001), again with support from English Nature. Marren (2000) notes that these species appear to be fairly widely distributed throughout England, but are rare outside 'core' areas, one of which is the New Forest, along with parts of east Berkshire, west Surrey and west Kent. They appear to be entirely absent over large areas of the UK. Marren (2000) also reports little evidence for decline of these species in England, noting that this may largely be attributed to the lack of suitable data for assessing trends in abundance over time. Survey work in Scotland has indicated that hydnoid fungi are widespread, but not common, in both Caledonian pine forests and oak woodland, again indicating little evidence of decline (Newton *et al.* 2002a,b).

In the New Forest, Ewald (2001) reports a total of 37 sites with records for stipitate hydnoid fungi. Eight of these were identified for the first time during a field survey undertaken in 2000, indicating that although

Table 24
Summary of the abundance of stipitate hydnoid species in the New Forest. Data from Ewald (2001).

Species	Number of records (to 2000)
Hydnellum concrescens	23
Hydnellum ferrugineum	1
Hydnellum scrobiculatum	4
Hydnellum spongiosipes	19
Phellodon confluens	6
Phellodon melaleucus	16
Phellodon niger	10
Phellodon tomentosus	1
Sarcodon squamosus	3
Sarcodon scabrosus	2

the area is relatively well known mycologically, information on the distribution of these fungi is still highly incomplete. Despite the number of sites located, hydnoid fungi are described by Ewald (2001) as 'extremely rare and scattered' in the New Forest, occurring primarily with broadleaved trees (especially oak), often on raised banks or ditches. The results of the survey confirm the importance of the New Forest as a stronghold for hydnoid fungi, but also provide some evidence of decline in one species. Specifically, in the 2000 survey, *Phellodon niger* was not recorded at five sites where it had previously been recorded, and only one new site was found for the species despite thorough searching of potential habitat (Ewald 2001). Further monitoring is required to verify whether this decline is genuinely occurring, and if so, what factors may be responsible. *Hydnellum concrescens* and *H. spongiosipes* consistently remain the most abundant species in the area (Table 24).

Waxcap grasslands

A distinctive and diverse community of saprotrophic larger fungi is associated with nutrient-poor grasslands, including members of the agaric genera *Hygrocybe* (waxcaps), *Camarophyllopsis*, *Dermoloma*, *Entoloma* and *Porpoloma*, and non-gilled fungi in the families Clavariaceae and Geoglossaceae. These fungi are associated with unfertilised or unimproved grasslands, lawns and pastures, often in swards that are shortened by grazing or mowing (Arnolds 1980, Boertmann 1995). Some evidence suggests that waxcap grasslands tend to be relatively old, with ecological continuity spanning many decades or even centuries (Keizer 1993, Feehan and McHugh 1992). Marren (1998) and Griffith *et al.* (2004) provide valuable overviews of this attractive group of fungi.

Waxcap grasslands have been the focus of increasing conservation concern in recent years as the community has undergone a rapid decline in many areas of north-west Europe (Newton *et al.* 2003a), primarily because of habitat loss and degradation (Arnolds 1991, Arnolds and de Vries 1993). Agricultural improvement and intensification, particularly use of fertilisers and the ploughing and resowing of grassland, nitrogen deposition from the atmosphere and decreasing numbers of grazing animals have all contributed to this process (Arnolds 1991, Boertmann 1995, Keizer 1993). For example, in Sweden, only 15% of grassland sites have remained unaffected by these factors over the past 20 years (Keizer 1993); some fungi have declined in range by more than 93% (Arnolds 1991). As a result, many grassland fungi are now considered to be threatened with extinction, with 268 grassland species included in Red Data Lists across Europe as a whole (Arnolds and de Vries 1993). An analysis of Red Lists for 11 European countries indicated that 89% of *Hygrocybe* species feature on one or more lists; the corresponding figure for *Entoloma* is 97% (Arnolds and de Vries 1993).

Concern about whether such declines have occurred in Britain has led to a substantial increase in survey effort over the past decade (Rotheroe *et al.* 1996), particularly after BAPs were developed for three grassland species, *Hygrocybe calyptriformis*, *H. spadicea* and *Microglossum olivaceum* (UK Steering Group 1999, Fleming 2001). As a result of these surveys, some species are now known to be much more widespread than previously thought (Newton *et al.* 2003a), and in consequence *H. calyptriformis* has been omitted from the latest revision of the BAP (2007, http://www.ukbap.org.uk).

As no systematic survey of grassland fungi has yet been undertaken in the New Forest, their current status and distribution is incompletely known. Extensive areas of apparently suitable habitat are distributed throughout the Forest, but records made to date do not indicate the presence of any individual sites of national or international importance. For example, Evans (2003) lists no New Forest sites among those considered the most important in England for grassland fungi. To qualify for this list, at least 17 *Hygrocybe* spp. or 15 *Entoloma* spp. would need to be recorded from a single site.

Available records indicate that two of the grassland species included in the BAP have been found in the New Forest (albeit at only two sites each), namely *Entoloma bloxamii* and *Microglossum olivaceum*, whereas the other two (*Hygrocybe spadicea* and *Geoglossum atropurpureum*) have not been recorded to date. A total of 27 *Hygrocybe* spp. are listed by Dickson and Leonard (1996), indicating that taken as a whole, the New Forest does support a high diversity of grassland fungi. However, these species tend to be distributed among a variety of different sites, and there is little evidence of any individual sites supporting exceptionally high diversity. This might be rectified, however, by a systematic survey such as those undertaken for stipitate hydnoids and *Hericium* spp. This might usefully focus on those sites that are somewhat base-rich, such as some of the abandoned airfields or grasslands that have been limed in the past. One particular challenge

is the short fruiting season for some grassland species, particularly *Entoloma* spp., which appear to require frost-free periods of relatively high rainfall (Newton *et al.* 2003a). It may therefore take many years of sustained survey effort to accurately determine the diversity of grassland fungi on a particular site (Newton *et al.* 2003a).

Poronia punctata 'Nail fungus'

Poronia punctata is the fungus species most closely associated with the New Forest in the minds of most mycologists. The species is an Ascomycete in the family Xylariaceae. In the UK it appears to be exclusively associated with horse or pony dung, although in other parts of the world it has been reported from cow dung (Whalley and Dickson 1986); records from rabbit dung (Reid 1986) are now referred to the closely related *P. erici* (Lohmeyer 1994). The fungus produces a stalked stroma, which raises the perithecia above the surface of the dung to assist in spore dispersal (Whalley and Dickson 1986). It is the nail-like shape of the stromata from which the common name of the fungus is derived. The 'nail' is typically rooted into the dung and is topped by a flat disc of up to 15 mm across, which is dotted with the black perithecia from which the spores are produced (Spooner and Roberts 2005).

The species is referred in the BAP as 'possibly the rarest fungus in Europe' (UK Steering Group 1995), and by Cox and Pickess (1999) as 'one of the rarest fungi in Europe', but this is surely an exaggeration. The global distribution of the species is not clearly established, particularly as it has been confused in the past with other *Poronia* spp. such as *P. erici* (Lohmeyer 1994), but the species is apparently known from the USA (Koehn 1978, Jumpponen and Johnson 2005) as well as in many parts of Europe. It may be accurate, however, to describe it as one of Europe's most threatened fungus species. For example, Ing (1993) lists it among 16 species that at the European scale have experienced widespread losses, rapidly declining populations and many national extinctions, and are the focus of a high level of concern. Its widespread decline reflects its close association with unimproved pasture, a habitat that has declined markedly in extent throughout the continent (Spooner and Roberts 2005). Other factors that have been implicated in its decline include widespread use of fertilisers, and other causes of changes in the characteristics of horse manure, including use of additives to feedstuffs and improvements in veterinary care (Spooner and Roberts 2005). As noted by these authors, year-round grazing on an individual site is required for the continuous provision of dung suitable for colonisation by the fungus, and therefore the decline in the species may also partly be attributable to loss of such continuous grazing. In Belgium, the decline in the Belgian donkey population has even been implicated in the decline of the fungus (Heinemann and Thoen 1981).

Reid (1986) provides a detailed account of previous records of the species made in Britain, noting that it was considered widespread and not uncommon until the late 19th century. It then appears to have undergone a rapid decline, indicated by the lack of any accessions in the Kew herbarium between 1899 and 1967 (Reid 1986), although it could be argued that the number of specimens lodged in a herbarium more accurately reflects the activity of mycologists rather than the actual status of a species in nature. Whalley and Dickson (1986) noted that nearly all recent records from Britain are from the New Forest area, although there have been occasional sightings elsewhere. Outside the New Forest, the species has been recorded on at least five sites scattered across southern England since 1990, including some Dorset heaths, and at a single site in southern Wales (http://www.searchnbn.net/).

In the New Forest, *P. punctata* was first recorded in 1893, and again in 1899, but thereafter it was not formally recorded again until 1967 (Reid 1986). Whalley and Dickson (1986) suggested that *P. punctata* has 'always been in the New Forest and is widespread but that no-one has bothered to record it'. In response to this suggestion, Reid (1986) rather testily suggested that while the species 'may have been present' during this period, 'this is of course unsubstantiated by either specimens or literature sources and there is nothing to account for the gap in records between 1899 and 1967'. He goes on to say that the species 'at no time could have ever approached the status of being "locally common" during the last 25–30 years'. This opinion is largely based on his own unsuccessful attempts to find the fungus, despite having made 'almost annual visits over a wide area' during this period. Intriguingly, Reid (1986) therefore suggests that within the New Forest the species may have declined in the early years of the 20th century, possibly even becoming extinct, but then recovered and spread during the 1960s and thereafter.

Is it possible therefore that *P. punctata* has increased in frequency within the New Forest in recent decades? Owing to the lack of any attempt at formal monitoring over this period, this suggestion is difficult to test. However, any fluctuations in the number of ponies within the Forest might be expected to influence abundance of the fungus, given its dependence on pony dung as a substrate. Tubbs (2001) presents data describing the number of ponies depastured on the Crown lands over the past 200 years, which suggest that numbers declined from the late 19th century until the middle of the 20th century – precisely coinciding with the gap in *Poronia* records identified by Reid (1986). Thereafter, the number of ponies has increased steadily, to reach current densities that apparently are as high as at any time over the past 200 years (Tubbs 2001, Mountford and Peterken 2003). It may be the case, therefore, that *Poronia* has undergone a recent increase in abundance in the Forest, and may even still be increasing, as a result of an increase in pony numbers. On the other hand, Whalley and Dickson (1986) may be correct to suggest that the species has always been widespread in the Forest, but has simply not been recorded.

As noted by Whalley and Dickson (1986), the ecology of the species is poorly understood. These authors suggest that it occurs only on horse droppings on open grass or heathland and not on dung located in woodland. They also suggest that the species may have exacting requirements for sporome production, 'not liking really wet weather nor drought'. Typically it is found on dung of a few weeks old, which is still in lumps (Whalley and Dickson 1986). Although slow-growing in culture, the species produces diffusible metabolites that are antagonistic to other fungi that appear earlier in the fungal succession on dung (Wicklow and Hirschfield 1979), emphasising the fact that it tends to occur later in the succession rather than on fresh dung. Cox and Pickess (1999) describe the ecology of the species on some Dorset heaths, where it has recently been recorded, confirming the findings of Dickson (1997) and Cox (1999) that the species tends to be found in dung in acidic heathy areas, whereas it is hardly ever recorded on grassland that has been limed in the past, and never on fertilised grassland.

Poland (2004) describes the first attempt to survey the species systematically within selected areas of the New Forest. Surveys were undertaken along seven transect routes, each 3–8 km in length, which were visited three times between October 2003 and February 2004. A total of 40 dungpiles supporting *Poronia* were recorded from five of the seven transects, with a maximum of 3% of dungpiles supporting the fungus. Most of the *Poronia* (68%) was recorded on humid heath (NVC community H3), with 18% and 13% from M16 (wet heath) and H2c (dry heath) communities, respectively, and only a single colony recorded on grassland (U3) (Poland 2004). On the basis of these results, Poland (2004) suggested that the species is primarily confined to a transitional heathland habitat, namely the damper sub-community of dry heath (H2c), through humid heath (H3) to the drier parts of wet heath (M16) communities. The species was not found on waterlogged microsites.

In total, Dickson and Leonard (1996) list some 56 locations of the species in the New Forest, spanning more than a century. Since 1996, some 49 records have been made as a result of the activities of the HFRG and the surveys described by Poland (2004). However, this underestimates the current distribution of the fungus in the New Forest area. Following several weeks of wet weather, *Poronia* began fruiting in mid-September 2008, providing an opportunity for some additional survey work. In just a few days, the current author recorded the species in 40 different 1 ha squares, distributed throughout the New Forest. When combined with previous data, recent records indicate that the species is widely distributed in the area (Figure 52), although the survey work undertaken in 2008 suggest that the species does vary in abundance, apparently occurring at higher densities in the south-east of the Forest than elsewhere. Further survey work is required to test whether this observation is valid, and to determine more accurately the current status and distribution of the species in the New Forest, as well as its habitat requirements. Further systematic

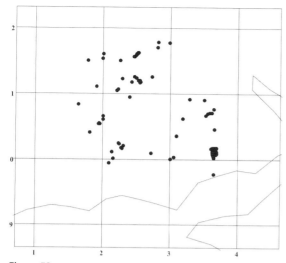

Figure 52
Current distribution of *Poronia punctata* in the New Forest, based on records made since 1996 (including foray records made by the HFRG, results presented by Poland (1994) and personal records of the author made during 2008). Each dot represents presence in a 1 ha square. Lines indicate the position of the Solent coast and the Isle of Wight. Gridlines represent OS 10 km × 10 km grid squares.

monitoring, such as that initiated by Poland (2004), is required to determine its trends in abundance.

Beech deadwood fungi

Recent research undertaken at the European scale has led to the identification of a group of fungi that could be considered as indicators of 'biotic integrity' or habitat value of old growth beech forests. An initial list of 42 species proposed for Denmark (Heilmann-Clausen and Christensen 2000) has since been extended to other European countries, with the aim of

developing a method for comparing sites both within and between countries. In the UK, this research has been pioneered by Dr Martyn Ainsworth (Ainsworth 2004, 2005), who has played a major role in raising awareness of this group of fungi, both among mycologists and conservation practitioners.

Assessments have focused on a suite of saprotrophic species that form relatively conspicuous sporocarps on trunks or large branches of beech trees (Ainsworth 2005). A list of 30 species was proposed for scoring British beechwood habitats, based on previous records and expert judgement, then applied to 11 English sites. Collaboration with mycologists in other European countries enabled a list of 21 species to be developed for assessing the quality of beech deadwood habitats at a European scale, of which 15 species also featured in the British list (Ainsworth 2004, 2005).

Results of the analysis indicated that two New Forest beechwoods (Wood Crates and Denny Wood) classify among the top 10 of the 127 European sites assessed for the presence of these fungi (Table 25). Both of these sites, according to the criteria presented by Heilmann-Clausen and Christensen (2000), would qualify as of international importance based on the number of beech deadwood fungi recorded to date (i.e. >11). Within the UK, according to the list of 30 indicator species proposed for British beechwoods, five of the top 10 sites are located in the New Forest (Ainsworth 2004). This emphasises the importance of the New Forest as a habitat for this group of fungi, at both national and international scales.

Many of these proposed indicator species are poorly known and are rarely collected; many are therefore of conservation interest in themselves. Their ecological requirements are also poorly understood. Ongoing survey work in the New Forest being undertaken by members of the HFRG and others continues to add to the number of known locations of these fungi, further emphasising the importance of the New Forest woodlands. Although insufficient monitoring information is available to determine whether any of these species are changing in abundance, it is possible

Table 25
Comparison of New Forest sites with other British sites for beech deadwood fungi, according to lists of British (30) and European (16) indicators. Adapted from Ainsworth (2004).

Ranking using British score	Ranking using European score	Site name	European score (out of 16)	British score (out of 30)
1	2	New Forest, Denny Wood	12	19
2=	1	New Forest, Wood Crates	13	17
2=	4	Windsor Highstanding Hill, Berkshire	10	17
4	5=	Norbury Park, Surrey	9	16
5=	3	Windsor Bears Rails, Berkshire	11	15
5=	8=	New Forest, Mark Ash Wood	7	15
7	7	Lullingstone Park, Kent	8	14
8	5=	New Forest, Whitley Wood	9	13
9=	8=	New Forest, Gritnam Wood	7	12
9=	11	Mens and Cut, West Sussex	6	12
11	8=	Ebernoe Common, West Sussex	7	11

that they have benefited from the recent trend towards increasing volumes of deadwood within New Forest woodlands (see Chapter 13).

Hericium spp. (spine fungi)

Hericium is a Basidiomycete genus with a spiny hymenophore (Pegler *et al.* 1997). Two species are considered as indicators of beech forests of high conservation value (see above; Ainsworth 2004), namely *H. coralloides* and *H. erinaceum*. Both are uncommon fungi internationally, as illustrated by their inclusion in a provisional European Red List of macrofungi (Ing 1993). Marren and Dickson (2000) provide an excellent introductory account.

In the UK, the two species are largely restricted to southern England, and the New Forest is believed to be an important stronghold of both. This is illustrated by records accessible via the National Biodiversity Network (http://www.searchnbn.net/ accessed September 2008), which indicate that *H. coralloides* has been recorded in nine 10-km squares in the UK since 1990, mostly clustered in south-east England. Four of these squares are located in the New Forest. *H. erinaceum* appears to be somewhat more widespread; of 30 records made nationally since 1990, four of these 10 km squares are again located in the New Forest. Surprisingly, given their relative frequency, *H. erinaceum* was included on the UK BAP, but the rarer *H. coralloides* was originally omitted. However, the latter species was proposed for inclusion in the revised (2007) BAP (http://www.ukbap.org.uk/).

In the late 1990s, a field survey of *Hericium* spp. was undertaken in the New Forest by the Hampshire Wildlife Trust, together with a compilation of previous records (Wicks 1999). In 1998, a total of 34 sites were surveyed, and locations of the fungi encountered were mapped. Records of either one or both of these two species were made at a total of 14 locations (Table 26). Four of these sites had no previous records, indicating once again the value of this type of targeted field survey for providing information about current status and distribution.

The results of this project indicate that *H. erinaceum* is the more widespread of the two species in the New Forest, reflecting the national situation. Neither species is commonly encountered, however. Observations indicate that *H. erinaceum* can persist on an individual tree for at least 20 years, although not necessarily fruiting every year (Wicks 1999). Although most records of this species were from mature beech, one was from oak; and although most were recorded on standing trees, sometimes still living, five were recorded from fallen trees. In contrast *H. coralloides* was usually found on fallen logs and on dead trees only (Wicks 1999). Fruiting *H. coralloides* tends to be associated with logs at a more advanced stage of decomposition than *H. erinaceum*. It is unknown how long this species can persist on a fallen log, although observations made by the author indicate that it can do so for at least six years.

Evidence from previous records of *Hericium* spp. provide no indication of declines in either species, and both appear to be maintaining populations within the New Forest. However, accurate assessment of population trends would require systematic monitoring over a number of years. The survey work described by Wicks (1999) provides a basis for such monitoring in future; regular resurveying of known colonies could be highly informative. Members of HFRG and others continue to identify new colonies of both species through foraying activities and ongoing survey work, and therefore the abundance of both species is likely to be underestimated by currently available information, emphasising the need for further exploratory surveys.

One of the main challenges to obtaining accurate assessments of status and distribution of any fungus species is that surveys of vegetative mycelia, rather than reproductive structures, are difficult to achieve. As most fungal surveys focus on locating sporomes, the abundance of species is likely to be routinely underestimated, because fruiting is typically sporadic and varies both seasonally and from year to year, being highly dependent on weather conditions. Analysis of the behaviour of these species in culture suggests that they are of average competitive ability, and fruit readily, suggesting that low fruiting potential and combative ability are unlikely to be major factors contributing to the rarity of these fungi (Wald *et al.* 2004). Research by Prof. Lynn Boddy and colleagues at Cardiff University has also involved the development of PCR primers for detecting the DNA of these species in wood (Pariftt *et al.* 2005). Use of such methods could transform our understanding of the distribution and ecology of these species, and research on this aspect is ongoing.

Harvesting of fungi

Over the past two decades, the global trade in wild mushrooms has increased substantially. The Pacific Northwest of the USA, Mexico, Russia, Poland and other countries of Eastern Europe have become significant exporters of fungi harvested from the wild (Amaranthus and Pilz 1996, Marshall *et al.* 2006, Pilz and Molina 2002). In Britain, despite less of a tradition of collecting wild fungi than in many other European countries, there has been a rapid increase in interest in recent years, stimulated by television programmes and books encouraging the use of wild fungi in cookery (Rotheroe 1998).

Table 26
Summary of the number of records of *Hericium* spp. made in the New Forest (adapted from Wicks 1999).

	Hericium erinaceum	*Hericeum coralloides*
Number of sites in 1998 survey	10	5
Total number of woods with records	21	6
Total number of 1-km grid squares	25	8

This developing commercialisation has been accompanied by increasing concern about its potential environmental impacts. Fungal declines across Europe were first noted in widely collected edible fungi in the late 1970s (Derbsh and Schmitt 1987), although the extent to which overcollection has been the cause of such declines remains unclear. The collection of fungal sporocarps could conceivably affect production of sporocarps in subsequent years, by damaging or exhausting fungal mycelia, by influencing competitive relations with other species or by causing reproductive failure as a result of decreased spore production (Arnolds 1995). However, as parallel declines in non-edible species have been recorded in mainland Europe, there is little evidence to suggest that overpicking has been a major factor in the decline of fungal populations (Arnolds 1995). Little information is available concerning what impact removal of the sporocarp has on the vegetative mycelium of the fungus, which accounts for the main proportion of fungal biomass and is intimately bound with the substrate. Although there is no evidence suggesting that the removal of sporocarps affects the survival of mycelia (Arnolds 1991), regular picking could conceivably reduce mycelial reserves and therefore growth potential (Arnolds 1995). However, this effect is difficult to quantify. Collection of sporocarps can even have positive effects on subsequent production; for example, when a mature sporocarp is collected it may allow smaller sporocarps to mature, by reducing competition for water.

The more demonstrable effects of fungal collection are impacts on the habitat. Raking or other harvesting techniques may disturb fungal mycelia, and the trampling that can occur during collection may also be damaging. Research by Egli et al. (1990) found that a plot trampled intensively every two days throughout summer and autumn was associated with a 95% reduction in sporocarp harvest the following year. Trampling may therefore be the element of the commercial harvest most likely to cause damage to fungal populations, simply because of the regularity with which sites are visited. Concern has also been expressed relating to the value of fungal sporocarps as a habitat for insects and other invertebrates (Stubbs 2001) and as a food source for other organisms, which could also be negatively affected by sporocarp collection (Rotheroe 1998).

In the New Forest, concern about the impacts of commercial fungus harvesting grew in the 1990s, when it attracted a significant amount of media coverage. For example, as noted by Rotheroe (1998), the renowned Italian chef Antonio Carluccio was the focus of a demonstration by environmental activists when giving a wild mushroom cooking demonstration in London in 1996. In that same year, commercial fungus picking was banned throughout the New Forest by the Department for Environment, Food and Rural Affairs (Defra), although as noted by Rotheroe (1998), collecting continued, with some pickers thought to be earning as much as £2000 a week. The ban was implemented under the Theft Act, England and Wales (1968), which specifically defines as theft the

gathering of fungi for commercial purposes without permission of the landowner (Section 4(3)).

The ban was tested in the courts in the case of Brigitte Tee-Hillman, who trades as 'Mrs Tee's Wild Mushrooms' in Lymington, Hampshire. Tee-Hillman was arrested by the police in 2002 while in possession of 6 kg of fungi (Cantharellus lutescens), after being repeatedly ordered to stop her commercial activities by the Forestry Commission. She then challenged in the courts the legal right of the UK Government to ban her from picking fungi. After a four year court battle, the judge finally dismissed the case on grounds of pettiness, and Defra dropped the action. As a result Tee-Hillman was granted a unique personal licence from Defra, leaving her the only person with legal dispensation to pick more than the allotted 1.5 kg of mushrooms a day in the New Forest, and to trade commercially. According to her website, the fungi are currently retailed at prices of up to £48 per kilo. The total value of this legalised trade is estimated at c. £75,000, described as 'the largest commercial operation in England' (Sanderson and Prendergast 2002).

Other protection has been provided by the Forestry Commission to fungi within the New Forest by use of a local bye-law, to prevent the removal of fungi from certain woodlands (indicated by signs) between September and March (Sanderson and Prendergast 2002). These woods are Burley Old / Dames Slough Inclosure near Burley and Whitley Wood near New Park, which have been protected to enable long-term comparisons to be made between areas that are picked and those that are not. Such protection has been attempted very rarely in the UK, although collecting controls are widespread on the continent. The Forestry Commission has also developed a 'New Forest Fungi Code', which stipulates (http://www.forestry.gov.uk/forestry/infd-6e3gaz):

- no commercial collecting;
- obey any signs;
- never remove all the fungi in one area;
- 1.5 kg personal limit;
- if you don't know what it is, leave it alone.

This code reflects a national guide to fungal conservation, which was produced in 1998 by English Nature (English Nature 1998). There is no evidence available to evaluate whether or not the code is being followed, or whether it has raised awareness of the issue.

Conclusions and implications for management

There is no doubt that the New Forest remains the principal stronghold of Poronia punctata in Britain, and one of the most important sites in Europe for this species. This may be attributed to the fact that the New Forest is one of very few areas where horses live in the 'wild' and are allowed to forage for themselves throughout the year (Whalley and Dickson 1986). The future of the species in the New Forest is clearly dependent on maintenance of a sufficiently large population of ponies, which is allowed to graze on unimproved grassland and heathland vegetation on low-nutrient, acidic soils. Any nutrient enrichment of the vegetation, for example through atmospheric pollution, would probably be detrimental to the fungus. Despite the limited amount of systematic survey and monitoring data, evidence suggests that the species is widespread throughout the Forest, and may even be increasing in abundance. Maintenance of grazing is likely to be important for other fungi associated with grasslands in the New Forest (Newton et al. 2003a).

Recent field evidence emphasises the importance of the New Forest as a stronghold for other internationally threatened fungi, such as the spine fungi Hericium coralloides and H. erinaceum (particularly the former). In this case it is availability of large areas of old-growth semi-natural woodland (particularly of beech) that is of importance (Wicks 1999). Surveys of these and other fungi associated with deadwood of beech indicate that a number of the New Forest woodlands are of international importance for this entire fungal community. Management should therefore seek to maintain substantial volumes of deadwood, both standing and fallen, to ensure that populations of these fungi are maintained. The recent loss of a Hericium host tree through forestry operations (http://www.ukbap.org.uk/library/Reporting_pdfs/UKListID361_2002.pdf) raises serious concerns about whether information on the distribution of threatened species is reaching those involved in day-to-day management decisions.

The New Forest is also home to important populations of ectomycorrhizal fungi, some of which (such as the stipitate hydnoids) are considered threatened at an international scale. In the case of the stipitate hydnoids, the New Forest is considered to be one of the main centres for this group of species in England (Marren 2000). Other internationally scarce ectomycorrhizal species not considered in this account include Podoscypha multizonata, for which some 80% of the world sites are in England (Spooner and Roberts 2005), Boletus torosus, Cantharellus melanoxeros and Phylloporus pelletieri. Each of these is included in the revised UK BAP (2007), and has been recorded previously in the New Forest. These form part of a very diverse and distinctive community of fungi associated with ancient, semi-natural woodland, and maintenance of this habitat and the mature individual trees associated with it should be a management priority.

One of the key priorities for the future should be greater emphasis on systematic survey and monitoring of threatened fungal species (Newton et al. 2003b). At present, the lack of survey data prevents an accurate assessment of conservation status for more than a handful of species. Insufficient information is available to assess the long-term trends in fungal abundance with any precision, but the substantial losses of semi-natural woodland through felling and establishment of exotic conifers that occurred in the New Forest in the 20th century (Tubbs 2001) must have had a major

deleterious impact on the fungi associated with them, as noted for lichens (Chapter 9).

Species such as those listed on the UK BAP would be a valuable target for future survey and monitoring efforts. The revised UK BAP (2007) lists 76 fungal species, at least 20 of which are known from the New Forest, which might usefully form the focus of future survey efforts. As noted above, a survey of grassland fungi might also be very worthwhile. Those surveys that have been completed in recent years have made a major contribution to improving our knowledge of fungi in the New Forest. In particular, the Hampshire Wildlife Trust should be commended for its role in coordinating the systematic surveys of Hericium spp., Poronia and the stipitate hydnoids, which are models of their kind, and illustrate what can be achieved with limited resources. Each of these surveys has highlighted deficiencies in our current knowledge of New Forest fungi, and future survey work is likely to emphasise still further just how important the area is mycologically. However it should not be forgotten that it is the efforts of volunteers, such as the members of HFRG and HWT, which are the backbone of fungus recording in the New Forest, and without which such surveys would not have been possible.

Although fungus collecting has been a major and controversial issue in the New Forest, its precise impacts are difficult to evaluate. It is possible that threatened fungi such as Hericium spp. (Marren and Dickson 2000) are among those that are being harvested for the pot, although evidence for this is lacking. The delineation of reserves where collection is prohibited is a novel initiative, but to date they have not provided any firm evidence regarding their effectiveness. Harvesting of fungi is not referred to in the latest management plan for the Crown lands (Forestry Commission 2007). While both personal and commercial collecting of fungi continue, informal observations made by the author suggest that collection intensity is currently lower than has been recorded in other parts of the UK, such as Scottish pine forests (Dyke and Newton 1999). The issue is attracting less media attention, and therefore perhaps less public interest, than it did a decade ago. Whether this represents an actual decline in collecting activity is unclear. Again, there is a need for more rigorous monitoring, both of the scale of fungus harvesting and of its impacts.

Other emerging threats to fungi potentially include climate change. Recent research has highlighted recent changes in the fruiting pattern of the fungal populations in areas near to the New Forest (i.e. within 30 km of Salisbury). When 315 autumnal fruiting species were analysed, the first fruiting date averaged across all species has become significantly earlier, whereas average last fruiting date has become significantly later, resulting in the fruiting period more than doubling in length, from 33.2 ± 1.6 days in the 1950s to 74.8 ± 7.6 days in the current decade (Gange et al. 2007). Whether such shifts are affecting the viability of fungal populations remains to be determined.

Acknowledgements

Many thanks to HFRG and BMS for access to fungal records, and to Alison Dyke for information about fungal harvesting.

References

Ainsworth, A. M. (2004). *Developing tools for assessing fungal interest in habitats. 1: Beech woodland saprotrophs.* English Nature Research Report Number 597. English Nature, Peterborough.

Ainsworth, A. M. (2005). Identifying important sites for beech deadwood fungi. *Field Mycology*, 6(2), 41–61.

Amaranthus, M. and Pilz, D. (1996). Productivity and sustainable harvest of wild mushrooms. In Pilz, D. and Molina, R. (eds.) *Managing forest ecosystems to conserve fungus diversity and sustain wild mushroom harvests*, pp. 42–61. USDA Forest Service, Pacific Northwest Research Station General technical Report PNW-GTR-371. Portland, Oregon.

Arnolds, E. J. M. (1980). De oecologie en sociologie van wasplaten (*Hygrophorus* subgenus *Hygrocybe* sensu lato). *Natura*, 77, 17–44.

Arnolds, E. (1989). Former and present distribution of stipitate hydnaceous fungi (Basidiomycetes) in the Netherlands. *Nova Hedwigia*, 48, 107–142.

Arnolds, E., (1991). Decline of ectomycorrhizal fungi in Europe. *Agriculture, Ecosystems and Environment*, 35, 209–244.

Arnolds, E. (1995). Conservation and management of natural populations of edible fungi. *Canadian Journal of Botany*, 73 (suppl. 1), 987–998.

Arnolds, E. and De Vries, B. (1993). Conservation of fungi in Europe. In Pegler, D., Boddy, L., Ing, B. and Kirk, P. M. (eds.) *Fungi of Europe: investigation, recording and conservation*, pp. 211–230. Royal Botanic Gardens, Kew.

Boertmann, D. (1995). *The genus Hygrocybe. Fungi of Northern Europe*, volume 1. Danish Mycological Society, Greve, Denmark.

Bramley, W. G. (1985). *A fungus flora of Yorkshire*. Mycological Section, Yorkshire Naturalists Union, Leeds.

Clark, M. C. (ed.) (1980). *A fungus flora of Warwickshire*. British Mycological Society, London.

Cox, J. H. S. (ed.) (1999). *The biodiversity of animal dung*. Hampshire and Isle of Wight Wildlife Trust, Eastleigh, Hampshire.

Cox, J. H. S. and Pickess, B. P. (1999). Observations concerning the ecology of Nail Fungus *Poronia punctata*, recently rediscovered in Dorset. *Dorset Proceedings*, 121, 129–132.

Dennis, R. W. G. (1986). *Fungi of the Hebrides*. Royal Botanic Gardens, Kew, Richmond, Surrey.

Dennis, R. W. G. (1995). *Fungi of South East England*. Royal Botanic Gardens, Kew, Richmond, Surrey.

Derbsch, H. and Schmitt, J. A. (1987). *Atlas der Pilze des Säarland*, Part 2: *Nachwiese, Ökologie, Vorkommen und Beschreibungen*. Ministerium für Umwelt, Saarbrücken, Germany.

Dickson, G. and Leonard, A. (eds.) (1996). *Fungi of the New Forest. A mycota*. British Mycological Society, London.

Dickson, G. (1997). Fungi are not plants – practical problems and conservation. *British Wildlife*, 9(1), 17–21.

Dyke, A. J. and Newton, A. C. (1999). Commercial harversting of wild mushrooms in Scottish forests: is it sustainable? *Scottish Forestry*, 53, 77–85.

Egli, S., Ayer, F. and Chatelain, F. (1990). Die Einfluss des Pilzsammelns auf die Pilzflora. *Mycologia Helvetica*, 3, 417–428.

English Nature (1998). *The wild mushroom picker's code of conduct*. Information and Marketing Team, English Nature, Peterborough, UK.

Evans, S. E. (2003). *Waxcap-grasslands: an assessment of English sites*. English Nature Research Reports Number 555. English Nature, Peterborough.

Evans, S., Marren, P. and Harper, M. (2001). *Important Fungus Areas. A provisional assessment of the best sites for fungi in the United Kingdom*. Plantlife, London.

Ewald, N. (2001). *Survey of the New Forest for stipitate hydnoid fungi*. Hampshire and Isle of Wight Wildlife Trust Ltd., Eastleigh, Hampshire.

Feehan, J. and McHugh, R. (1992). The Curragh of Kildare as a *Hygrocybe* grassland. *Irish Naturalist Journal*, 24 (1), 13–17.

Fleming, L. V. (2001). Fungi and the UK Biodiversity Action Plan: the process explained. In Moore, D., Nauta, M. M., Evans, S. E. and Rotheroe, M. (eds.) *Fungal conservation: issues and solutions*, pp. 209–218. Cambridge University Press, Cambridge.

Forestry Commission (2007). *Management Plan*, part B: *The Crown Lands*. Draft, November 2007. http://www.forestry.gov.uk/newforest

Gange, A. C., Gange, E. G., Sparks, T. H. and Boddy, L. (2007). Rapid and recent changes in fungal fruiting patterns. *Science*, 316, 71.

Griffith, G. W., Bratton, J. H. and Easton, G. (2004). Charismatic megafungi: the conservation of waxcap grasslands. *British Wildlife*, 16(1), 31–43.

Hrouda, P. (1999). Hydnaceous fungi of the Czech Republic and Slovakia. *Czech Mycology*, 51(2–3), 99–155.

Heilmann-Clausen, J. and Christensen, M. (2000). Svampe på bøgestammer – indikatorer for værdifulde løvskovslokaliteter. *Svampe*, 42, 35–47.

Heinemann, P. and Thoen, D. (1981). *Distributiones fungorum Belgii et Luxemburgii 1*. Jardin Botanique National de Belgique, Brussels.

Ing, B. (1993). Towards a Red List of endangered European macrofungi. In Pegler, D. N., Boddy, L., Ing, B. and Kirk, P. M. (eds.) *Fungi of Europe: investigation, recording and conservation*, pp. 231–237. Royal Botanic Gardens, Kew, Richmond, Surrey.

Jansen, E. J. and van Dobben, H. F. (1987). Is decline of *Cantharellus cibarius* in the Netherlands due to air pollution? *Ambio*, 16, 211–213.

Jumpponen, A. and Johnson, L. C. (2005). Can rDNA analyses of diverse fungal communities in soil and roots detect effects of environmental manipulations – a case study of tallgrass prairie. *Mycologia*, 97(6), 1177–1194.

Keizer, P. J. (1993). The influence of nature management on the macromycete flora. In Pegler, D. N., Boddy, L., Ing, B. and Kirk, P. M. (eds.) *Fungi of Europe: investigation, recording and conservation*, pp. 251–269. Royal Botanic Gardens, Kew.

Koehn, R. D. (1978). New localities for the genus *Poronia* (Ascomycetes) in Texas. *The Southwestern Naturalist,* 23(3), 529–539.

Leonard, P. and Evans, S. (1997). A scientific approach to a policy on commercial collecting of wild fungi. *Mycologist,* 11(2), 89–91.

Lizon, P. (1993). Decline of macrofungi in Europe: an overview. *Transactions of the Mycological Society of the Republic of China,* 8(3–4), 21–48.

Lizon, P. (1995). Macrofungi reported as extinct or threatened with extinction in European Red Data Lists. *Fungi and Conservation Newsletter,* 3, 3–4.

Lohmeyer, T. R. (1994). New European and Australian records of *Poronia erici* Lohmeyer and Benkert, and a fairy tale concerning their possible relationship. *Mycologist,* 8(1), 16–20.

Marren, P. (1998). Fungal flowers: the wax caps and their world. *British Wildlife,* 9(3), 164–172.

Marren, P. (2000). *Stipitate hydnoid fungi in England.* English Nature Research Reports No. 420. English Nature, Peterborough.

Marren, P. and Dickson, G. (2000). British tooth-fungi and their conservation. *British Wildlife,* 11, 401–409.

Marshall, E., Schreckenberg, K. and Newton, A. C. (eds) (2006). *Commercialization of non-timber forest products: factors influencing success. Lessons learned from Mexico and Bolivia and policy implications for decision-makers.* UNEP World Conservation Monitoring Centre, Cambridge, UK.

Moore, D., Nauta, M. M., Evans, S. E. and Rotheroe, M. (eds.). (2001). *Fungal conservation: issues and solutions.* Cambridge University Press, Cambridge.

Mountford, E. P. and Peterken, G. F. (2003). Long-term change and implications for the management of wood-pastures: experience over 40 years from Denny Wood, New Forest. *Forestry,* 76(1), 19–43.

Newton, A. C. and Davy, L. M. (1997). *BMS autumn foray 1997 Kindrogan. Summary list of previous fungus records.* Unpublished report for the British Mycological Society.

Newton, A. C., Davy, L. M., Holden, E., Silverside, A., Watling, R., Ward, S. D. (2003a). Status, distribution and definition of mycologically important grasslands in Scotland. *Biological Conservation,* 111, 11–23.

Newton, A. C., Holden, E., Watling, R. and Davy, L. M. (2003b). Fungal conservation in Scotland: recent progress and future priorities. *Botanical Journal of Scotland,* 55(1), 39–53.

Newton, A. C., Holden, E., Davy, L. Ward, S. D., Fleming, L. V., Watling R. (2002a). Status and distribution of stipitate hydnoid fungi in Scottish coniferous forests. *Biological Conservation,* 107, 181–192.

Newton, A. C., Watling R., Davy, L., Holden, E., Ward, S. D. (2002b). Progress towards implementing the Biodiversity Action Plan for stipitate hydnoid fungi in Scotland. *Botanical Journal of Scotland* 54(1), 89–110.

Parfitt, D., Hynes, J., Rogers, H. J. and Boddy, L. (2005). Polymerase Chain Reaction (PCR) assay detects rare tooth fungi in wood where traditional approaches fail. *Mycological Research,* 109, 1187–1194.

Pegler, D. N., Roberts, P. J. and Spooner, B. M. (1997). *British chanterelles and tooth fungi.* Royal Botanic Gardens, Kew, Richmond, Surrey.

Pegler, D. N., Boddy, L., Ing, B., Kirk, P. M. (eds.) (1993). *Fungi of Europe: investigation, recording and conservation.* Royal Botanic Gardens, Kew, Richmond, Surrey.

Pilz, D. and Molina, R. (2002). Commercial harvests of edible mushrooms from the forests of the Pacific Northwest United States: issues, management, and monitoring for sustainability. *Forest Ecology and Management,* 155, 3–16.

Plantlife International (2008). *Saving the forgotten kingdom. A strategy for the conservation of the UK's fungi: 2008–2015.* Plantlife International, Salisbury, Wiltshire.

Poland, J. (2004). *Survey of Nail Fungus* Poronia punctata *in the New Forest during 2003–4.* A report produced for the Hampshire and Isle of Wight Wildlife Trust. English Nature. 26 pp.

Reid, D. (1986). A collection of *Poronia punctata* from Surrey. *Bulletin of the British Mycological Society,* 20(1), 58–59.

Rotheroe, M. (1998). Wild fungi and the controversy over collecting for the pot. *British Wildlife,* 9(6), 349–355.

Rotheroe, M., Newton, A. C., Evans, S. and Feehan, J. (1996). Wax capgrassland survey. *Mycologist,* 10(1), 23–25.

Sanderson, H. and Prendergast, H. D. V. (2002). *Commercial uses of wild and traditionally managed plants in England and Scotland.* Royal Botanic Gardens, Kew, Richmond, Surrey.

Spooner, B. and Roberts, P. (2005). *Fungi.* The New Naturalist library. Collins, London.

Stubbs, A. E. (2001). Flies. In Hawksworth, D. L. (ed.) *The changing wildlife of Great Britain and Ireland,* pp. 239–261. Taylor and Francis, London and New York.

Tubbs, C. R. (2001). *The New Forest. History, ecology and conservation.* New Forest Ninth Centenary Trust, Lyndhurst, Hampshire.

UK Steering Group (1995). *Biodiversity: The UK Steering Group Report,* volume 2: *Action Plans (Tranche 1, Vol 2).* HMSO, London.

UK Steering Group (1999). *UK Biodiversity Group. Tranche 2 Action Plans,* volume 3: *Plants and fungi.* HMSO, London.

Wald, P., Pitkänen, S. and Boddy, L. (2004). Interspecific interactions between the rare tooth fungi *Creolophus cirrhatus, Hericium erinaceus* and *H. coralloides* and other wood decay species in agar and wood. *Mycological Research,* 108(12), 1447–1457.

Watling, R. (2001). Larger fungi. In Hawksworth, D.L. (ed.) *The changing wildlife of Great Britain and Ireland,* pp. 103–113. Taylor and Francis, London and New York.

Watling, R. (1992). *The fungus flora of Shetland.* Royal Botanic Garden, Edinburgh.

Watling, R. (1983). Fungi of Skye. *Glasgow Naturalist,* 20(4), 269–311.

Watling, R., Eggeling, T. and Turnbull, E. (1999). *The fungus flora of Orkney.* Royal Botanic Garden, Edinburgh.

Whalley, A. J. S. and Dickson, G. C. (1986). *Poronia punctata,* a declining species? *Bulletin of the British Mycological Society,* 20(1), 54–57.

Wicklow, D. T. and Hirschfield, B. J. (1979). Evidence of a competitive hierarchy among coprophilous fungal populations. *Canadian Journal of Botany,* 25, 855–858.

Wicks, D. (1999). *Survey of the New Forest for the tooth fungi* Hericium erinaceum *and* Hericium coralloides. Hampshire and Isle of Wight Naturalists' Trust, Eastleigh, Hampshire.

11 **Bryophytes**

Rod Stern

The New Forest National Park has many good sites for bryophytes. Further north and east there are good sites on heathland in north-east Hampshire and Surrey, and in localities in East and West Sussex, particularly on the sandrocks, so it would be wrong to claim that the New Forest is the best area in lowland England for bryophytes, but it is generally recognised as being one of the best.

The main bryophyte habitat that is missing is rock, although, as in many other lowland areas, churches and churchyards have at least some interest for bryophytes. Most of the habitats are acid and the extensive areas of heathland are not very rich in bryophytes, but the valley bogs are rich in *Sphagnum* species and liverworts. The old pasture woodlands are of interest with a few species growing as epiphytes on the old oak and beech, and also on decaying logs. Ditch and stream banks can be good for both mosses and liverworts (also for the two hornwort species of *Anthoceros* and *Phaeoceros*); the restoration of streams to their former courses is to be welcomed. The conifer plantations are generally of less interest, and the clearance of the younger plantations established in the 1950s and 1960s and restoration of heathland should be beneficial bryologically.

One of the most important habitats for bryophytes is on the southern parts of the Crown lands where the underlying Headon Beds are of particular interest, with a high basic content. Some of the best heathland is not within the Crown lands; there are considerable areas on the west side and especially the north-east, where the National Trust owns much open common.

Some of the most interesting sites for mosses and liverworts include the old pasture woodlands in Denny Wood, Mark Ash Wood, Bramshaw Wood, Wood Crates, near the Rufus Stone, and Burley Old Inclosure; the valley bogs and wet heaths at Cranes and Vales Moors, Matley Heath, and in or near Wilverley; and on the Headon Beds near Crockford Bridge, Forest Lodge, Norleywood and Holmsley.

As far as the bryophytes themselves are concerned, 19 species of *Sphagnum* have been recorded – a very high number for lowland England, and including the very local (in lowland England) twisted bog-moss *S. contortum*, blushing bog-moss *S. molle*, rigid bog-moss *S. teres*, and slender cow-horn bog-moss *S. subsecundum*. The only protected moss is knothole yoke-moss *Zygodon forsteri*, which occurs on old beech trees in four places; this is legally protected under Schedule 8 of the Wildlife and Countryside Act of 1981. It is also covered under a Biodiversity Action Plan, as are two other bryophytes: varnished hook-moss *Hamatocaulis vernicosus* and ribbonwort *Pallavicinia lyellii*. The latter occurs frequently on Cadnam Common and rarely in three other localities in the National Park.

Species that occur in Crown lands but are very rare elsewhere in lowland England include spotty scalewort *Frullania fragilifolia*, mainly found on old trees; western pouncewort *Lejeunea lamacerina*, found by rivers and streams; narrow mushroom-headed liverwort *Preissia quadrata* on some basic sites; long fringe-moss *Racomitrium elongatum* on some dry heathland sites; cruet collar-moss *Splachnum ampullaceum* on pony and cattle dung; golden-head moss *Breutelia chrysocoma* on damp heathland; birds-foot wing-moss *Pterogonium gracile* on old beeches; and delicate tamarisk-moss *Thuidium delicatulum*, mainly found on damp heathland.

The main work of reference is Paton (1961). The New Forest is covered in some detail in this work. Work is currently in progress on an *Atlas of Bryophytes of South Hampshire*. It seems clear that as far as the New Forest is concerned, there have not been significant changes in the bryoflora in the past 40–50 years. There seems to be no reason why the situation for bryophytes should not continue as relatively stable; some of the management operations being undertaken now could in time be beneficial in this respect.

Reference

Paton, J. A. (1961). A bryophyte flora of South Hants. *Transactions of the British Bryological Society*, 4, 1-83.

12 The condition of the New Forest habitats: an overview

Elena Cantarello, Rachel Green and Diana Westerhoff

Introduction

The area of the New Forest protected for the purposes of nature conservation covers over 29,000 hectares (ha). There are a number of different types of conservation designation applied to the New Forest, ranging from national-scale legislation (e.g. Site of Special Scientific Interest (SSSI), designated under the Wildlife and Countryside Act 1981 as amended by the Countryside and Rights of Way Act 2000), through European designations (e.g. Special Protection Area (SPA) and Special Area of Conservation (SAC) designated under the Birds and Habitats Directives 79/409/EEC and 92/43/EEC), to global-scale designations (e.g. Ramsar Site under The Convention on Wetlands of International Importance, Ramsar, Iran, 1971) (Figure 53). This chapter provides an overview of the current condition of New Forest habitats, with a specific focus on those occurring within the New Forest SSSI.

The New Forest SSSI embraces the largest area of semi-natural vegetation in lowland England, and includes the representation on a large scale of habitat formations formerly common but now fragmented and rare in lowland Western Europe. The major components are the extensive wet and dry heath with their rich valley mires and associated wet and dry grassland, the ancient pasture and enclosed woodlands, the network of clear rivers and streams and frequent permanent and temporary ponds. Outstanding examples of thirteen habitats of European interest (according to the Habitats Directive) are represented together with two priority habitat types, namely bog woodland and riverine woodland. Nowhere else do these habitats occur in combination and on such a large scale. The existence of this dynamic habitat mosaic is of fundamental importance in creating enormous niche separation for exploitation by a wide range of plants, invertebrates, reptiles and birds and animals of national and international conservation importance (Wright and Westerhoff 2001).

Nature conservation agencies devote a substantial proportion of their resources to the management and

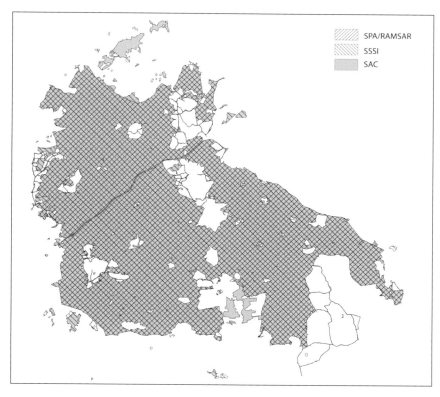

Key:
- SPA/RAMSAR
- SSSI
- SAC

Figure 53
Areas in the New Forest designated for nature conservation (see text for details). SPA and Ramsar areas coincide. This map illustrates the SSSI area considered in this chapter in relation to other designated areas for nature conservation. For geographic context, see Figures 1 and 2.

protection of the designated sites (SSSI, SPA, SAC and Ramsar sites), and mechanisms are needed to assess how successful these activities have been in achieving nature conservation objectives. An assessment of these activities is also required to test the effectiveness of policy measures, such as the Habitats Directive, in contributing to biodiversity conservation on protected sites. Natural England, in parallel with the other statutory conservation agencies in the UK, assesses the condition of the SSSIs using standard methods that have been designed to implement the Joint Nature Conservation Committee (JNCC) Common Standard Monitoring system (CSM) (JNCC 2004).

The CSM programme was developed in 1998 by JNCC in agreement with the statutory country conservation agencies to provide common principles for monitoring all of the features of interest (e.g. habitats, species, or geology) for which the protected sites were designated. To assess the condition of each feature a number of attributes with targets were identified (e.g. extent, floristic composition for habitats; population size, distribution of species), which allow assessment of whether the feature is in a favourable or unfavourable condition. If all of the targets are met, the feature is considered to be in favourable condition.

All interest features on all designated sites are assessed at least once within a six year period, which corresponds to the six-year reporting cycle used for the Habitats Directive. The results of the first cycle are reported in Williams (2006). Given the considerable number of features to assess (with an estimate of 22,000–23,000 nationwide), the CSM approach was not intended to give statistically significant results, but to facilitate rapid and simple judgements of the interesting features by local conservation officers and to provide consistent and comparable results on the condition of designated sites by habitat or site and at a UK level.

In England the condition assessment of SSSIs is undertaken by Natural England advisors. Each SSSI is divided into units and each one is assessed against a set of targets that have to be met for the unit to be judged as in favourable condition. In particular, the CSM defines six standard terms for assessing the condition of interest features: favourable, unfavourable-recovering, unfavourable-no change, unfavourable-declining, partially destroyed and destroyed (JNCC 2004).

Methodology

In the New Forest SSSI there are 582 units to assess. The boundaries of these units were defined considering habitat type, land management and land ownership (Figure 54). Standard field recording forms were developed for each habitat type based on the conservation objectives of the interest features. These include eleven habitat types, i.e. dry heath, wet heath, dry grassland, wet grassland, pasture woodland, riverine woodland, bog woodland, enclosed woodland,

temporary ponds, permanent ponds, and valley mires; and species including amphibians (e.g. great crested newts, *Triturus cristatus*), invertebrates (e.g. southern damselfly *Coenagrion mercuriale*, stag beetle *Lucanus cervus*), birds (e.g. Dartford warbler *Sylvia undata*, nightjar *Caprimulgus europaeus*, woodlark *Lullula arborea*, honey buzzard *Pernis apivorus*, wintering hen harrier *Circus cyaneus*) and reptiles (e.g. sand lizard *Lacerta agilis*, smooth snake *Coronella austriaca*), together with various species of wading birds, lichens and vascular plants. Each field form reports attributes and targets compiled in a questionnaire, which is completed during structured walks, and used to assess the condition of each unit. In the following sections the habitats assessed and the field forms developed are summarised; a detailed description of the habitats can be found in Wright and Westerhoff (2001).

Dry heath and dry grassland

The New Forest dry heaths comprise a suite of vegetation communities defined largely along a soil moisture gradient (Table 27). The dry heath occurs in close association with dry grassland. Together the dry heathland and dry grassland units cover 9,343 ha (Natural England 2008).

According to the dry heath standard field form, dry heaths are in favourable condition when: their area is maintained; there is between 1% and 10% bare ground forming an intimate mosaic with the vegetation, but not in an extensive form as a result of intensive stock feeding or human disturbance; there is a structural mosaic of ericaceous vegetation with at least 10% young and between 20% and 50% old heather *Calluna vulgaris* and cover of *C. vulgaris* lies between 25% and 90%; the cover of invasive species such as *Rhododendron ponticum* is less than 1%, and pine trees or seedlings less than 5%; not more than 10% of gorse *Ulex europaeus* is in a degenerate condition; and bracken *Pteridium aquilinum* cover does not exceed 25% cover in any unit (Alonso *et al.* 2003).

The New Forest dry grasslands, outside those mentioned above, occur in some of the enclosed, unimproved meadows throughout the Forest. These isolated areas cover 370 ha (Natural England 2008) and comprise a suite of vegetation communities subjected to a high and relatively uniform grazing pressure (Table 27). Soil fertility and soil moisture retention are the main factors determining their distribution.

According to the dry grassland standard field forms, dry grasslands are in favourable condition when: their area is maintained; there is up to 10% bare soil in an intimate mosaic with the vegetation; the sward height is 5 cm or less or between 3–10 cm for U20; the plant litter is less than 25% cover or between 5–50 % for U20; the scrub cover does not exceed 30% for *Ulex europeaus*, 1% for *Rhododendron* and 5% for other scrub; the bracken cover is less than 10% for U1b, U1d, U1f and CG7, less than 20% for U1e, U3 and U4 and between 50–90% for U20; unfavourable species such as rosebay willowherb *Chamerion angustifolium*, creeping thistle *Cirsium arvense* and spear thistle *C. vulgare*, greater plantain *Plantago major*, common nettle *Urtica dioica* and cover of coarse grasses (e.g. Yorkshire-fog *Holcus lanatus* and cock's-foot *Dactylis glomerata*) do not exceed 10% (Robertson and Jefferson 2000). Note that the codes used here (such as U1, U3 etc.) refer to communities defined in the National Vegetation Classification (NVC) (see Table 27).

Wet heath, wet grassland and mire

The New Forest wet heaths comprise a suite of vegetation communities defined by soil moisture, nutrient and base status, and are profoundly influenced by burning and grazing (Table 27). The wet heath is usually found in an intimate mosaic with mire habitats and occasionally wet grassland. These wet habitats together total 6,035 ha (Natural England 2008) of which approximately 2,100 ha is wet heath (Wright and Westerhoff 2001).

According to the wet heath standard field form, wet heaths are in favourable condition when: their area is maintained; there is up to 5% bare peaty soil in an intimate mosaic with the vegetation; soils are seasonally waterlogged, but may be dry at surface in summer; at least 25% cover is provided by ericoid shrubs (heather *Calluna vulgaris* and cross-leaved heath *Erica tetralix*) and a further minimum of 20% cover by *Sphagnum*; purple moor-grass *Molinia caerulea* does not exceed 50% in scattered tussocks; *Rhododendron* cover is below 1%, tree seedlings or tree cover are below 5% and bog myrtle *Myrica gale* and gorse *Ulex europaeus* cover are below 30% and 20%, respectively (Alonso *et al.* 2003).

The New Forest wet grasslands, outside those covered above, also occur in isolated, enclosed meadows throughout the Forest and they total c.600 ha in area (Natural England 2008). They comprise a suite of generally tightly grazed plant communities affected by high ground water levels, which are waterlogged in the winter but which dry out to some extent in the summer (Table 27). According to the wet grassland standard field form, wet grasslands are in favourable condition

Table 27
Relationship between the New Forest SAC management plan habitat classification, the NVC and the Habitats Directive classifications. Sources of the vegetation classification: (1) Wright and Westerhoff (2001); (2) Rodwell (1991a, b, 1992, 1995).

SAC management plan[1]	National Vegetation Classification (NVC)[2]	Habitats Directive
Dry Heath	H2a, H3c H2a, H3c and unclassified *Calluna-Molinia-Erica tetralix-Leucobryum glaucum* heath	European Dry Heath
Wet Heath	M16a, M16b and more base-rich extreme form of M16b M16c	North Atlantic Wet Heaths with *Erica tetralix* Depressions on peat substrates (*Rhynchosporion*)
Dry grassland	U1b, U1d/f, U1f, H2/U1d, U1e, CG7 ('Parched acid grasslands') U3 ('Heathy acid grasslands') U4 ('Moist acid grassland') MG6b ('Neutral greens') U20 ('Herb-rich Bracken grassland')	No equivalent No equivalent No equivalent No equivalent No equivalent
Wet grassland	M23a, M24c, M25b, M16b	*Eu-Molinion* grassland
Pasture woodland and Inclosure woodland	W15, W14 W16, W10a/W11 W14, W8b W10b/W11	*Atlantic acidophilous* beech forests with *Ilex* and sometimes *Taxus* in the shrub layer Old *acidophilous* oak woods with *Quercus robur* on sandy plains *Asperulo-fagetum* beech forests No equivalent
Riverine woodland	W7, W8	Alluvial forests with *Alnus glutinosa* and *Fraxinus excelsior*
Bog woodland	W4b W5b	Bog Woodland No equivalent
Mire	M16c M29, M9 M10 W5 M21, M6, M1, M14	Depressions on peat substrates of the *Rhynchosporion* Transition mires Alkaline fens Alluvial forests with *Alnus glutinosa* and *Fraxinus excelsior* No equivalent
Temporary ponds	M30, OV35, M29 S22 OV31, OV30	Oligotrophic waters containing very few minerals of sandy plains: *Littorelletalia uniflorae* No equivalent No equivalent
Permanent ponds	No equivalent	Oligotrophic waters in medio-European and perialpine area with amphibious vegetation: *Littorella* or *Isoetes* or annual vegetation on exposed banks

when: their area is maintained; there is up to 10% bare soil in an intimate mosaic with the vegetation; the sward height is less than 2 cm for M23 or between 2 and 15 cm for M24c; the plant litter is less than 25% cover; the scrub cover does not exceed 10% for bog myrtle and 5% for other scrub; unfavourable species such as marsh thistle *Cirsium palustre*, tufted hair-grass *Deschampsia cespitosa* and *Juncus* spp. cover are less than 20%, 10% and 80%, respectively and curled dock *Rumex crispus*, broad-leaved dock *R. obtusifolious*, common nettle, creeping thistle, spear thistle and marsh ragwort *Senecio aquaticus* are occasional (Robertson and Jefferson 2000).

The New Forest mires comprise a suite of communities with elements that are typical of both bogs and fens (Table 27). Bogs are typically rain-fed, mineral and nutrient poor and acidic; fens are groundwater fed, have a higher nutrient status and are generally neutral or alkaline. Together with the other closely associated habitats they cover c.5,169 ha (Natural England 2008), of which c.2,000 ha is mire (Wright and Westerhoff 2001).

According to the mire standard field form, mires are in favourable condition when: their area is maintained; there is between 1% and 10% bare peaty soil; presence of high water level all year and open bog pools with standing water in mires larger than 5 ha; unfavourable species such as *Rhododendron*, bramble *Rubus fruticosus*, gorse are rare or absent; *Sphagnum* cover is at least 10% and there is no species dominant to the exclusion of all others; purple moor-grass cover is less than 75%, bog myrtle cover is less than 50% and alder *Alnus glutinosa* and *Salix* spp. cover are less than 90%.

Pasture, riverine and bog woodland

The New Forest pasture woodland covers c. 4,400 ha (Natural England 2008) and includes all of those woodland stands that depend upon grazing by livestock to maintain the special interest features (Table 27). They have a great structural diversity with a complete range of tree age classes and a wide range of tree density; they are also characterised by an exceptionally rich lichen, bryophyte and fungal flora, and invertebrate and bird fauna.

According to the pasture woodland standard field form, pasture woodlands are in favourable condition when: the area of ancient woodland is maintained; there is at least one native sapling, oak or beech contributing 10% of the saplings seen within 30 minutes walking and fallen branches allowing scrub and sapling development; there is less than 1% non-native species in the canopy; there is no evidence of felling of native trees, less than 1% local ground disturbance, no ditch maintenance or other safety work; the canopy cover is between 30 and 90% and the holly thickets cover less than 50%; less than 55% of big trees show severe stress; deadwood is classed as average to good; there is less than 10% of the soil surface poached; less than 10% of the vegetation is heavily modified, improved or exhibiting disturbed communities attributable to recreational activities; and

less than 50% of the vegetation reaches 10 cm in height (Table 28) (Kirby *et al.* 2002).

The New Forest riverine woodland comprises those woodland stands with occasional to abundant alder and frequent ash *Fraxinus excelsior* on wet mineral or peaty soils along water courses (Table 27). Riverine woodlands are often in close association with scrub and other broadleaved woodland. The total units cover 492 ha (Natural England 2008), of which c. 212 ha is riverine woodland (Wright and Westerhoff 2001).

According to the riverine woodland standard field form, riverine woodlands are in favourable condition when: the area of ancient woodland is maintained; in open forest occasional saplings are present and in restoration areas 10% of the area show saplings of native species; there is less than 1% non-native species; there is no evidence of native trees being felled, local ground disturbance, planting, ditch maintenance, safety work; the canopy cover is between 30 and 90% and thorn, bramble and rose thickets protect the regeneration; the stream dynamics and the deadwood are classed as average to good; less than 5% of dead trees is attributable to alder die-back; and there is less than 10% of the soil surface poached and less than 10% of the vegetation heavily modified, improved or exhibiting disturbed communities attributable to recreational activities (Kirby *et al.* 2002).

The New Forest bog woodlands cover c.33 ha (Wright and Westerhoff 2001) and comprises woodland communities on peat with a significant component of bog species in the ground flora (Table 27). According to the bog woodland standard field form, bog woodlands are in favourable condition when: the area of ancient woodland is maintained; sallow and alder are dominant in the canopy, there is less than 1% cover of non-native species and less than 5% of birch; there is no expanse of woodland at expense of mire; no evidence of felling of native trees, planting, ditch maintenance or safety work; less than 1% ground disturbance; high water level all year; *Sphagnum* more than 10% cover, *Molinia* less than 75% and *Myrica gale* less than 50% (Kirby *et al.* 2002).

Inclosure woodland

The New Forest Inclosure woodland comprises woodland communities that are not subject to livestock grazing until most trees are past browsing height (Table 27). On the Crown lands they are relatively recent plantations on former heathland or ancient woodland stands (AWS), fenced off from the commoners' animals, but accessible by deer. Off the Crown lands they are remote from commoners' animals. Together with the ancient semi-natural woodland, they cover c.8,186 ha (Natural England 2008).

According to the Inclosure woodland standard field form, Inclosure woodlands are in favourable condition when (i) in the 19th century stands (or older): their area is maintained; there is a successful establishment of saplings; there is less than 1% non-native species in the canopy; (ii) in non-intervention sites: there is no

Table 28
Example of standard field monitoring form the New Forest (see text for details).

Site name: **New Forest**	Site unit name and number:	Date visited:

Assessed by:

Level 1 Habitat Type: **Pasture Woodland** (Habitats Directive: Beech forests with *Ilex* and *Taxus*, rich in epiphytes (*Ilici-Fagion*), Old acidophilous oak woods with *Quercus robur* on sandy plains, *Asperulo-fagetum* beech forests. NVC: W15, W16, W14, W10a/W11, W10b/W11, W8b)

Condition assessment:

Favourable	Unfavourable – maintained	Partially destroyed
Unfavourable – recovering	Unfavourable – declining	Destroyed

Recommended visiting period: Anytime

Recommended frequency of visits : All Pasture Woodland units to be visited within 3 years

Level 1 Attribute	Target	Yes	No	Samples										
Area of A&O Woodland	Maintain existing area of ancient woodland on existing sites													
Regeneration (native species only)	At least 1 native sapling (>1.5 m, <15 cm dbh) (excluding birch), or leader out of reach of grazing animals within 30 minutes walking.													
	Oak and Beech contributing at least 10% of the saplings seen													
	Fallen branch wood present allowing scrub and sapling development													
Composition	<1% non-native species in canopy or shrub layer													
Natural processes and structural development	No evidence of recent (within last 5 yrs) felling of native trees													
	<1% (local) ground disturbance													
	No evidence of recent (within last 5 yrs) planting													
	No evidence of recent (within last 5 yrs) drainage/ ditch maintenance													
	No evidence of essential safety work, e.g. felling, drainage etc.													
	Canopy cover present over 30–90% of unit area													
Characteristic features of Pasture Woodland	<55% trees >80 cm dbh 2.5 m girth showing severe stress or death attributable to disease or pollution													
	Deadwood : *Good*: 1 or 2 large fallen trees or trunks (>50cm dia) visible, plenty 5–50 cm pieces in view													
	Average: 1 or 2 large pieces, little smaller material; or only smaller material (5–50 cm) in view.													
	Poor: Even small material (5–50 cm) scarce													
	Absent: Nothing >15 cm diameter													
	Fallen dead wood classed as average to good over most of unit													
	Holly thickets occasional or frequent NOT dominant over most of unit (<50% ground cover)													
	Ground vegetation: <10% soil surface poached or trampled													
	<50% of vegetation more than 10 cm high (except bracken)													
	<10% vegetation heavily modified, improved or exhibiting disturbed communities attributable to recreational activities													

evidence of felling of native trees, local ground disturbance, planting, or ditch maintenance; and (iii) in the managed compartments: there is between 5–20% permanent open space, at least 5 native trees per hectare and ditch maintenance restricted to roadsides for the AWS; deadwood is classed as average to good; there is less than 10% of the soil surface poached and the vegetation heavily modified; less than 50% of the vegetation reaches 10 cm height, there is at least 30% of oak as final crop and less than 5% in rotational stage other than high forest for the AWS (Kirby *et al.* 2002).

Temporary and permanent ponds

The New Forest temporary and permanent ponds are numerous and scattered across the Forest. The temporary ponds, in particular, are often so small that their area has not been measured. A few larger ponds forming individual units total 5.7 ha (Natural England 2008). Temporary ponds support a range of distinctive vegetation communities restricted to water-filled shallow depressions on poorly drained soils that dry out temporarily during the summer months; permanent ponds maintain a water level throughout the year (Table 27).

According to the temporary pond standard field form, temporary ponds are in favourable condition when: their area is maintained; there is between 25 and 75% bare ground present at the end of each summer; the water chemistry is maintained; *Juncus bulbosus* var. *fluitans* growth is less than 50%; unfavourable species

such as New Zealand pigmyweed *Crassula helmsii* and parrot's-feather *Myriophyllum aquaticum* are absent. Permanent ponds are in favourable condition when: the water level, the water quality and the sediment quality are maintained throughout the year; unfavourable species such as *Crassula helmsii* and *Myriophyllum aquaticum* are absent.

Temporary and permanent ponds (5 units), and rivers and streams (1 unit) were not considered in the present study as their condition assessment has only recently started and their actual condition needs further study to be carefully determined. A total of 576 out of 582 units were therefore assessed in this study.

Results

Data analyses
Data analyses were performed by using SPSS 16.0 for Windows (© 2008 SPSS Inc., USA) and ArcGIS 9.2 (© 1999–2006 ESRI Inc., USA).

Overall situation
Of the 576 units assessed using the standard field monitoring forms from September 1998 to August 2008 (see the previous section on Methodology), 32% of their area is assessed as being in favourable condition, and 68% in unfavourable condition; a very small percentage of their area is considered partially or totally destroyed (Figure 54). Of the 68% unfavourable units, 62.5% are in unfavourable–recovering category

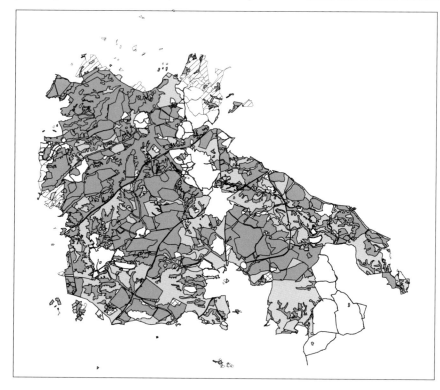

Figure 54
The New Forest SSSI condition (data compiled from 8 September 1998 to 4 August 2008). Pale grey, favourable (31.9%); dark grey, unfavourable recovering (62.46%;) hatched, unfavourable declining (4.62%); cross-hatched, unfavourable no change (0.85%); black, part destroyed / destroyed (0.01%).

and 4.6% in the unfavourable–declining category; thus, 94.4% of the units' area is in favourable condition or is recovering towards favourable condition. Drainage, forestry and woodland management are most often mentioned as adverse activities affecting the condition of the habitats.

Dry heathland and dry grassland
Dry heathland and dry grassland fare relatively well with 88% of their coverage assessed in favourable or unfavourable recovering condition (8,520 ha, of which 5,770 ha is in favourable condition and 2,750 ha in unfavourable recovering) (Figure 55). 1,191 ha are in unfavourable no change or declining condition. The main factors affecting the unfavourable condition are: overgrazing, spread of bracken *Pteridium aquilinum*, Scots pine *Pinus sylvestris* and birch *Betula pendula* for the dry heath; undergrazing off the Crown land and spread of bracken for the dry grassland.

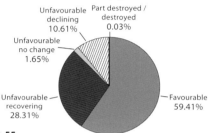

Figure 55
Condition of dry heath and dry grassland. Percentages represent the proportion of the area falling into each of the assessment categories on the 4 August 2008 over a span of 10 years (for details see text and Figure 54 caption).

Wet heath, wet grassland and mire
Wet heath, wet grassland and valley mire achieve good results with 97% of their area in favourable or unfavourable recovering condition (5,881 ha, of which 977 ha in favourable condition and 4,904 in unfavourable recovering condition) (Figure 56). A relatively small area totalling 168 ha is in unfavourable no change or declining condition. The main factors responsible for the unfavourable condition are: inappropriate scrub control, past drainage, and establishment of Scots pine for the wet heath; excess scrub and past drainage for the wet grassland and valley mire.

Figure 56
Condition of wet heath, wet grassland and mire habitats. For details see caption to Figure 55.

Pasture, riverine and bog woodland
Pasture, riverine and bog woodland achieve the best results with 99% of their area in favourable or unfavourable recovering condition (4,914 ha, of which 2,049 in favourable condition and 2,865 in unfavourable recovering condition) (Figure 57). Only 50 ha are in unfavourable no change or declining condition. The main factors affecting the unfavourable condition are: low dead wood volume, insufficient canopy and trees collapsing for pasture woodland; and past drainage, channel morphology changes and non-native species for riverine and bog woodland.

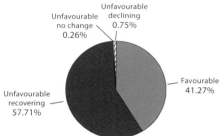

Figure 57
Condition of pasture, riverine and bog woodland. For details see caption to Figure 55.

Inclosure woodland
In the case of Inclosure woodland, 98% of its coverage assessed is in favourable or unfavourable recovering condition (8,002 ha, of which 459 ha in favourable condition and 7,543 ha in unfavourable recovering condition) (Figure 58). 184 ha are in unfavourable no change or declining condition. The main factors affecting the unfavourable condition are: forestry, woodland management and past drainage.

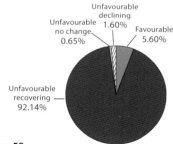

Figure 58
Condition of Inclosure woodland. For details see caption to Figure 55.

Discussion

There are a number of ways in which the condition assessment results are used, from the site level to the European scale. At the site level, the assessments provide information on which adverse activities are affecting the habitats, which issues are needed to be addressed and which management measures need to be undertaken to restore the favourable condition. With regards to the Inclosure woodland, for example, where 94% their area is in unfavourable condition (Figure 58), much effort is currently being focused on addressing the following issues: management of broadleaf woodland, non-native trees and scrub management, drainage and soil disturbance, felling and planting, timber extraction, damage by machinery and ride management. The management actions that are currently under way include: to remove non-native species; to set different grazing options; to restore appropriate hydrological regimes and to remove drainage channels; to assist the natural regeneration; to retain fallen and standing deadwood, and to retain existing veteran trees and identify future ones; to manage scrub and bracken where required, to support other species; to minimise ground disturbance; and to keep rides open and to widen them as required.

European projects funded by LIFE-Nature programme (i.e. LIFE II Project 'Securing Natura Objectives in the New Forest' and LIFE III Project 'Sustainable Wetland restoration in the New Forest; see Chapter 17), Government projects (e.g. the 'Rural Pathfinder Project', set up by the Hampshire County Council in partnership with Natural England) and other projects funded by the Department for Environment, Food and Rural Affairs (DEFRA), are essential to support the management actions needed to achieve the favourable condition and their emphasis is likely to increase in the future.

Natural England has a Public Service Agreement (PSA) with DEFRA. The PSA target is for 95% of SSSIs, by area, to be in favourable condition by 2010. In the New Forest much has been achieved in recent years to restore those areas of unfavourable habitat condition, which totalled some 11,000 ha. Many of the areas within the enclosed woodlands have been restored to unfavourable recovering condition under the Pathfinder Project. In 2008 a Memorandum of Agreement was signed between the Forestry Commission, the New Forest National Park Authority and Natural England to restore most of the remaining area of approximately 4,000 ha. Most of the area involved includes wetlands damaged by past drainage and the agreement is a commitment to restore these areas following consultation with other interested parties such as the New Forest Verderers and the Commoners' Defence Association. On the strength of this agreement those units have been changed to unfavourable recovering condition.

At the national scale, the condition assessment results are used to help prioritise conservation funding by focusing on particular habitats or species of particular interest, or on addressing broad-scale adverse conditions. The results are also used to help conservation agencies meet national and international reporting obligations, and to evaluate the implementation of international convention and directives. It is pertinent here to consider whether the condition assessment results could be used to assess the Favourable Conservation Status (FCS) as defined in Article 1(e) and 1(i) of the Habitats Directive. However it should be noted that whilst the UK nature conservation agencies agree that the FCS can be applied at a variety of levels, there is an ongoing debate as to the degree to which the concept can be applied directly at the site level. However, key elements that contribute to the determination of FCS can be applied to sites. For example, Cantarello and Newton (2008) presented a detailed evaluation of three monitoring methods, including the CSM, which could potentially be used to assess the FCS of forested habitats at the individual site scale.

Further and updated information on the condition assessment results can be found at:

- *http://www.english-nature.org.uk/Special/sssi*
- *http://www.naturalengland.org.uk/*

References

Alonso, I., Sherry, J., Turner, A., Farrell, L., Corbett, P. and Strachan, I. (2003). *Lowland heathland SSSIs: Guidance on conservation objectives setting and condition monitoring.* English Nature, Peterborough.

Cantarello, E. and Newton, A. C. (2008). Identifying cost-effective indicators to assess the conservation status of forested habitats in Natura 2000 sites. *Forest Ecology and Management,* 256, 815–826.

JNCC (2004). *Common standard monitoring. Introduction to the guidance manual. Issue date: February 2004.* Joint Nature Conservation Committee, Peterborough.

Kirby, K., Latham, J., Holl, K., Bryce, J., Corbett, P. and Watson, R. (2002). *Objective setting and condition monitoring within woodland Sites of Special Scientific interest.* English Nature, Peterborough.

Natural England (2008). *Condition of SSSI units in the New Forest – detailed agreement compiled 04 August 2008.* Unpublished data provided by D.V. Westerhoff and R. Green. Natural England, Lyndhurst.

Robertson, H. J. and Jefferson, R. G. (2000). *Monitoring the condition of lowland grassland SSSIs: Part 1 – English Nature's rapid assessment method.* English Nature, Peterborough.

Rodwell, J. S. (1991a). *British Plant Communities Volume 1 – Woodlands and scrub.* Cambridge University Press, Cambridge.

Rodwell, J. S. (1991b). *British Plant Communities Volume 2 – Mires and heath.* Cambridge University Press, Cambridge.

Rodwell, J. S. (1992). *British Plant Communities Volume 3 – Grassland and montane communities.* Cambridge University Press, Cambridge.

Rodwell, J. S. (1995). *British Plant Communities Volume 4 – Aquatic communities, swamps and tall-herb fens.* Cambridge University Press, Cambridge.

Williams, J. M. (2006). Monitoring the condition of UK protected sites: results from the first six years. *British Wildlife,* 18, 1–9.

Wright, R. N. and Westerhoff, D. V. (2001). *New Forest SAC Management Plan.* English Nature, Lyndhurst.

13 The condition and dynamics of New Forest woodlands

Adrian C. Newton, Elena Cantarello, Gillian Myers, Sarah Douglas and Natalia Tejedor

Introduction

In his classic account of the New Forest, Tubbs (2001) refers to its ancient native woodlands as 'collectively the finest remnants of comparatively undisturbed deciduous forest in the lowlands of Western Europe'. This is a remarkable claim, but comes from someone who knew the woodlands intimately, and who recognised their special character and exceptional ecological value.

Tubbs' statement referred to unenclosed ancient pasture woodlands, called 'Ancient and Ornamental' (A&O) woods in the 1877 Act, of which he estimates that 3,671 ha remain. As noted by Peterken *et al.* (1996), most of the substantial A&O woods are distributed in a broad belt of near-continuous woodland centred on Lyndhurst, with additional outlying woods surviving in western and southern districts (Figure 59). This same general pattern of distribution has persisted for at least two hundred years, although during that time substantial areas of

A&O woodland have been incorporated within Silvicultural Inclosures and replaced by plantations.

The A&O woodlands are dominated by beech, oak (both pedunculate and sessile), birch (both downy and silver), and holly. Typically beech and oak dominate the canopy, with birches occurring on the edges of main woodland blocks, and holly in the understorey (Peterken *et al.* 1996). Other species occurring at low density include yew, hawthorn, crab apple, rowan and whitebeam. Most of these woodlands classify as acid and oak beechwood types (National Vegetation Classification (NVC) vegetation types W10a, W10b, W11, W14–17), but other woodland types are present in limited areas, including ash-rich riverine woodland (W7), sallow and alder carrs (W4b and W5b respectively), and ash–field maple–dog's mercury woodland (W8b) on relatively base-rich soils (Peterken *et al.* 1996, Table 29). Scots pine is also widely distributed, having spread naturally following its reintroduction in the 18th century, often colonising heathland.

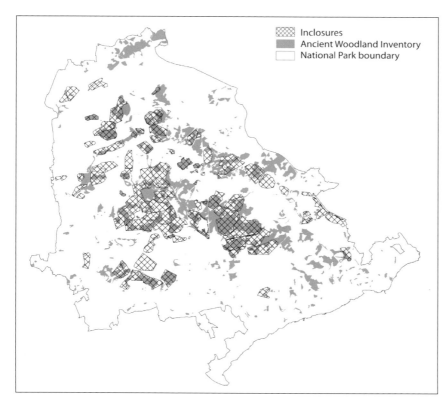

Inclosures
Ancient Woodland Inventory
National Park boundary

Figure 59
Map of the Inclosures and ancient woodland within the New Forest. The distribution of ancient woodland is based on the results of the national Ancient Woodland Inventory (see Goldberg *et al.* 2007 for details). For geographic context, see Figure 1.

Many of the A&O woods are 'ancient', in that they have been in existence for at least 400 years. Some appear to be 'primary', in that they have never been completely cleared since the arrival of humans in the area, and may therefore be considered direct descendents of the original 'wildwood' (Peterken *et al.* 1996, Rackham 2003). This continuity of woodland cover is thought to be an important factor in conferring their high value as habitat for wildlife. While the structure and composition of the woodlands has been greatly influenced by a long history of human intervention, and in particular the activities of livestock and deer, the presence of large trees and large quantities of dead wood create a structure that is believed to resemble that of wildwood (Peterken *et al.* 1996). Tubbs (2001) suggests that the riverine woodlands may be among the least disturbed of the Forest's A&O woodlands, possessing great diversity of age structure and substantial accumulations of dead wood, and may represent the only substantial examples of ancient floodplain forests remaining in England (Peterken and Hughes 1995).

According to Tubbs (2001), a further 344 ha of ancient pasture woods occur within the Silvicultural Inclosures, which with some other remnants, gives a total of approximately 4,035 ha. The Inclosures themselves primarily comprise plantations established after the Acts of 1698, 1808 and 1851, together with the results of replanting or natural regeneration, most of which originated in the 20th century as a result of harvesting of the earlier plantations (Tubbs 2001). Much of this replanting was of exotic conifer species, but the earlier plantations were mainly of oak, of which extensive areas still survive. Further areas of conifer plantation were established (in the 'Verderers' Inclosures') on open heathland in the 1950s and 1960s (Tubbs 2001). The current area covered by the New Forest Inclosures is 8,493 ha (Forestry Commission 2007). As described by Tubbs (2001), livestock have often been excluded from Inclosures at various times in their history through the use of banks, ditches and fences, with the aim of protecting tree regeneration from herbivory, but individual Inclosures have not always been continuously enclosed. In addition, measures taken to exclude livestock have not always been completely successful.

The aim of this chapter is to provide an overview of previous ecological research and survey work that have been undertaken on New Forest woodlands, with a focus on woodland dynamics. It is widely recognised that effective conservation management of woodlands depends critically on understanding the ecological processes influencing their dynamics, but in the case of the New Forest, such processes have been the focus of some debate and uncertainty. The current condition of New Forest woodlands is then considered, in the light of available information. Survey data describing the distribution of dead wood are also summarised, to provide an indication of the current status of this important habitat resource. The potential management implications of current trends in woodland composition and structure are then briefly explored.

Table 29
Distribution of Ancient and Ornamental woodlands following a survey undertaken in 1996 (after Peterken *et al.* 1996). (Note that the estimate of total area differs slightly from that of Tubbs 2001.) The term 'emergent woods' refers to those secondary woodlands that have developed since 1850.

Compositional group	Area (ha)	% of total area
Old oak and/or beech woodlands	1,174	31
Emergent broadleaved woodlands	485	13
Ash-rich riverine woodland	157	4
Other riverine woodland	133	3
Stands of Scots pine	184	5
Area of Ancient and Ornamental Woodlands surveyed in 1996	3,684	98
Total area of Ancient and Ornamental Woodlands in 1996	3,770	100

For detailed accounts of the natural history and management history of the New Forest woodlands, the reader is referred to Tubbs (1968, 2001). Wright and Westerhoff (2001) provide a detailed ecological description of New Forest woodlands, whereas Goriup (1999) provides a useful introductory account.

Previous surveys and research

In order to illustrate how an understanding of the ecology of New Forest woodlands has developed over recent decades, a summary is provided here of the survey and research investigations that have been undertaken, listed by author and structured chronologically. This account does not claim to be comprehensive; one of the features of previous research and survey work in the area is that the results have not always been made widely available, and are often difficult to access. The emphasis here is on those investigations that have contributed to an increased understanding of woodland dynamics, rather than woodland ecology more generally.

(i) Peterken and Tubbs
The first detailed analysis of woodland structure and dynamics in the New Forest was presented by Peterken and Tubbs (1965). Analysis of the age structure of woodlands and evidence relating to the dynamics of herbivore populations suggested that phases of active tree regeneration have occurred over the past 300 years, which were related to the fluctuations in grazing and browsing pressure, and the incidence of heathland burning. Trees were divided into three age classes (old, intermediate and young, referred to as 'A', 'B' and 'C' respectively). The ages of each generation were established by counting annual growth rings from a representative sample of trees, obtained from a variety of different woods. Results indicated that generation A dates from 1649–1764, whereas generation B primarily originates from 1858–1923. In contrast, very little recruitment was recorded in the period 1765–1850.

Generation C results from a period of 'vigorous and widespread' regeneration that coincides roughly with the period of World War II. However, at time of writing, the authors reported that regeneration was prevented or held in check by browsing of livestock and deer in most of the unenclosed woodlands, 'although not always in unshaded sites' (Peterken and Tubbs 1965).

Comparison between tree age structures and herbivore numbers suggested some correlations between the two. Most notably, the B generation appeared to date from the almost complete removal of deer following the 1851 Deer Removal Act, whereas C regeneration coincided with the decline in browsing pressure during World War II. Similarly, browsing pressure was high during 1760–1850, when little regeneration took place. However, generation A appears to have arisen during a period of high browsing pressure, a result that the authors were unable to explain (Peterken and Tubbs 1965).

The survey undertaken by Peterken and Tubbs (1965) was limited in scope, as ring counts were obtained from only 141 trees in 31 woodlands (Table 30). Information on herbivore numbers must also be considered to be somewhat uncertain, particularly for relatively early dates. However, Tubbs continued to collect ring count data in subsequent years, increasing the sample size to 530. In his final account, Tubbs (2001) reiterated the existence of three principal age classes, with the A generation dating from 1660–1760, the B generation mainly during 1840–1870 and the C generation between 1900 and 1960, with least

regeneration occurring between 1920 and 1935. Tubbs (2001) stated that after 1970, tree and shrub regeneration 'petered out... over most of the Forest'. This apparently confirmed the prediction made by Peterken and Tubbs (1965), that as a result of elevated browsing pressure, 'successful regeneration in unenclosed woods will become impossible in the next few years'. However, this observation was not supported by any quantitative survey data.

Mention should also be made of George Peterken's research into the ecology of holly, the subject of his PhD dissertation. Peterken (1966) refers to one of the 'outstanding problems of 19th century holly regeneration', namely the fact that at that time holly regeneration was confined to woodland clearings and margins, 'with the result that characteristic holly rings developed'. Yet in other woods, regeneration occurred throughout the woodland, to form the present-day closed understorey. This he attributed to an interaction between browsing pressure and light availability; although holly is a shade-tolerant species, he suggested that on relatively shaded sites, the species grows less vigorously, and is therefore more susceptible to the negative impacts of browsing on growth.

(ii) Small and Haggett

Concern about the state of A&O woodlands, and the limited extent of natural regeneration, led to a survey undertaken by Small and Haggett (1972). This was incorporated into the management plan for the New Forest for the period 1972–1981, and formed the basis for management for many years (Peterken et al. 1996).

Table 30
Summary of woodland surveys undertaken in the New Forest.

Sample	Measurements	Scope	Reference
141 trees sampled in 31 woodlands	Ages estimated from ring counts, for holly, oak and beech	Unenclosed woodlands only	Peterken and Tubbs (1965)
'All high forest and park sub-compartments visited'	Visual assessment of whether regeneration (including trees of up to 100 years old) was 'adequate'	Unenclosed woodlands only	Small and Haggett (1972)
24 woods including oak-dominated woods important for lichens, plus representatives of four other woodland types	20 random points in each wood, used to sample point-centred quarters; four trees nearest each point measured for girth at breast height	Unenclosed woodlands only	Flower (1977)
All woodland compartments visited	Presence of oak and beech saplings (>2 m height and <0.2 m girth) noted; girths of largest trees measured	Unenclosed woods plus woods of 'mostly similar origins' in Statutory Inclosures	Flower and Tubbs (1982)
310 sample sites, each of 200 m², located by overlaying randomly orientated grids on maps of the woodland units, with 500 m spacing	Counts of seedlings (<130 cm height), saplings (>130 cm height, <5 cm diameter) and trees, size data, and visual estimates of canopy density and litter layer	Unenclosed woods	Morgan (1977, 1987a,b)
173 sample sites, including all units used for monitoring of woodland condition by Natural England; each plot 2,500 m²	Stand structure and composition, including seedlings classified as trees <1.5 m in height, saplings as = 1.5 m in height and < 10 cm dbh, and trees as = 10 cm dbh. Also surveyed browsing damage	Unenclosed woods and Inclosures	This chapter

Analysis of historic maps indicated that woodland area increased substantially during 1867–1909, and between 1909 and 1963, largely as a result of tree regeneration on former parkland. In total, some 517 ha of woodland was estimated to have been established during the period 1867–1963, representing a gain of some 21% in the area of broadleaved native woodland in the unenclosed ('Open') Forest during this period of 96 years. The authors suggested, on the basis of map analysis supported by field observations, that in some areas regeneration has occurred between large, open-grown trees, which formerly occurred at relatively low density in areas subjected to heavy grazing pressure. This resulted in conversion of scattered trees to extensive blocks of continuous-canopy woodland, an increase in connectivity between woodland fragments, and an increase in area of some individual woods. These two phases of woodland expansion correspond roughly to the periods of low grazing pressure identified by Peterken and Tubbs (1965).

Small and Haggett (1972) visited every 'high forest and park subcompartment' (Table 30) and classified each according to the amount and extent of regeneration, defined as 'an adequate distribution throughout the stand of healthy oak or beech trees up to an estimated 100 years of age that will ensure continuity of high forest (diameter at breast height of 6.5–38.8 cm)'. According to this definition, only limited areas (17.4 ha in total) were found to be lacking regeneration, most of which were relatively homogeneous stands of beech. Approximately 901 ha were classified as areas without adequate regeneration, i.e. 26.7% of the total broadleaved woodland area. However, the assessment of regeneration was purely subjective, and no quantitative data were collected on density of juvenile trees. It is also unclear, therefore, precisely what constitutes 'adequate' regeneration according to these authors.

Small and Haggett (1972) conclude that broadleaved tree species have regenerated successfully on a wide range of site types over a long period, over much of the area of unenclosed woodlands of the New Forest. According to Peterken et al. (1996), these authors also noted that 'younger age classes have regenerated in small groups no more than a few square yards in extent, often arising, particularly in the case of oak, by growing through blackthorn scrub which has given protection against browsing animals'. Those areas where regeneration is lacking are typically those where 'the die back of old beech is a main feature. Under such areas 'lawns' and bracken beds develop with no regeneration'.

(iii) Flower and Tubbs

The report produced by Flower and Tubbs (1982) details a thorough study of the historical origins and use of the New Forest, and results of fieldwork undertaken during 1977–1978. This survey involved visits to woodland compartments, defined on the basis of their species composition and age structure. Girths of the largest trees were measured, to assess the age of the oldest trees present. Regeneration was assessed by noting the presence of oak or beech saplings >2 m height and <0.2 m girth. Results indicated that oak saplings were present in 182 compartments, and beech in 153 compartments, with both oak and beech present in an additional 128 compartments (giving a total of 563). The authors noted that few seedlings appeared to have survived in very recent years, most of those recorded representing recruitment in the early and mid-1970s rather than the late 1970s. However, overall, regeneration was considered to have taken place recently despite high herbivore populations, though its distribution was patchy. The authors found no evidence that beech regenerates more successfully than oak, and no correlation was found between soil type and species dominance, when data from a subset of 20 woods were analysed (Flower and Tubbs 1982).

This report built on work undertaken previously by Flower (1980a,b) towards his PhD (Flower 1977; see also Flower 1983). This involved a survey of 24 woods, involving the measurement of trees using a point-centred quarter method (Table 30), although trees <1.5 m in height were not included in the survey. Data were used to classify the plant communities using a phytosociological ordination method, enabling primary and secondary woods to be differentiated. On the basis of age profiles (derived from girth measurements), Flower (1977) concluded that 'the Forest is quite capable of perpetuating itself', and noted that the regeneration phases described by Peterken and Tubbs (1965) are clearly discernible (Flower 1980a). Analysis of historical records also enabled Flower (1980a) to identify a period of intensive felling of oak in the late 17th century, which gave rise to the oldest generation of oak now found in the unenclosed woods, and led to a marked increase in the representation of beech in many woods (Flower 1980a).

(iv) Morgan

Richard Morgan also undertook a programme of field research towards his PhD in the 1970s (Morgan 1977), at about the same time as that of Nicholas Flower, although his results were not published until many years later (Morgan 1987a,b). This research was later supplemented by further field survey work (Morgan 1991).

Unlike the surveys described above, Morgan (1977, 1987a) employed a systematic design, involving surveys of 310 sample plots located on a regular grid (Table 30), distributed throughout the unenclosed woodlands of the New Forest. Results indicated that almost 47% of stands were dominated by a single species, either oak or beech, with *Fagus* being the more frequent (27.7% of stands surveyed). When all sites were pooled together, stem diameter classes for both oak and beech displayed a similar, 'negative exponential' frequency distribution, with beech displaying generally higher frequencies in the middle size classes (35–75 cm dbh) and oak in the 15–35 cm dbh size classes (Morgan 1987a). Seedlings of both species occurred widely but were generally of low density (i.e. most often <5 seedlings per 200 m^2); oak and beech seedlings were recorded on 36.1% and 17.1% of sites, respectively, the corresponding figures for saplings being 17.4% and 13.9% (Morgan 1987a).

These data were used by Morgan (1987b) to challenge the model proposed by Peterken and Tubbs (1965) and supported by Flower (1980a), with three main phases of tree recruitment coinciding with periods of relatively low herbivore pressure. Specifically, Morgan (1987b) identified three main weaknesses in the model: (i) the evidence of three generations remains equivocal, (ii) the anomalies identified by Peterken and Tubbs (1965) themselves undermine the model (such as the occurrence of a relatively high herbivore density during recruitment of the 'A' generation), and (iii) the model does not provide an adequate explanation for the observed changes in regeneration occurrence, both temporally and spatially.

Morgan (1987b) rightly points out that Peterken and Tubbs (1965) did not adopt a formal sampling scheme in their work (Table 30), and as a result, their results may be biased. In addition, samples for ring-counts were selected to be representative of the already identified age groups, risking circularity. Coupled with the low sample sizes employed, Morgan (1987b) was surely right to state that the model has not yet been rigorously tested (despite the additional ring counts reported by Tubbs 2001). Morgan (1987b) also highlighted inconsistencies in the results of Flower (1980a) compared with those of Peterken and Tubbs (1965), as well as the limitations of the point-centred quarter method that Flower adopted. The size-frequency distributions presented by Morgan (1987a) failed to provide any evidence in support of discrete phases of recruitment, yet his data were derived from a survey that was more comprehensive than any other undertaken previously.

Morgan (1987b) went further in his critique, highlighting the probable role of timber extraction in stimulating periods of increased tree regeneration, a point also recognised by Flower (1980a). He concluded that explaining patterns of woodland structure purely in terms of changes in browsing pressure is over-simplistic, a point supported by the fact that regeneration has apparently occurred in the past at times of high browsing pressure. This he ascribes to the role of understorey shrubs, such as holly, in protecting seedlings from herbivory. This process was investigated further by Morgan (1991), by assessing regeneration in a single plot (36 m × 24 m) in a single site (Ridley Wood). The position of each seedling was recorded, together with information on a variety of environmental variables. Larger oak and beech seedlings were found to be associated with protective conditions, namely sites with young holly or fallen branches, or adjacent to canopy gaps. However, saplings of both oak and beech were absent.

The research described by Morgan (1991) can similarly be criticised, for being limited to a single site of limited size, and at a single point in time. In the analysis that he presents, it is also difficult to tease apart the relative role of protection and light

availability in enabling tree establishment. However, the data presented do provide some evidence for tree seedling establishment of beech and oak seedlings occurring under a woodland canopy, on microsites protected from herbivores.

(v) Putman and colleagues

In the 1970s and 1980s, populations of large herbivores in the New Forest were the focus of an intensive programme of research undertaken by Rory Putman and others at the University of Southampton. This research is profiled in another chapter in this volume (see Chapter 14), as well as by a series of publications (Putman 1986, 1995, 1996; Putman et al. 1987, 1989) and is therefore not described here in detail.

In the context of woodland dynamics, one of the more important pieces of research was that described by Putman et al. (1989). Two 5.6 ha fenced exclosures were established in Denny Lodge Inclosure in 1963, one of which was kept free of all large herbivores, and the other of which was subjected to herbivory by fallow deer at a density of 1 ha^{-1}. Vegetation in both plots was surveyed after intervals of 6, 14 and 22 years. In the grazed plot, tree regeneration was completely absent; in the ungrazed plot, rapid regeneration of a range of tree species (including both beech and oak) occurred within the first six years, with sapling densities reaching 7,115 ha^{-1} after 22 years. Differences in vegetation structure were also apparent, with much of the vegetation between 10 and 70 cm above ground being composed of bracken, while a range of understorey species were recorded in the ungrazed plot. The results of this experiment therefore provide a clear demonstration of the potential impact of herbivory on tree regeneration within woods.

(vi) Vera and colleagues

In 2000, the Dutch researcher Franciscus Vera published a highly influential book, based on his PhD thesis, which examined the potential role of vertebrate herbivory in the dynamics of woodlands in the lowlands of Central and Western Europe (Vera 2000). While not without criticism (Bradshaw et al. 2003, Rackham 2003, Mitchell 2005, Svenning 2002), the book has stimulated a great deal of debate about the role of herbivores in woodland ecology, and has contributed to a major shift in thinking regarding the role of grazing animals in conservation management of woodlands (Hodder et al. 2005, Kirby 2003, 2004; see also Olff et al. 1999 and Vera et al. 2006).

Vera (2000) presented what he described as 'the theory of the cyclical turnover of vegetations' (Figure 60). This is based on the idea that the original vegetation of the lowlands of Europe was a park-like landscape, in which successional processes are determined by large herbivorous mammals and birds (such as the jay) that act as seed dispersal agents. Specialised grass eaters, such as wild cattle and wild horses, produce grassland vegetation in which thorny shrubs become established, into which species of tree may become established. These are then protected from herbivory, and develop into groves of trees, which

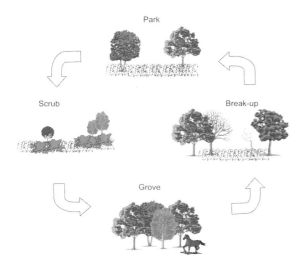

Park

Scrub

Break-up

Grove

Figure 60
Schematic diagram of Vera's cyclical theory of vegetation turnover. This consists of the three phases of Open Park, Scrub and Grove, to which a fourth has been added (following Kirby 2003), 'Break-up', representing the transition from woodland back to open habitats. Following Kirby (2003), after Vera (2000), the Park phase is a largely open landscape with a thin scatter of trees left from the previous grove; vegetation is mainly grassland or heath species. In the Scrub phase, spread of thorny shrubs excludes herbivores; young trees grow up with the shrubs and eventually overtop them. In the Grove phase, which is the tree-dominated phase of the cycle, a closed tree canopy shades out the shrubs, and herbivores return, preventing regeneration. In the Break-up phase, the canopy opens out as trees die; vegetation shifts from woodland to grassland species.

advance into the grassland as the thorny shrubs advance. Regeneration of trees within the grove is prevented because of shade, and because of herbivory, as animals are able to enter the grove as it matures. As a result, the forest grove eventually degenerates into grassland, and the cycle begins again (Figure 60).

Vera (2000) considered the New Forest in detail, examining the evidence provided by the studies listed above with reference to the 'cyclical theory'. Key statements include:

- In woodland, there is little or no regeneration of trees, because of the high densities of herbivores.
- Interpretation of data presented by Flower (1980a) and Putman (1986) showed that the regeneration of trees in the New Forest occurred with densities of animals (1.4–1.5 feeding units ha⁻¹) at which Peterken and Tubbs (1965) considered regeneration was not possible.
- Both Peterken and Tubbs (1965) and Flower (1980a) failed to consider regeneration on the margins of woods in thorny scrub, instead focusing on regeneration in canopy gaps within woodlands.
- In the New Forest, 'woodlands have spread in concentric circles in an expanding ring of mainly young oak, which emerged from the advancing blackthorn scrub…', and 'throughout the New

Forest this has resulted in a concentric expansion of forests in the form of successive generations of trees'.
- The regeneration of trees in thorny scrub explains how regeneration can take place, outside woodlands, even with very high densities of herbivores.

Although Vera's cyclical theory appears plausible, the account is based largely on a critical evaluation of the scientific literature, rather than on a substantive body of original data. Statements such as the spread of woodland in 'concentric circles' are not supported by any quantitative evidence presented either by Vera (2000) or any of the references he cites in support of this contention, or by the analyses of historical maps presented by Small and Haggett (1972), although concentric expansion of holly is mentioned by Peterken (1966). The question remains, therefore, whether Vera's theory accurately depicts woodland dynamics in the New Forest.

Some efforts have subsequently been made to test Vera's theory. For example, Bakker *et al.* (2004) examined the role of thorny shrubs in protecting palatable tree species across four floodplain woodlands in north-west Europe, including a site near to the Beaulieu River in the New Forest. Exclosure experiments indicated that oak grew best in grassland exclosures and on the edge of thorny shrub thickets. Field observations indicated that oak was found to be able to regenerate in the presence of large herbivores through spatial association with blackthorn. However, spatial expansion of both blackthorn and oak coincided with periods of low rabbit abundance and not with livestock density.

(vii) Mountford and colleagues

For his doctoral research, Ed Mountford examined the long-term dynamics of six lowland British woodlands, based on resurveys of permanent sample plots (Mountford 2004). One of these sites was Denny Wood in the New Forest, the results of which were presented in two publications (Mountford and Peterken 2003, Mountford *et al.* 1999). The research involved resurveys of two transects 20 m wide, established by ecologists at Southampton University in the 1950s, one of which was located within Denny Inclosure and the other in the unenclosed part of Denny Wood. The two publications present an exceptionally detailed account of the changes that have occurred in the woodland in recent decades.

Results from the unenclosed transect indicate that (Mountford and Peterken 2003):
- Woodland structure has changed markedly over the past 40 years. In 1959 the transect comprised closed beech-oak forest with abundant holly understorey. Forty years later, this had become an open oak-beech parkland with little understorey.
- Species-rich lawns and stands of bracken had spread extensively, and large herbivores had become far more numerous.
- Survival of oak was higher than that of beech, which suffered particularly from drought in 1976 and debarking by grey squirrels.

- Holly was reduced mainly by browsing and debarking by ponies and deer.
- A total of 21 established seedlings (≥40 cm height and <1.3 m) of seven tree species were recorded in 1999, mostly in clumps of protective bramble or under bracken. However, recruitment of tree species has been very limited since the 1950s.

On the enclosed transect, results indicate that (Mountford et al. 1999, Mountford and Peterken 2003):
- The stand was denser than the unenclosed transect in 1959, but also comprised closed beech–oak–holly forest at that time.
- Substantial canopy gaps were created during the past forty years, primarily as a result of mortality of large oak and beech trees as a result of the 1976 drought, coupled with the effect of subsequent storms.
- Canopy gaps tended to be colonised by species-poor grassland and stands of bracken; areas of closed high forest were associated with little ground vegetation.
- Holly was much reduced, principally owing to browsing and debarking by deer and ponies. Browsing almost completely prevented tree regeneration.

Based on these results, Mountford and Peterken (2003) concluded that tree regeneration has largely been prevented in Denny Wood in recent decades as a result of heavy browsing, largely by ponies. This is despite the presence of possible protective features such as spiny shrubs, fallen trees and bracken. Coupled with the reduction in the understorey, the accelerating break-up and mortality of old-growth stands, and damage by grey squirrels, Denny Wood – and potentially the other wood pastures of the New Forest – are currently at a vulnerable point in their history, according to these authors.

The results provide some insight into Vera's hypothesis. Most importantly, populations of herbivores have largely prevented tree regeneration since 1964, despite a substantial increase in the area of canopy gaps. The recruitment that has occurred has largely been restricted to sites protected from browsing. The understorey itself, composed of holly and bramble, which could potentially protect oak and beech saplings, has itself been almost destroyed by heavy browsing. The results therefore contradict those of Morgan (1987a,b), who suggested that regeneration can occur widely within woods can because of the presence of protective cover (Mountford et al. 1999). According to the Vera hypothesis, such regeneration should occur primarily outside woodlands; canopy dieback of woodland groves should lead to their replacement by grassland (Vera 2000). In this respect, therefore, the results obtained for Denny Wood support Vera's cyclic regeneration model.

The study by Mountford and colleagues is of exceptional importance. As the most detailed example of long-term monitoring of permanent plots in the New Forest, it provides a unique insight into the long-term changes that have been occurring in the woodlands of the area. The level of detail and rigour of the investigation make it a model of its kind, and the results highlight the enormous value of this kind of long-term

investigation. Despite this, as the authors would readily admit, the study is limited in scope, to just two plots within a single woodland. Questions remain, therefore, whether the results obtained are representative of the New Forest A&O woodlands as a whole.

(viii) Other work
Peterken et al. (1996) provided a review of the distribution, composition and structure of the A&O woodlands, based on a review of existing data and a resurvey of the woodlands. This involved revisiting most A&O woodlands, with the primary aim of refining the survey undertaken by Flower and Tubbs (1982). The report is appended by a series of digitised maps, largely based on the hand-drawn maps produced by Flower and Tubbs (1982), but updated in the light of the survey data. The report provides a valuable and detailed overview of the A&O woods, but provides only limited quantitative information on the structure and composition of the woodlands. However the report presents the important finding that overall, some 5% of the A&O woodlands show signs of canopy collapse, similar to that recorded for Denny Wood by Mountford et al. (1999).

Peterken et al. (1996, Annex 8) list a number of long-term ecological research studies undertaken in New Forest woodlands, including the Denny Wood transects resurveyed by Mountford (see above). Five additional transects were recorded during the project described by Peterken et al. (1996), three in Woodfidley Beeches (Denny Old Inclosure), and one in each of Denny Wood (northern A&O regeneration plot), and Stubbs Wood. These were accurately mapped but not permanently marked. Data from the transects were not presented in the report, although results from Woodfidley were briefly described, indicating that complete exclusion of stock and deer had led to the development of abundant beech regeneration, but very little oak regeneration was observed on this site. However, frequent regeneration of oak was observed in the Denny Wood regeneration plot (such fenced plots having been established from time to time in various woods, to encourage regeneration).

Peterken et al. (1996) also mention research by Prof. Henk Koop of the Instituut voor Bos- en Natuuronderzoek, Wageningen, Netherlands, which involved the creation of ten transects in unenclosed woodlands. These were mapped in detail in the early 1980s as part of a European-wide study of forest dynamics, and resurveyed several times thereafter. Some of the results obtained are presented by Drenth and Oosterbaan (1984), Koop (1989) and Siebel and Bijlsma (1998). None of these studies reported significant regeneration (Mountford et al. 1999). The main results reported by Koop (1989) indicate that the central parts of A&O woods that were included in the survey, including Denny Wood, Mark Ash Wood, Bratley Wood and Berry Wood, were characterised by a relatively homogeneous structure of beech with stem diameters of around 100 cm. These were interpreted as belonging to the A generation of Peterken and Tubbs (1965) (i.e. mid-17th century in origin). Koop (1989) also refers to the spread of bracken following the collapse of old beech-dominated stands, which he suggests may completely limit tree regeneration. However, it is possible that bracken could act as a protective nurse for tree species such as oak; whether this occurs in the New Forest has not yet been rigorously determined. Tubbs (2001, p. 355) notes that the ecological role of bracken is poorly understood.

Pyatt *et al.* (2003) described additional work undertaken in the New Forest Inclosures, focusing on application of the Ecological Site Classification. This is a method developed by Forestry Commission researchers to characterise the ecological characteristics of forested sites, based on an assessment of soil conditions, climate and ground vegetation. The approach is designed to assist in choice of species for timber production, and as a guide to silvicultural operations, including those in native woodland (Pyatt *et al.* 2003). Surveys of plant communities were carried out in 153 2 m × 2 m quadrats, and used in combination with preexisting soil survey data to define and map the different site types present. Key findings include the fact that the climatic factor most limiting tree growth in the New Forest is summer moisture supply; soil limitations include generally low fertility and a predominance of shallow winter water tables. The results are of value for understanding the association between different plant communities and edaphic variables, but as the analyses are restricted to the Inclosures, the report is of limited value for understanding New Forest woodlands as a whole.

Results of a recent survey

In order to assess the current structure, composition and condition of New Forest woodlands, a new survey was undertaken during 2005–2007 by the current authors. Unlike previous surveys, both Inclosures and A&O woodlands were included in the sample, to provide an overview of New Forest woodlands as a whole. The sampling approach adopted the woodland units defined by Natural England (formerly English Nature), which are used as a basis for monitoring the condition of woodlands designated as SSSIs (see Chapter 12). The habitat category is referred to by Natural England as 'Broadleaved, mixed and yew woodland – lowland', and covers all wooded areas in the New Forest including A&O woodlands, exotic and native plantations, within open forest and enclosed forest areas. In some parts of the New Forest, these units follow the compartment boundaries used by the Forestry Commission in their management plans, but in others, such as the Open Forest, unit boundaries are defined by the shape of the woodland derived from habitat maps (Wright and Westerhoff 2001). The precise boundaries of these units continue to be modified; the survey employed unit boundaries as they were defined in 2005.

A total of 173 woodland units were sampled (Figure 61), representing all units defined as this habitat type, with the exception of those that were too small to accommodate a survey plot, or were located on private land or were otherwise inaccessible. In each

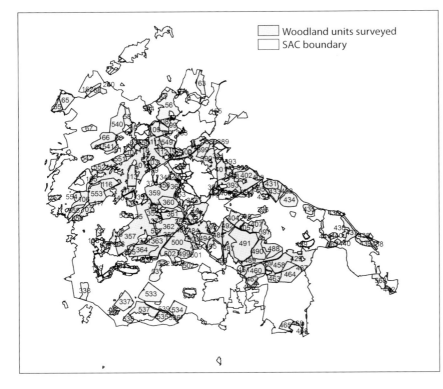

Figure 61
Map of woodland units (see text for definition) included in the woodland survey undertaken during 2005–2007. The numbers of the units refer to those employed by Natural England for monitoring the condition of SSSI units, from which the boundaries are also derived.

Legend: Woodland units surveyed / SAC boundary

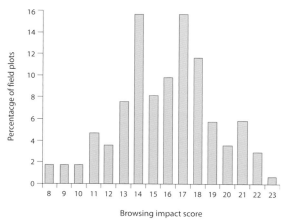

classified as Moderate browsing, 76.3% as Heavy, and 18.6% as Very Heavy, following the definitions presented by Reimoser *et al.* (1999).

Despite this, saplings of 41 tree species were encountered in the survey, 18 of which (44%) were non-native. Overall mean sapling density was 7.8 ha⁻¹. However, regeneration was patchy, with zero saplings recorded in 11% of sample plots. The sapling size-class was dominated by holly and hawthorn; oak saplings were relatively scarce, at a mean density of 2.7 ha⁻¹, and recorded in only 16% of plots. Corresponding figures for beech were 17.6 ha⁻¹ and 25.7%. These results indicate that tree regeneration within New Forest woodlands is widespread, although patchy and often at low density. It should be noted that introduced species feature prominently in the sapling flora; for example, both Douglas fir and pine were among the ten most abundant species as saplings (Figure 63).

Figure 62
Results of the survey of browsing impacts, undertaken throughout New Forest woodlands (see text for details). The browsing impact score is based on the variables presented by Reimoser et al. (1999). Scores of < 10 presented here would classify as Moderate browsing pressure, 11–18 as Heavy, and ≥ 19 as Very Heavy, according to the definitions presented by Reimoser *et al.* (1999).

Current condition of New Forest woodlands

The monitoring of habitat condition of SSSIs currently carried out by Natural England (see Chapter 12) employs an approach called Common Standards Monitoring (CSM), developed by the JNCC (JNCC 2004). This involves a questionnaire survey of a range of indicators, which is completed by performing a subjective visual assessment during structured walks. The latest results of this process (see http://www.english-nature.org.uk/Special/sssi/, accessed August 2008) indicate that 113 (32% of the units area) of the New Forest woodland units are currently in favourable condition, 75 (5%) are classified as unfavourable declining, 20 (1%) as unfavourable no change, and 366 (62%) as unfavourable recovering. The reasons for unfavourable condition are not

unit, a 50 m × 50 m plot was located randomly, and surveyed for woodland structure and composition (Table 30). In addition, a series of ten variables were assessed as indicators of browsing impact, based on Reimoser *et al.* (1999). Data from the survey of browsing impact indicated that browsing pressure does vary between woodlands; for example, a browse line was evident on 62% of plots surveyed. Overall, however, almost all of the New Forest woodlands are being browsed heavily, or very heavily (Figure 62): 5.1% of field plots (and therefore woodland units) were

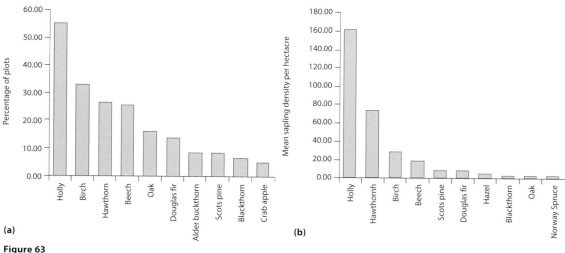

(a)

(b)

Figure 63
Regeneration of tree species in New Forest woodlands, based on a survey undertaken in 2005–2007. The data presented relate to saplings (i.e. trees = 1.5 m height and <10 cm dbh), assessed in randomly located 50 x 50 m plots. (a) percentage of plots in which saplings of different tree species were present, the ten most abundant species being illustrated; (b) mean sapling densities for the 10 species occurring at highest densities.

systematically reported in this assessment, but widely cited factors include lack of dead wood, presence of exotic species (principally conifers), presence of *Rhododendron*, poor development of ground flora, extensive areas of bare ground, lack of tree regeneration and overgrazing. Many of these problems are currently being addressed by management interventions, such as the widespread removal of conifers and the hydrological restoration undertaken in the LIFE projects (see Chapters 12 and 17). The introduction of such management interventions accounts for why such a high proportion of woodland units are currently considered to be unfavourable recovering rather than unfavourable.

Although monitoring of habitat condition is clearly an essential source of information to guide management action, the effectiveness of the CSM approach has not been widely evaluated. Concerns stem from the fact that the assessment is subjective and therefore potentially unreliable (Gaston *et al.* 2006). Another key issue relates to which indicators should be used to assess condition, referred to in the context of Natura 2000 sites (such as the New Forest Special Area of Conservation, or SAC) as 'favourable conservation status (FCS)'. The selection and testing of FCS indicators has previously received very little attention from researchers, and limited information is available regarding how FCS should be assessed. Potentially, indicators of forest biodiversity that have been developed to support assessment of sustainable forest management (SFM) (e.g. see Lindenmayer *et al.* 2000, Angelstam and Dönz-Breuss 2004, Newton 2007) could be of value in this context.

To examine the use of such indicators in the New Forest, Cantarello and Newton (2008) selected a suite of indicators on the basis of a literature review, relating to forest structure and composition, dead wood volume,

tree regeneration and ground flora composition. Thirty units used by Natural England for monitoring condition were randomly selected for survey. Two different methods, namely (i) sample plots and (ii) a point-transect method, were used to assess the conservation status of the units by using 17 indicators in the sample plots and 6 in the point-transect method (Table 31). Results were compared with a third approach, namely a visual assessment method based on CSM, as employed in the formal monitoring undertaken in the New Forest to assess FCS. Results suggested that mean values of indicators did not differ between the plot and the point-transect based methods ($P> 0.05$; paired *t*-test and Wilcoxon signed rank test). However, values obtained from these methods were poorly correlated with those obtained from the subjective CSM approach (Cantarello and Newton 2008). In addition, a significant association was recorded between sampling method and assessment of condition ($P<0.001$, correlation test). These results raise doubts about the reliability of the CSM approach, which is currently used for assessing woodland condition in the New Forest.

Results from this random sample of 30 units can also be compared with the results of the intensive survey of Denny Wood undertaken by Mountford *et al.* (1999). This provides some insight into how representative Denny Wood is of New Forest woodlands in general. Results indicate that in terms of stem density (number of trees), tree species diversity (Shannon-Wiener index for native trees) and % big trees (>80 cm dbh), values from Denny Wood are similar to those obtained from the larger sample. However, indicators such as mean sapling density, tree basal area and stem diameter were substantially higher for the sample of 30 woodlands than for Denny Wood (Table 31). This raises the question of what constitutes a reasonable target or reference value for woodland condition. Remarkably

Table 31
Characteristics of 30 randomly selected New Forest woodlands, surveyed by using sample plot and point-transect methods. For comparison, values provided by Mountford *et al.* (1999) for the enclosed transect at Denny Wood are also presented. Adapted from Cantarello and Newton (2008).

	Plot			Point-transect			Denny Wood
	$\bar{x}$	x_{min}	x_{max}	$\bar{x}$	x_{min}	x_{max}	
Number of trees (no. ha⁻¹)	256	72.0	536	251	67	602	222
Shannon–Wiener index for native trees	0.90	0.00	1.58	0.98	0.00	1.66	0.87
Basal area (m² ha⁻¹)	33.8	13.5	49.1	31.2	10.3	76.3	23
Mean diameter of trees (cm)	43.4	25.9	80.5	43.5	27.3	75.1	32
% of big trees (i.e. dbh >80 cm)	7.25	0.00	47.4	7.3	0.00	36.2	7
Number of total saplings (no. ha⁻¹)	356	0.00	1924	–	–	–	91
Number of saplings of native tree species (no. ha⁻¹)	351	0.00	1924	–	–	–	91
Volume of downed dead wood (m³ ha⁻¹)	12.0	0.00	37.6	–	–	–	26
Volume of snags (m³ ha⁻¹)	5.40	0.00	25.0	–	–	–	16
Total number of tree seedlings (no. ha⁻¹)	21,397	100	295,300	–	–	–	63,219
Number of native seedlings (ha⁻¹)	21,143	100	295,300	–	–	–	63,219
Shannon–Wiener index for native seedlings	0.53	0.00	1.27	–	–	–	0.89
Number of ground vegetation species	4.00	0.00	13.0	–	–	–	33

Abbreviations: $\bar{x}$ = mean value, x_{min} = minimum value, x_{max} = maximum value.
For further details, see Cantarello and Newton (2008).

Table 32
Measurements of dead wood length and volume for selected New Forest woodlands. Adapted from Kirby *et al.* (1998). (SE refers to standard error of volume measurements.)

Woodland name	Site details	Length m/ha	Volume m³/ha	SE volume
Red Shoot	Largely mature oak–holly wood pasture	3,078	62	36
Tantany	Old beech, oak, holly, with occasional blowdowns	4,649	65	20
Stubbs	Old beech, oak–holly wood pasture	3,204	35	8
Frame	Old beech, oak–holly wood pasture	4,335	76	20
Mark Ash	Old beech, oak–holly wood pasture	2,576	58	24
Denny	Open old beech–oak pasture woodland. Close to car park	816	14	7
Lyndhurst	Oak, beech, holly high forest, largely closed canopy	816	13	4
Wood Crates	Patches of old oak, beech interspersed with young birch	1,068	9	4

little research has been undertaken on this issue. There is an urgent need to define such reference values for European forests, as described by Keddy and Drummond (1996) for North America. This issue is considered further below, in relation to dead wood volume.

Dead wood

Volume of dead wood (also referred to as Coarse Woody Debris) is widely recognised as an important indicator of woodland condition, reflecting its importance as habitat for organisms such as insects and other invertebrates, fungi, lichens and bryophytes. A number of surveys of dead wood in New Forest woodlands have been carried out, including visual assessments made as part of the condition monitoring of SSSI units, performed by Natural England (see above). Overall, lack of dead wood was cited for seven woodlands as a reason for failing to meet favourable condition status in the latest assessment of SSSI units (http://www.english-nature.org.uk/Special/sssi/; accessed October 2008).

Kirby *et al.* (1998) presented an overview of dead wood estimates for a range of woodlands (87 stands on

Plate 5
Denny Wood, in the permanent transect surveyed by Mountford *et al.* (1999) (see text). This stand of beech has undergone canopy collapse, resulting in conversion to grassland, perhaps illustrating part of the cyclical dynamics described by Vera (2000) (see text).

Plate 6
Cathedral Beeches in Denny Wood, another stand of beech that has undergone canopy collapse (see text), and also an important habitat for lichens.

Table 33
Sites of primary importance for dead wood, according to the survey by Wilson (1986). The results are based on a survey of 56 A&O (unenclosed) woodlands.

Name of woodland	Species	E. White's assessment [1]
Red Shoot Wood	Oak	Good
Mark Ash	Beech	Poor/good
Burley Old Inclosure	Oak, beech	–
Little Huntley Bank	Beech	Poor
Great Huntley Bank	Beech	Good
Camel Green	Beech, oak	Good
Wood Crates	Beech	Intermediate
The Knowles	Beech	Intermediate
Spaniard's Hole	Beech, oak	Intermediate
Stubbs Wood	Oak	Good/Intermediate
Eyeworth Wood	Beech, oak	Intermediate
Great Wood	Oak, beech	Intermediate
Bramshaw Wood	Oak	Good
South Ocknell Wood	Oak, ash	–
Stubby Hat	Beech	Good

1 Refers to subjective visual assessment by White 1975

63 sites) throughout Britain. Events such as the drought of 1976 and the great storm of 1987 were found to have had a major impact on the amount of fallen dead wood in many areas. On the basis of their survey results, these authors proposed provisional benchmarks for the amount of dead wood in British broadleaved forests, with values of <20 m³ ha⁻¹ considered as low, 20–40 m³ ha⁻¹ as medium, and   >40 m³ ha⁻¹ as high. Old-growth forests in eastern North America and in continental Europe typically have values in the range 50–150 m³ ha⁻¹ (Kirby *et al.* 1998). Eight stands were assessed in the New Forest (Table 32), indicating dead wood volume values in the range 9–76 m³ ha⁻¹. On the basis of the benchmarks defined by Kirby *et al.* (1998), three of these woodlands would classify as low, one as medium and four as high in terms of the volume of dead wood present. The sites assessed by Cantarello and Newton (2008), which can be considered as a random (and therefore arguably representative) sample of New Forest woodlands, indicated that on average, dead wood volumes in New Forest woodlands are relatively low. A mean value of 12.0 ± 9.99 m³ ha⁻¹ was reported from the 30 randomly selected woodlands units that they surveyed in detail, with values ranging from 0–37.6 m³ ha⁻¹ (Table 31).

The most extensive dead wood survey in the New Forest is probably that undertaken by Wilson (1986), who identified 15 woods as of particular importance for dead wood (Table 33). Individual woodlands were thoroughly surveyed and each dead wood feature was noted (including fallen trees, standing dead trees, stumps, dead limbs, etc.), to provide total numbers of each type of feature. A total of 56 A&O woodlands were included in the survey. This was preceded by an earlier survey of 43 unenclosed woodlands by White (1975). Unfortunately, because no estimates of dead wood volume were provided by either Wilson (1986) or White (1975), it is difficult to compare these data with those obtained by more recent surveys. The two surveys also employed different survey methods, further hindering comparative analysis. However, Wilson (1986) concluded that there had been only local changes in the dead wood habitat in the Forest over the previous decade. Areas that had apparently deteriorated badly included Denny Wood, whereas in others (such as Wood Crates) the amount of dead wood had increased since the 1976 drought. Wilson (1986) noted that removal of dead wood from New Forest woodlands had 'drastically escalated… in   recent years', such that many woods were 'completely bare of fallen wood'. Areas particularly badly affected included areas to the north of Lyndhurst, including Brockis Hill, Hazel Hill, Shave Wood and Denny Wood. This was attributed to the relatively easy vehicular access to these woods, enabling collection of fuelwood.

Mountford and Peterken (2003) recorded volumes of fallen dead wood in Denny Wood of 26 and 201 m³ ha⁻¹ in the unenclosed and enclosed transects respectively. The latter value is exceptionally high (see above), and reflects the canopy collapse that has occurred there as a result of the 1976 drought and subsequent storms.

Conclusions and management implications

Despite their undoubted conservation importance, the New Forest woodlands have attracted surprisingly little attention from ecological researchers. As a result, the current understanding of their dynamics is still limited. As documented by Tubbs (2001), the New Forest woodlands have been subjected to numerous management interventions over the past 150 years, many of which with hindsight appear to have been inappropriate or misjudged. The conservation value of the woods must have declined significantly over this period, as their habitat condition has deteriorated, but such trends are difficult to identify with precision because of the lack of systematic, long-term monitoring. As highlighted by Tubbs (2001), it is the loss of some old-growth stands of trees that is likely to have been most damaging in this context. Inappropriate interventions have resulted from a lack of appreciation of particular woodland characteristics, such as the habitat value of large, old trees, as well as a lack of understanding about woodland dynamics. This is exemplified by the oft-cited concerns about the perceived lack of regeneration in many woodlands. Yet it is only relatively recently that regeneration has been systematically and quantitatively surveyed throughout the New Forest woodlands.

The debate surrounding the impact of large herbivores on woodland regeneration is symptomatic of our current lack of understanding. Vera's model has undoubtedly stimulated much interest in the role of herbivory in woodland ecology, but it still awaits rigorous testing. The only way of achieving this would be through the long-term monitoring of appropriate permanent sample plots, to test (for example) whether seedlings apparently protected by spiny shrubs successfully survive into adulthood. The detailed results obtained by Mountford and colleagues (Mountford and Peterken 2003, Mountford et al. 1999) illustrate the value of this kind of investigation. However, the situation in Denny Wood as documented by these authors may not be typical of the New Forest A&O woodlands as a whole. At this location, beech has undergone canopy collapse as a result of the effects of drought and storm damage. The phenomenon of canopy collapse itself deserves greater research attention; while apparently widespread in the New Forest (Peterken et al. 1996), the characteristics of those locations where it has occurred have not been analysed in detail. Is it possible, for example, that collapse of beech has occurred on sites that are marginal for this species, such as the waterlogged, gleyed soils of Denny Wood?

The conversion of old-growth beech stands to grassland, as recorded in Denny Wood, is an interesting phenomenon that provides some support for Vera's model. Does this occur on only particular site types, or under especially high browsing pressure?

Plate 7
Young stand of regenerating beech in Mark Ash Wood, apparently establishing without the protection of spiny shrubs as hypothesised by Vera (2000). Photo: Arthur Newton

The influence of soil type on woodland succession under conditions of high browsing pressure has not so far been investigated. Other issues not addressed by Vera (2000) relate to the rate at which the processes of woodland dynamics occur, and the fact that tree species differ in their regeneration ecology. It has been documented that species such as pine and birch, for example, can colonise heathland under intense herbivory without protection from spiny shrubs (Putman 1986).

Potential limitations of the Vera model are highlighted by the work of Morgan (1991), who suggested that the thorny shrub protection process can occur within woodlands and is not limited to the margins; other areas important for tree establishment within woodlands include fallen trees and dead wood accumulations (Morgan 1991). It is notable that the only two studies that have systematically and quantitatively examined regeneration in large numbers of New Forest woodlands, namely Morgan (1987a,b) and the 2005–2007 survey reported here, both suggest that tree regeneration occurs at low density but is widespread. This is despite the fact that browsing pressure is almost uniformly heavy or very heavy. This suggests that within woodlands, some young trees (at least of relatively shade-tolerant species such as beech) are successfully able to establish themselves, in contradiction to the Vera model. If this is true, then this also casts doubt on the close linkage between herbivore pressure and tree regeneration proposed by Peterken and Tubbs (1965).

Whether Vera's model is correct or not has major implications for how the New Forest should be managed. This is explicitly recognised in the New Forest SAC management plan, which states (Wright and Westerhoff 2001):

'This theory based on vegetation dynamics at the ecosystem scale is hugely appealing and is highly significant for ecologists and foresters alike. It is **highly consistent** with what happens in the New Forest' (our emphasis).

Such a statement may be considered premature, given that the theory has not been adequately tested. The problem is exemplified by the current management practice of clearing scrub at woodland margins. If the Vera model is correct, it is precisely in such scrub that tree regeneration is expected to occur. Maintenance of scrub may therefore be critical to the long-term dynamics of woodland within the New Forest, particularly with respect to oak. Scrub clearance is undertaken to provide increased grazing opportunities for livestock, but as noted by Tubbs (2001), as the impacts of this management intervention are not systematically monitored, it is unclear whether it actually provides the benefits that are intended. This again highlights the importance of adequate monitoring to support management.

Uncertainty about the ecological dynamics of the New Forest woodlands leads to uncertainty about how their condition should be monitored. The lack of correspondence recorded between the subjective (CSM) approach currently used as a basis for condition monitoring, and data derived from more rigorous, quantitative methods (Cantarello and Newton 2008), raises further doubts about the adequacy of current monitoring approaches. As a result, managers arguably do not have access to adequate information to ascertain whether their current management interventions are being effective. This can only be resolved by investment in an adequate and robust monitoring system, supported by a programme of appropriate research.

A critical evaluation of current management approaches is beyond the scope of this chapter. Spencer (2002) provides a valuable overview of current approaches, which are further detailed in current management plans (Wright and Westerhoff 2001, Forestry Commission 2007). Examples of recent management interventions include restoration of hydrological features, clearance of exotic species such as *Rhododendron* and conifers, reintroduction of pollarding and grazing to some woodlands, pollarding of holly to improve habitat quality for rare lichens and to provide winter fodder for ponies, and restoration of bog woodland (Spencer 2002). With respect to dead wood management, the most recent management plan (Forestry Commission 2007) refers to the recent introduction of stricter controls on collection of firewood, while noting the need to maintain access along tracks within the A&O woodlands. Dead wood can be removed from such areas according to a strict set of criteria, but aside from lawns or tracks no dead wood can now be removed or sold for firewood from within A&O woodland unless it is part of an agreed management programme and in a suitable area for removal (Forestry Commission 2007). Such initiatives should undoubtedly have a positive impact on the condition of New Forest woodlands and their associated biodiversity in years to come. However, a number of problems still require attention; for example, illicit removal of dead wood was reported from some woodlands in the latest SSSI condition assessment (see earlier).

Peterken *et al.* (1996) note that the New Forest A&O woodlands occur in a complex mosaic, which 'must be managed as a unified whole'. We propose that this unified approach to management should be extended to include the Inclosure woodlands as well, given the need to manage woodlands and their associated biodiversity at the landscape scale (Lindenmayer and Franklin 2002). It is striking that the field survey described here is apparently the first systematic, quantitative ecological assessment of both A&O and Inclosure woodlands ever to have been undertaken (Table 30). The recently collected field survey data are currently being used to parameterise a spatially explicit model of woodland dynamics (LANDIS II), which can be used to explore the potential impacts of different forms of disturbance, including herbivory, on woodland structure and composition across the entire New Forest. Using this approach, future research work will examine the dynamics of woodlands at the landscape scale, with the aim of identifying the potential impacts of management interventions and other forms of environmental change. Ultimately, use of such approaches might also enable the historical development of the New Forest to be examined, following the suggestion made by Bradshaw *et al.* (2003). Our hope is that this will help reduce the current uncertainty regarding the ecological dynamics of New Forest woodlands, and help support their improved management in future.

Acknowledgements

Thanks to Andrew Brown, who assisted with the field survey, and to Richard Reeves (museum, Lyndhurst), Ed Mountford (JNCC), Jonathan Spencer, Berry Stone and Simon Weymouth (Forestry Commission) for assistance with accessing information about previous surveys of the New Forest woodlands.

References

Angelstam, P. and Dönz-Breuss, M. (2004). Measuring forest biodiversity at the stand scale – an evaluation of indicators in European forest history gradients. In Angelstam, P., Dönz-Breuss, M. and Roberge, J.-M. (eds.) Targets and tools for the maintenance of forest biodiversity. *Ecological Bulletin*, 51, 305–332.

Bakker, E. S., Olff, H., Vandenberghe, C., De Maeyer, K., Smit, R., Gleichman, J. M. and Vera, F. W. M. (2004). Ecological anachronisms in the recruitment of temperate light-demanding tree species in wooded pastures. *Journal of Applied Ecology*, 41, 571–582.

Bradshaw, R. H. W, Hannon, G. W. and Lister, A. M. (2003). A long-term perspective on ungulate-vegetation interactions. *Forest Ecology and Management*, 181, 267–280.

Cantarello, E. and Newton, A. C. (2008). Identifying cost-effective indicators to assess the conservation status of forested habitats in Natura 2000 sites. *Forest Ecology and Management*, 256, 815–826.

Drenth, W. and Oosterbaan, M. (1984). *Bossen en begrazing. Een onderzoek naar de invloed van begrazing op de bosstructuur en bosontwikkeling in het New Forest.* Rijkinstituut voor Natuurbeheer, Leersum, Netherlands.

Flower, N. (1977). *An historical and ecological study of inclosed and uninclosed woods in the New Forest, Hampshire.* PhD thesis, University of London.

Flower, N. (1980a). The management history and structure of unenclosed woodlands in the New Forest, Hampshire. *Journal of Biogeography*, 7, 311–328.

Flower, N. (1980b). Early coppice sites in the New Forest, Hampshire. *Forestry*, 43, 187–194.

Flower, N. (1983). The Ancient and Ornamental woods of the New Forest. A brief history of their origins, and details of the oldest remaining trees. *Hampshire*, 23, 55–57.

Flower, N. and Tubbs, C. R. (1982). *The New Forest, Hampshire: Management proposals for the unenclosed woodlands and woodlands of special importance in the Statutory Inclosures.* Nature Conservancy Council, Lyndhurst, Hampshire.

Forestry Commission (2007). *Management Plan. Part B: The Crown Lands.* Draft, November 2007. http://www.forestry.gov.uk/newforest

Gaston, K. J., Charman, K., Jackson, S. F., Armsworth, P. R., Bonn, A., Briers, R. A., Callaghan, C. S. Q., Catchpole, R., Hopkins, J., Kunin, W. E., Latham, J., Opdam, P., Stoneman, R., Stroud, D. A. and Tratt, R. (2006). The ecological effectiveness of protected areas: The United Kingdom. *Biological Conservation*, 132, 76–87.

Goldberg, E., Kirby, K., Hall, J. and Latham, J. (2007). The ancient woodland concept as a practical conservation tool in Great Britain. *Journal for Nature Conservation*, 15, 109–119.

Goriup, P. (Ed.) (1999). *The New Forest woodlands. A management history.* Pisces Publications for the Forestry Commission, Newbury, Berkshire.

Hodder, K. H., Bullock, J. M., Buckland, P. C. and Kirby, K. J. (2005). *Large herbivores in the wildwood and modern naturalistic grazing systems.* English Nature Research Reports no. 648. English Nature, Peterborough, UK.

JNCC (2004). *Common Standard Monitoring guidance for woodland habitats.* Joint Nature Conservation Committee, Peterborough, UK.

Keddy, P. A. and Drummond, C. G. (1996). Ecological properties for the evaluation, management, and restoration of temperate deciduous forest ecosystems. *Ecological Applications*, 6, 748–762.

Kirby, K. J. (2003). *What might a British forest-landscape driven by large herbivores look like?* English Nature Research Reports, No. 530, English Nature, Peterborough, UK.

Kirby, K. J. (2004). A model of a natural wooded landscape in Britain as influenced by large herbivore activity. *Forestry*, 77(5), 406–420.

Kirby, K. J., Reid, C. M., Thomas, R. C. and Goldsmith, F. B. (1998). Preliminary estimates of fallen dead wood and standing dead trees in managed and unmanaged forests in Britain. *Journal of Applied Ecology*, 35(1), 148–155.

Koop, H. (1989). *Forest dynamics. Silvi-Star: a comprehensive monitoring system.* Springer Verlag, Berlin.

Lindenmayer, D. B. and Franklin, J. F. (2002). *Conserving forest biodiversity. A comprehensive multiscaled approach.* Island Press, Washington, D.C.

Lindenmayer, D. B., Margules, C. R. and Botkin, D. B. (2000). Indicators of biodiversity for ecologically sustainable forest management. *Conservation Biology*, 14, 941–950.

Mitchell, F. J. G. (2005). How open were European primeval forests? Hypothesis testing using palaeoecological data. *Journal of Ecology*, 93, 168–177.

Morgan, R. K. (1977). *The influence of anthropogenic activities on the regeneration of the open woodlands of the New Forest, Hants.* PhD thesis, University of Birmingham.

Morgan, R. K. (1987a). Composition, structure and regeneration characteristics of the open woodlands of the New Forest, Hampshire. *Journal of Biogeography*, 14, 423–438.

Morgan, R. K. (1987b). An evaluation of the impact of anthropogenic pressures on woodland regeneration in the New Forest, Hampshire. *Journal of Biogeography*, 14, 439–450.

Morgan, R. K. (1991). The role of protective understorey in the regeneration system of a heavily browsed woodland. *Vegetatio*, 92, 119–132.

Mountford, E. P. (2004). *Long-term patterns of mortality and regeneration in near-natural woodland*. PhD thesis, Open University.

Mountford, E. P., Peterken, G. F., Edwards, P. . and Manners, J. G. (1999). Long-term change in growth, mortality and regeneration of trees in Denny Wood, an old-growth wood-pasture in the New Forest. *Perspectives in Plant Ecology, Evolution and Systematics*, 2(2), 223–272.

Mountford, E. P. and Peterken, G. F. (2003). Long term change and implications for the management of wood-pastures: experience over 40 years from Denny Wood, New Forest. *Forestry*, 76(1), 19–43.

Newton, A. C. (2007). *Forest ecology and conservation. A handbook of techniques*. Oxford University Press, Oxford.

Olff, H., Vera, F. W. M., Bokdam, J., Bakker, E. S., Gleichman, J. M., De Maeyer, K. and Smit, R. (1999). Shifting mosaics in grazed woodlands driven by the alternation of plant facilitation and competition. *Plant Biology*, 1, 127–137.

Peterken, G. F. (1966). Mortality of Holly (*Ilex aquifolium*) seedlings in relation to natural regeneration in the New Forest. *Journal of Ecology*, 54(1), 259–269.

Peterken, G. F. and Hughes, F. M. R. (1995). Restoration of floodplain forests in Britain. *Forestry*, 68, 187–202.

Peterken, G. F., Spencer, J. W. and Field, A. B. (1996). *Maintaining the Ancient and Ornamental woods of the New Forest*. Consultation document. Forestry Commission, Lyndhurst.

Peterken, G. F. and Tubbs, C. R. (1965) Woodland regeneration in the New Forest, Hampshire, Since 1650. *Journal of Applied Ecology*, 2(1), 159–170.

Putman, R. J. (1986). *Grazing in temperate ecosystems: large herbivores and the ecology of the New Forest*. Croom Helm, Beckenham.

Putman, R. J. (1995). *Competition and resource partitioning in temperate ungulate assemblies*. Chapman and Hall, London.

Putman, R. J. (1996). Ungulates in temperate forest ecosystems: perspectives and recommendations for future research. *Forest Ecology and Management*, 88, 205–214.

Putman, R. J., Edwards, P. J., Mann, J. C. E., How, R. C. and Hill, S. D. (1989). Vegetational and faunal changes in an area of heavily grazed woodland following relief of grazing. *Biological Conservation*, 47, 13–32.

Putman, R. J., Pratt, R. M., Ekins, J. R. and Edwards, P. J. (1987). Food and feeding behaviour of cattle and ponies in the New Forest, Hampshire. *Journal of Applied Ecology*, 24, 369–380.

Pyatt, G., Spencer, J., Hutchby, l., Davani, S., Fletcher, J. and Purdy, K. (2003). *Applying the Ecological Site Classification in the lowlands. A case study of the New Forest inclosures*. Forestry Commission Technical Paper 33. Forestry Commission, Edinburgh.

Rackham, O. (2003). *Ancient woodland*, rev. edn. Edward Arnold, London.

Reimoser, F., Armstrong, H. and Suchant, R. (1999). Measuring forest damage of ungulates: what should be considered. *Forest Ecology and Management*, 120, 47–58.

Siebel, H. N. and Bijlsma, R. J. (1998). *Patroonontwikkeling en begrazing in boslandschappen: New Forest en Fontainebleau als referenties*. INB-rapport 357. Instituut voor Bos- en Natuuronderzoek, Wageningen, Netherlands.

Small, D. and Haggett, G. M. (1972). A study of broadleaved woodland changes and natural regeneration of broadleaves in the Ancient and Ornamental woodlands from 1867–1963. In: *New Forest, Forestry Commission Management Plan 1972–1981*. Appendix D. Forestry Commission, Lyndhurst.

Spencer, J. W. (2002). Managing wood pasture landscapes in England; the New Forest and other more recent examples. In Redecker, B., Finck, P., Härdtle, W., Riecken, U. and Schröder, E. (eds.) *Pasture Landscapes and Nature Conservation*, pp. 123–136. Springer-Verlag, Berlin.

Svenning, J.-C. (2002). A review of natural vegetation openness in north-western Europe. *Biological Conservation*, 104, 133–148.

Tubbs, C. R. (1968). *The New Forest: an ecological history*. David & Charles, Newton Abbott, Devon.

Tubbs, C. R. (2001). *The New Forest. History, ecology and conservation*. New Forest Ninth Centenary Trust, Lyndhurst, Hampshire.

Vera, F. W. M. (2000). *Grazing ecology and forest history*. CABI Publishing, Wallingford, Oxon, UK.

Vera, F. W. M., Bakker, E. S. and Olff, H. (2006). Large herbivores: missing partners of western European light-demanding tree and shrub species? In Danell, K., Duncan, P., Bergström, R. and Pastor, J. (eds.) *Large herbivore ecology, ecosystem dynamics and conservation*, pp. 203–231. Cambridge University Press, Cambridge, UK.

White, E. (1975). *Survey of dead wood habitats in the unenclosed woodlands of the New Forest, Hampshire, August–September 1975*. Unpublished report. Nature Conservancy Council, Lyndhurst, Hampshire.

Wilson, P. (1986). *The dead wood resource of New Forest unenclosed woodlands*. Unpublished report. Nature Conservancy Council, Lyndhurst, Hampshire.

Wright, R. N. and Westerhoff, D. V. (2001). *New Forest SAC Management Plan*. English Nature, Lyndhurst, Hampshire.

14 The effects of grazing on the ecological structure and dynamics of the New Forest

Rory Putman

Introduction

While other chapters in this volume focus on particular habitats, species or species groups, and highlight their especial character, or value, one of the recurring themes in all such analyses is the unique character of the Forest; or, put another way, its essential oddness.

This, to me, is one of the main characteristics of the Forest (and one of its major interests to an ecologist): that the composition and dynamics of the woodlands are not quite like those of other, more 'normal' woodlands; the same might also be said of other habitats, such as heathlands and grasslands.

Aspects of this unique character include the following.

- The vegetation structure is unusual (both in terms of its physical three-dimensional structure and its age-structure).
- The age-structure of the trees in the ancient woodlands is bizarre. Instead of what might more normally be expected in a woodland, namely a continuous age-profile of trees of a whole range of ages, the Forest woodlands have a curiously discontinuous age-structure, consisting of trees that established in the 1750s, some from the late 1850s, some from the 1930s, and some more recently from the late 1980s (Peterken and Tubbs 1965, Putman 1986, 1996; see Chapter 13).
- Much of the Forest is nutrient-poor, but this is grossly distorted in most communities by nutrient dislocation and translocation (*sensu* Spedding 1971).
- Whether in woodlands or more open communities, there are virtually *no* small mammals at all, and a remarkable scarcity of resident predatory birds and mammals – in terms of both number of species and density. Roe deer, until very recently, were declining sharply in numbers – at a time when roe populations were expanding dramatically throughout the rest of southern England.

However, in adoption of the old philosophical device of taking an argument to extremes in order to expose weaknesses, or flaws of logic not apparent within more 'normal' boundaries, it is sometimes instructive to study such 'atypical' situations in more detail, for the insights they may offer into the underlying ecological processes. Therein lies a great deal of the Forest's interest (and charm!). For, in the case of the New Forest, its rather off-beat ecology is a reflection of some 950 years of heavy grazing by large mammalian herbivores – at levels that I believe are unique and probably higher than anywhere else in Europe.

In this chapter, therefore, I want to take a somewhat wider perspective than have many of the other contributions to this book, and explore what have been the effects of this unbroken history of heavy grazing pressure on the wider ecology of the New Forest. In a sense, this chapter uses the Forest as a case-study to exemplify the effects of grazing and browsing by large herbivores on communities more generally. This review draws heavily on work undertaken by myself and my colleagues and students from the University of Southampton through the late 1970s and the 1980s, and summarises work already published elsewhere (e.g. Pratt *et al.* 1986, Putman 1986, 1996; Putman *et al.* 1987, Langbein and Putman 1999).

The vegetation of the New Forest

Perhaps only the English, with their unwitting natural irony, could have retained the name New Forest for an area that is neither new (it is one of the oldest semi-natural areas of woodland in Great Britain, as well as one of the largest), nor what most would regard as a forest. It was 'New' only when it was first created as the latest in a series of 'Royal Forests' in the 11th century, and it is also a 'forest' only in the medieval sense of an area set aside as a Royal hunting preserve (and thus coming under Forest rather than Common law). In practice this 'New Forest' comprises a diverse mix of vegetational communities: only some 10,000 hectares (of a total administrative area at the current time of approximately 37,500 ha) are actually forested in the sense of covered with trees; the remaining area is a complex mixture of wet and dry heathlands, grasslands and bog (see Chapter 12), all patchworked together into an intimate mosaic.

Heavily leached and base-poor plateau gravels are widespread, particularly to the north, and support a *Calluna*-dominated dry-heath community. At lower altitudes, and where the plateau gravel has been eroded, more fertile clays and loams support mixed deciduous woodland. These are predominantly of beech and oak, with an understorey of holly; common bent *Agrostis capillaris* colonises the woodland floors in openings and glades. Many of the more fertile woodland sites have been enclosed over the past 100 years and now support commercial plantations, which are largely coniferous (see Chapter 13). Also common on these more fertile soils are a range of natural acid-grassland communities, dominated by the coarse bristle bent *Agrostis curtisii* and to a lesser extent by the purple moor-grass *Molinia caerulea*, usually also colonised to a greater or lesser extent by bracken *Pteridium aquilinum* and often by extensive brakes of gorse *Ulex europaeus*.

Where drainage is impeded on the lower slopes, domination of the heathland community by *Calluna* is reduced and the species diversity of the whole heathland increases. A clear gradation is observed from the dry-heath association through humid and wet heath, with increasing abundance of cross-leaved heath *Erica tetralix* and purple moor-grass and the appearance of true wetland plants such as bog asphodel *Narthecium ossifragum* and *Juncus* species. This progression frequently ends in the development of a bog community.

The valley bogs offer some of the richest communities in the New Forest in terms of plant diversity, and are one of the formations unique to this area. The species composition varies considerably in relation to the degree of eutrophication and several distinct communities may be recognised. Perhaps the most widespread in base-poor water is that dominated by tussocks of purple moor-grass with common cottongrass *Eriophorum angustifolium* and *Sphagnum* mosses abundant between the tussocks. In many heathland catchments, carr woodland communities develop in the valley bottoms where drainage waters have a definite axis of flow. These carrs are composed of willows, alder buckthorn *Frangula alnus*, alder *Alnus glutinosus* and other tree species, and have a diverse herb layer including the greater tussock-sedge *Carex paniculata*.

In areas that are well drained by one of the many small streams that dissect the Forest, the bogs are replaced, and the heathland progression terminates abruptly at the edge of alluvial strips bordering the streams. These alluvial deposits are covered by grassland, often dominated by velvet bent *Agrostis canina*, interrupted with patches of riverine woodland. These streamside lawns are particularly nutrient-rich because of regular annual flooding from the rivers they border, which carry base-rich compounds from north of the Forest area.

Very little of the New Forest vegetation can be considered as entirely natural, and most areas have at various times been subjected to management by people. Heathland communities, for example, were created originally by extensive livestock grazing, but nowadays are maintained in a programme of regular cutting or controlled burning, so that any extensive area of heath contains a patchwork of sub-communities from 0 to 15 years of maturity. Woodlands, even ancient deciduous blocks, are commonly of artificial structure and origin, planted initially by people for timber production, even if subsequently left more to processes of natural regeneration and decay. The 8,000-odd hectares of commercial coniferous forest established mostly in the past 100 years are clearly also of entirely artificial origin.

In addition there are other distinct community-types of anthropogenic origin. A number of areas of the natural acid grassland of the Forest were fenced during the Second World War, ploughed, fertilised and cropped for potatoes or oats. At the end of the War, these areas were reseeded with a commercial ley, and after the grassland had become established, the fences were removed to return these reseeded areas to the

Forest grazing. In the late 1960s and early 1970s a number of other attempts were made to improve the Forest grazing, by clearing bracken from other areas of acid grassland and liming them. These improved areas once again form a distinct and characteristic plant community.

The Forest's large herbivores and their management

At least 2,500 wild deer currently have access to the entire New Forest (Table 34).

Of the four main deer species present on the Forest today, red deer *Cervus elaphus* and sika deer *Cervus nippon* populations are of relatively recent origin and are essentially local in distribution. Populations of these species are restricted to relatively limited areas of the Forest, although both are currently expanding their range. Roe deer *Capreolus capreolus* are distributed more widely, but the distribution is patchy and they are everywhere uncommon. Fallow deer *Dama dama* are both widespread and abundant. Reeves muntjac *Muntiacus reevesi* are also more regularly reported, but numbers are thought to be low and as yet they have had no pronounced impact upon the Forest vegetation.

Fallow deer have long been the dominant deer species within the Forest; indeed William I's declaration of the area as a Royal Forest was chiefly to conserve hunting interests for this species. It is difficult to assess what numbers may have occurred on the Forest at that time. The earliest complete 'census' is that of 1670, when the Knights Regarder charged with administration of the Forest returned an estimate of 7,593 fallow deer and 357 red deer within the Forest boundaries. (Painfully aware myself of the difficulties of assessing population sizes of any deer species in a huge area of difficult terrain, and the lengthy debates in the literature about the accuracy and application of alternative survey methods, I cannot help but marvel at the delightful precision of these figures, and take them with a pinch of salt!).

A government report of 1789 gave a more global estimate of the average number of fallow deer present as 5,900 and numbers seem to have remained at roughly

Table 34
Current numbers of different deer species in the New Forest, in relation to recommended sustainable population size.

Species	Recommended sustainable population size (after Putman & Langbein 1999)	Estimated current numbers (2004/5) in the Crown lands (after Forestry Commission 2007)
Fallow deer	1,200	1,728
Red deer	100	183
Sika deer	100	<100
Roe deer	Up to 400	468
Muntjac	Prevent population establishment	Not censused, but numbers appear to be increasing

this same level until the 1850s. In 1851, the New Forest Deer Removal Act, in relinquishing the Crown's rights to an exclusive hunting reserve, provided for the 'removal' of all deer from the Forest within three years of the enactment. Total extermination of such a large population of animals, scattered over so large an area, was of course as impracticable as a precise count, but numbers were certainly dramatically reduced and population estimates in 1900 gave a figure of 200 head (Lascelles 1915). Since that time the population has gradually expanded and is now maintained by culling at a level that has been estimated at about 2000 animals (Putman and Sharma 1987, Putman and Langbein 1999; Table 34).

Red deer were also established in the New Forest at the time of the Conqueror, but numbers were always substantially lower than those of fallow, and the population throughout seems to have been barely self-sustaining. Populations have indeed continuously been 'subsidised' by introductions, not merely in an attempt to improve the perceived 'quality', but also simply to bolster numbers. Both James I and Charles II introduced fresh blood from France, Charles II importing no fewer than 375 red deer that were released near Brockenhurst in the south of the Forest. Further introductions continued throughout the 19th century and even into the early 20th century.

Census records are patchy. During Henry VII's reign there were several records of red deer being killed within the Forest; the Regarders' survey of 1679 estimated numbers at 357, with 103 male and 254 female deer. By the late 18th century, however, the Forest's red deer population was almost certainly extinct; certainly returns of 1828–1830 of deer in Royal Forests omit any mention of red deer within the New Forest. References to sightings in the 19th century probably relate to escapes from nearby deer parks, and in the past 200 years numbers have probably never exceeded 80–100 animals. Current populations derive in the main from reintroductions to two distinct areas of the Forest in the 1960s.

Roe may also be presumed to have been native in the New Forest area, but by medieval law, red deer were beasts of the Forest (reserved for Royalty), whereas fallow and roe, the lesser beasts of the 'Chase', were generally less jealously protected. During the Middle Ages roe deer became virtually extinct throughout England and much of Scotland. As with the red deer, modern populations of roe in southern England have resulted from reintroductions of animals into several areas during the 19th and 20th centuries (Prior 1973). Roe recolonised the New Forest from 1870 onwards, spreading across from Dorset (Jackson 1980). Census figures suggested a population of perhaps 400–500 animals in the early 1970s; for a period thereafter numbers declined substantially to really very low values (estimated in 1990 at between 250 and 350 animals across the whole of the Forest). Populations are now showing some recovery but are still somewhat patchily distributed within the Forest.

Sika deer are a much more recent and completely exotic introduction to the New Forest. Sika were first introduced to Great Britain in the 1860s and to the New Forest in the early 1900s. Current populations are descended from animals that escaped from a collection in the nearby Manor of Beaulieu. For many years they were restricted to a small area in the south of the Forest, an area seemingly bounded to the north by a major railway line, by the sea to the south, and to the east and west by the waters of the Beaulieu and Lymington Rivers. These boundaries were hardly impassable, at least those to the north and west. Populations were contained until perhaps the late 1970s or early 1980s, but by the late 1980s, increasing reports were made of sika spreading beyond this initial localised area. By the late 1980s numbers were assessed as in excess of 200–300 animals, and while still restricted to the southern part of the Forest, sika were recorded over a far more extensive range. Numbers were reduced by heavy culling in the late 1980s and are now held at approximately 100.

As an aside here, we may note that recent DNA analysis of samples of both sika and red deer taken from the New Forest confirmed that current populations of red deer were of fairly mongrel origin (as would be expected for a population derived from introductions from various sources), but offered no evidence for recent hybridisation with sika deer (Diaz et al. 2006). Further analysis (using STRUCTURE, a procedure that calculates the proportion of the DNA profile that is sika and red deer DNA) detected low-level hybridisation, with presence of at least some red deer genetic 'markers' in 12.5% of sika deer from the Purbeck region of Dorset, while only 3.7% of New Forest sika contained any red deer markers (Diaz et al. 2006). These small, but perhaps important, genetic differences between the populations support the earlier deduction based on cranial morphometrics (Putman and Hunt 1994) that New Forest sika may be more pure genetically than other populations of feral sika in Britain.

Domestic animals (chiefly cattle and ponies) have of course also been depastured on the Forest alongside the deer, ever since its designation as a Royal Forest, and probably considerably before that time. One of the concessions granted to the local populace after the declaration of the area as a Royal Hunting Forest, was the right of Common Grazing. On the payment of an appropriate 'marking fee', local cottagers and farmers could turn out cattle and horses to exploit the rough grazing of the Forest lands. These rights are still honoured and large numbers of cattle and ponies are regularly pastured at free range upon the Forest grazings. Ancient rights of 'pannage' also provide for the turning out of pigs into the Forest's woodlands for a restricted period in the autumn, to feed upon the rich crop of tree-fruit: acorns and beechmast. Small numbers of sheep and donkeys are also pastured under Common Rights in small areas of the Forest.

The numbers and relative importance of all these herbivores have fluctuated over the years (Tubbs 1986). However, in the past numbers of domestic livestock were probably much lower than at present, and in addition a far larger area of land was unenclosed and available for common grazing (Putman 1986, 1996).

As a result, the impact of the common stock was historically probably secondary to that of the deer. Throughout this time, the deer would have been predominantly fallow, with at most a few hundred red deer. At the end of the 19th century, however, the area was 'disafforested'; with the passing of the Deer Removal Act in 1851, deer populations were decimated and have only recently recovered to their present numbers. With the reduction of numbers of deer and simultaneous increased effective density of domestic stock, cattle and ponies emerged as the major grazing influence on the Open Forest and have remained so to this day.

The impacts of grazing on the fauna and flora

Some seven species of large ungulate co-occur within the boundaries of the New Forest, giving it not only an unusually high biomass of grazing herbivores, but also a remarkably high diversity of species. Whether by deer or domestic stock, the New Forest area has always sustained a tremendous grazing pressure from large herbivores. At present, 20,000 ha of some of the poorest possible grazing (current land-use survey maps class the majority of the area as grade 5, or non-agricultural land) support a total large herbivore biomass in excess of 2,500 tonnes (Putman 1996), and it is clear that equivalent grazing pressure must have existed over the centuries.

This history of continued grazing has stamped its mark on the Forest vegetation, and indeed the current ecology of the open ground outside the Forest enclosures can in my view *only* be correctly interpreted in relation to the various effects of past and present grazing. Any attempt to explain the ecology of the Forest – in accounting for the curious lack of diversity of many of the vegetational systems, the low numbers and diversity of small mammals, curious behaviour of birds of prey and other predators – forces the attention back to the dominating effect of grazing in the shaping of this ecosystem.

The effects of grazers and grazing upon vegetational systems in general are far-reaching. Grazing may directly affect the species composition, diversity, productivity, and even physical architecture of the plant community. Patterns of foraging, trampling and elimination may affect nutrient dynamics and patterns of nutrient flow, with further implications for plant species composition, distribution and productivity. In addition, effects of grazing are not limited to an influence on vegetational structure and dynamics. Through their impact on the composition and productivity of the vegetation, herbivores immediately have a secondary and equally significant influence upon all other animals dependent on that same shared vegetation, affecting the composition and dynamics of the entire community.

Almost all of these effects may be registered within the various communities of the New Forest. None of these effects is of course unique to the New Forest: equivalent examples of the effects of grazing upon the structure and species composition of vegetation are legion, and are extensively reviewed elsewhere (e.g. Putman 1994, Gill and Beardall 2001). 'Knock-on' effects of such changes upon other herbivores or their predators are also increasingly commonly reported (e.g. Petty and Avery 1990, Stewart 2001, Feber *et al.* 2001, Flowerdew and Ellwood 2001, Fuller 2001). But what is perhaps unusual is that in the New Forest, all of these various changes are clearly documented within a single system. Analysis of the ecological dynamics of this one site allows us to clearly illustrate all of the potential effects of heavy grazing within the one area.

Changes in species composition
Clear changes in species composition in response to grazing, with selective elimination of species particularly sensitive to defoliation, or others more tolerant but heavily preferred, are apparent in most of the Forest communities. This is accompanied by a gross shift in community structure towards those species that are in some way more resistant to, or tolerant of grazing impact. Such changes may be recorded quite quickly, as in the grassland areas ploughed and reseeded ('reseeded lawns') after the Second World War and only opened to the Common grazing in the early 1960s (Pickering 1968, Putman *et al.* 1981, Putman 1986). Significant changes were already apparent in the species composition of the sward by the mid 1960s, and certainly by the end of the 1980s. This resulted in the establishment at equilibrium of communities dominated by stoloniferous grasses (such as common bent) and prostrate or rosette-forming herbs such as daisies *Bellis perennis*, cat's-ear *Hypochaeris radicata* or ribwort plantain *Plantago lanceolata*, which by their growth form are more able to withstand or escape grazing (Table 35).

Species composition and horizontal patterns of distribution within these same grassland communities are also affected by clear 'dislocation' of nutrient

Table 35
Percentage cover of Long Slade reseeded lawn in 1963 and 1979, by comparison to the proportional composition of the seed mixture applied in 1958. Data for 1958 and 1963 from Pickering (1968); data for 1979 from Putman *et al.* (1981). This table presents only a summary; more detail is presented as Table 7.13 in Putman (1986).

		1958	1963	1979
Grasses	*Agrostis capillaris*	–	47.8	51.0
	Dactylis glomerata	58	6.8	2.4
	Festuca rubra	–	–	2.9
	Lolium perenne	–	2.0	2.5
	Vulpia bromoides	–	5.3	0.1
	Other grass species	–	5.5	4.3
Forbs	*Bellis perennis*	–	4.7	6.3
	Hypochoeris radicata	–	3.2	3.8
	Leontodon autumnalis	–	3.7	1.8
	Plantago lanceolata	–	0.3	7.4
	Trifolium pratense	10	0.6	0
	Trifolium repens	32	12.8	3.2
	Other forbs	–	5.9	6.0

Figure 64

A schematic representation of the mosaic of grazing and latrine areas on a reseeded lawn (redrawn after Edwards and Hollis 1982). Areas grazed by ponies (with grass usually too short to be grazed by cattle) extend to 38% of the total area (illustrated in black), while pony latrines (areas also grazed by cattle) cover 62% of the area (illustrated in white).

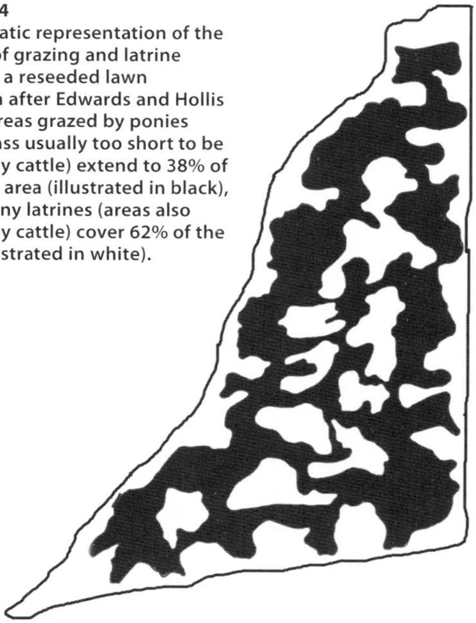

Table 36

Differences in the species composition of pony-grazed and latrine areas in reseeded lawns (from Putman *et al.* (1981) and Putman (1986)).

Status	Species	% age cover in latrines	% age cover in grazed areas
Confined to latrines	Cirsium arvense		–
	Cirsium vulgare		–
	Senecio jacobaea		–
More abundant in latrine areas	Hypochoeris radicata	7.7	4.8
	Lolium perenne	2.2	0.3
	Trifolium repens	5.3	1.3
More abundant in pony-grazed areas	Poa compressa	1.8	2.8
	Sagina procumbens	1.2	2.2

Table 37

Species composition of trees and shrubs in two woodland enclosures: one grazed, one ungrazed (from Mann 1978). Data shown as number of trees or saplings per 10 m-radius circular plot.

Species	Grazed	Ungrazed
Fagus sylvatica	2.5	22.4
Quercus sp.	1.8	12.9
Pinus sylvestris	1.0	43.3
Betula sp.	0.3	65.3
Salix sp.	0	23.8
Ilex aquifolium	0	17.1
Ulex europaeus	0	19.7
Crataegus monogyna	0	1.0
Prunus spinosa	0	0.6

return, whereby feeding patterns of the various large herbivores result in a very patchy and discontinuous return to the system of abstracted nutrients. Animals that forage over a relatively wide area but defaecate in a smaller area can have a substantial impact on local nutrient availability. Sheep, for example, graze widely over a pasture during daylight hours but congregate in camps at night or for shade. In consequence 35% of their faeces are deposited on less than 5% of the grazing area, resulting in a gradual impoverishment of the wider grazing range but continued enrichment of small areas within it (Spedding 1971). These patterns of grazing and elimination result in the development of a fine-scale heterogeneity of species associations within swards grazed by sheep (Bakker *et al.* 1983 a,b).

Such 'nutrient dislocation' has also been recorded for horses (Archer 1973, Edwards and Hollis 1982), which establish distinct and fixed grazing and latrine areas in different parts of their foraging range. Edwards and Hollis (1982) showed that free-ranging ponies of the New Forest, like their more domesticated counterparts in fields, established within their grazing grounds distinct and traditional sites for grazing and for elimination. The animals cropped swards close in areas selected for grazing, and undertook specific and purposeful movements away from these areas to defaecate and urinate in traditional latrine sites, within which they did not graze except in occasional periods when other forage was extremely scarce.

These traditional latrine sites were fixed and persisted in the same areas for year after year (Figure 64), establishing a clearly non-random pattern of return of nutrients within the community that was not masked or reversed by the activities of other grazers. Although cattle and deer also utilised these Forest grasslands, their feeding was restricted to the pony latrines. With incisors in both upper and lower jaw, the ponies can crop the sward in grazing areas so close that ruminants such as cattle or deer cannot themselves utilise those patches. Neither cattle nor deer establish distinct latrine and grazing sites. Both dung wherever they happen to be at the time, and since they spend most of their time grazing within the pony latrines, their dung, too, accumulates in these latrine sites.

Over time this dislocation in nutrient return even within a single community leads to continued impoverishment of pony-grazing areas and continuous nutrient enrichment of latrines. Already, in grasslands ploughed and reseeded after the War, consistent differences are recorded in the potassium and phosphorus content of soils, with nutrient concentrations being higher in the latrine areas by a factor of about 1.2 (phosphorus) to 1.7 (potassium) (Putman *et al.* 1981). Organic matter content of latrine areas is also consistently a little higher. Differences between latrine and non-latrine patches reflect both the nutrient status and grazing regime experienced (given that plants growing in pony grazing areas are subjected to a closer cropping than those in latrine areas foraged only by cattle or deer). Such factors have led to significant differences in species composition, producing a fine-scale mosaic in species associations

Plate 10
Typical catch from a shaded stream (Highland Water) (left) and an unshaded stream (Ober Water) (right). Species in the Highland water include trout, minnows, bullheads and brook lampreys. Ober Water species include chub, pike, minnows and perch.

Over many years, the management of the New Forest for timber and coppicing resulted in many of the streams being deepened and straightened to improve drainage, particularly for oak and conifer plantations (Tubbs 1986, 2001). This led to increased erosion in many reaches where bankfull channel depths exceeded 2 m instead of the more natural depths of 0.3–0.5 m. Stream management also included the routine removal of timber debris from channels, reducing their structural and hydraulic diversity. However, some streams have retained their natural sinuosity and many of the characteristics of pristine lowland forest streams (Sear and Arnell 2000).

Over centuries, travellers and naturalists visiting or working in the New Forest have commented on the streams (e.g. Cornish 1895, Begbie 1934, Everard 1957), but they have rarely attracted the great attention afforded to the sparkling chalk streams that characterise the remainder of Hampshire, Dorset and Wiltshire. For the most part, the Forest streams are small with peat-coloured water, which can vary in depth from 2–5 cm to more than 1.5 m within short distances. Latchmore Brook, flowing westward, was described as comprising *'deep grottos, fox holes (so large that they look more like dens for wolves) and bogs which heave'* (de Bairacli-Levy 1958). The iron-rich (chalybeate) springs and stream-waters in some areas were noted for their value as treatments for leprosy in the Middle Ages, for example Iron or Lepers' Well near Fritham in the northern area of the Forest (SU 22951485). In the 19th century, chalybeate springs and streams such as Passford Brook were recommended as cures for mange in dogs and for treatment of eye disorders (SZ 91053175) (Langford 1996).

The streams have never been regarded as significant venues for angling despite records of sea trout *Salmo trutta* of above 5 kg in weight (de Crespigny and Hutchinson 1899, Langford 2000). Only one fishing club regularly uses the streams, mainly the Lymington River, and pleasure angling mostly takes place only in a few artificial pools on the Forest. An opinion expressed in the 19th century was that *'practically speaking there is no fishing on the Forest'*, although the authors did note the presence of *'large sea-trout'* in the Avon Water and remarked that timber and trees were a hindrance to fly-fishers. Today, most visitors to the Forest are surprised to see large numbers of fish such as minnows *Phoxinus phoxinus*, bullheads *Cottus gobio* and small trout *Salmo trutta* caught during research sampling in various streams. Large chub *Leuciscus cephalus*, pike *Esox lucius* and other coarse fish are present in streams such as the Ober Water and Dockens Water but are rarely seen by the casual visitor (Plate 10).

Channel structure and hydrology

Land use in the stream catchments comprises mostly woods, open grazing lawns, heathland and a few small urban areas, but no significant arable areas. The wooded areas include conifers and managed young stands of hardwoods with old-growth woodland (see Chapter 13). Oak, ash and beech dominate the deciduous trees, often interspersed with holly. Alder lines the margins of many streams. In the unfenced areas the vegetation pattern is mostly maintained through a mixture of grazing by large herbivores and anthropogenic forest and lawn management practices. This system has been maintained for many centuries (Tubbs 1968, 1986, 2001). The pattern of riparian vegetation and land use can, as noted below, have significant implications for the ecology of the streams.

Stream channels rarely exceed bankfull widths of 7 m across the Forest, although the lower reaches of the Lymington River are up to 10 m wide. Straightened and deepened reaches of all streams are interspersed with more natural, meandering reaches. There is a defined riffle-pool structure in most streams, with minimum depths on riffles at base-flow of between 2 and 7 cm. Pools vary in depth from 20 cm to 1.3 m, and in dry periods upper reaches of streams may consist only of pools interspersed with dry riffles. At moderate discharge rates, some reaches show smooth,

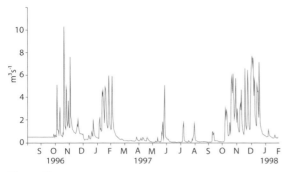

Figure 67
Hydrograph of the Lymington River at Brockenhurst, 1996–1998. The 'flashy' nature of the flow patterns is typical of New Forest streams and rivers.

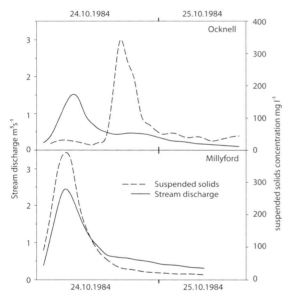

Figure 68
Effects of heavy rainfall on stream discharge and suspended solids concentrations over a two-day period. Highland Water, New Forest, 1984. (After Futter 1985.)

laminar flow and can be categorised as glides. In extremely dry years, such as 1976 and 2006, some streams dry out completely in their upper reaches, sometimes for up to 1 km, and historically such dry periods may last for up to 6–8 weeks (Shore 1890). Typically, riffles tend to be between 5 and 15 m long and pools from 5 to 30 m long, depending on the location within the stream system. Pools become more common in lower reaches. The substrate is dominated by sand and clay overlain with gravel, pebbles and small flint cobbles with diameters from approximately 1 cm to 12 cm. The phi scale, describing substrates, is typically from 3 to minus 6, indicating small to moderate-sized particles. There are no large rocks, boulders or bare bedrock reaches. Common depositing

substrates are silt, leaf packs, sand and silt-sand with small twigs and small woody debris.

Hydrologically, New Forest streams are described as 'flashy' (Gurnell and Gregory 1987), with a tendency to rise and fall quickly after rainfall (Figure 67). Streams with extensive mires and bogs in their catchments tend to have more consistent flows in summer (Tubbs 1986). Run-off from the few large roads that cross the area and from the small urban areas would be expected to affect stream flows. For example, Gregory (1992) suggested that increases in the peak flow of the upper Highland Water were caused by storm run-off from a large dual carriageway following road improvements in the 1980s.

The streams can carry large amounts of sediments during spates with even tiny streams removing from 0.64–0.75 m³ yr⁻¹. Such values increase where human impact or cattle access occurs (e.g. Tuckfield 1964, 1973, 1976, 1980). As an extreme example, 1084 m³ of sediment was removed from one gulley in 10 years. Channelisation of unshaded reaches also leads to large growths of silt-loving plants such as Nuttall's waterweed *Elodea nuttalli* (Brookes 1983). Suspended solids concentrations can rise from between 5 and 25 mg l⁻¹ at low discharge to over 300 mg l⁻¹ during high discharge (Figure 68) (Futter 1985). The rate of erosion and sediment removal from the riparian zone depends upon the dryness of the soils, the intensity of the rainfall and the stream discharge (e.g. Gregory 1992). Spores and pollen may reach concentrations of 230 grains ml⁻¹ at high discharge, although at low flows the values are typically 1–2 grains ml⁻¹. Tree pollen can dominate the contributions at high flows, though not at lower flows (Brown 1985).

Water chemistry

The waters of the New Forest are typically circum-neutral with pH values normally ranging from 6 to 7.3 in the larger streams, but in the headwaters draining mires pH may be as low as 3–4 (Arbuthnott 1996). Nutrient and calcium concentrations are naturally very low, although they can vary with underlying rocks, soils and with riparian land use (Table 38). Natural acidity was measured in the late 19th century when Brierly (1890) noted the *'very great corrosive nature of the waters….upon metals'* and the presence of humic acids. A good measure of the mineral content of the water is 'conductivity' or 'specific conductance' (Buttle *et al.* 1970), which is measured by passing an electric current though a sample of the water in a cell of known dimensions and represented in units of micro-siemens per centimetre (µS cm⁻¹). Forest streams show typical conductivities (adjusted to be 25 °C) of 120– 200 µS cm⁻¹ with less common higher and lower values depending on the underlying geology. In the smallest feeders conductivities can be as low as 50–75 µS cm⁻¹ and where sewage effluents, road drainage or small domestic effluents enter streams, conductivities can range from 500 to 1150 µS cm⁻¹, usually for very short distances (Le Rossignol 1977). In comparison, chalk streams range naturally from 350 to 600 µS cm⁻¹, a

Table 38

Typical chemical constituents of New Forest stream water in relation to underlying geology. Values are means of five samples (from Langford 1996, after Le Rossignol 1977). Lead (Pb) and Copper (Cu) were below detection level.

Rock type	Conductivity	TDS	Ca	Mg	Na	K	Li	Fe	Mn	Zn
Headon Beds	396	428	41.5	12	27.5	8.44	25	2,300	600	47
Headon Beds	486	540	62.5	16	42	4.7	33	460	1525	33
Barton Clay	156	193	11.0	6.3	12.7	3.2	36	1,840	119	34
Plateau Gravel	120	124	5.0	4.5	12.7	1.05	25	1,250	113	30
Barton Sand	156	170	6.0	5.2	16.9	3.2	14	630	80	25
Barton Sand	147	212	13.5	6	12	4.35	24	4,800	381	72
Barton Clay	373	349	26.0	25.8	17.9	6.1	86	460	440	440
Barton Clay	129	123	6.5	4	11.2	2.43	16	2,010	116	1

factor of 2–3.5 greater than natural Forest streams. There is some variation in the mean natural concentrations of the major constituents (Table 38), but in streams draining urban areas, improved farm land or standing waters, conductivities, nutrient concentrations and pH may be higher than in the more natural streams (Environment Agency data 1988–96). Marker (1976) recorded nitrate (as NO_3-N) concentrations of 0.1–0.8 mg l^{-1} and 0.1–1.4 mg l^{-1} in the Ober Water and Dockens Water, respectively, during 1969–1972, which were very similar to the values for 1996–2000 (Langford 2000). The chemical characteristics of the Forest streams are a main defining factor in their ecology and they form a hydrological and biochemical geographical and ecological island, surrounded by calcareous lands and high-quality chalk streams.

Sources of pollution

Pollution has been, historically, relatively rare. The most serious consistent polluting industrial discharge was that from the Schultze Gunpowder Factory at Fritham to the Latchmore Brook, where leakages of various acids 'so tainted the water that cattle refused to drink it and the fish, holding their noses, fled, in the case of the salmon never to return' (Begbie 1934). In 1871, soon after the opening of the factory, dead eels and fish were found in the brook five miles downstream of the factory (Pasmore 1993), although as the pollution problems became worse, the Company suggested that because the substances in use were 'nitre and sulphuric acids', both used in medicine and as tonics, 'there was no cause for alarm' (Pasmore 1993). The factory closed and the discharge ceased in the 1940s. The Company also built a substantial reservoir for water supply to the factory by blocking the Latchmore Brook and tapping into springs nearby. This is now known as Eyeworth Pond (SU 22851470).

Present discharges to Forest streams now mainly originate from sewage disposal works serving the small towns and villages such as Lyndhurst, Brockenhurst, Fritham and Burley (Tubbs 2001). Occasional discharges from some of these works, usually as a result of storms or the breakdown of equipment, exceed threshold limits and cause fish mortalities and ecological damage downstream. Other point-sources may be sited at farms, businesses or factories that discharge effluents intermittently (usually accidentally). Also, storm overflow pipes designed only to operate during heavy precipitation may cause occasional problems. Diffuse pollution, mainly run-off from roads and impervious urban surfaces can introduce sediments, oil and rubber residues and organic material deposited on the hard surface. These sources are relatively rare in the Forest proper, and are restricted to the small central urban areas, the urbanised fringe and the few large roads that cross the Forest. Diffuse run-off from agriculture, trackways and areas where ponies and cattle congregate also contribute nutrients and nitrogenous materials, though concentrations tend to be low.

Large woody debris

A noted feature of New Forest stream channels is the presence of varying amounts of large wood debris in the form of fallen trees, large fallen branches and cut tree sections (see also Chapter 13). These may be in the form of single items or, more commonly aggregated into larger accumulations forming matrices or dam-like structures traversing the channel. The effects of such woody debris on channel structure and sediments have been studied for over 30 years (e.g. Gregory et al. 1985, Gregory and Davis 1992, Gurnell and Sweet 1998, Jeffries et al. 2003). The number and density of dams has varied over the years, mainly as a result of stream and forest management practices. Until the 1980s, debris dams were often removed from channels to enhance drainage but more recently, many dams have been retained to try to reinstate a more natural regime of flow and sediment transport (e.g. Jeffries et al. 2003).

The presence of debris dams is not universally appreciated by the various users of the New Forest. For example, ecologists and conservationists mostly consider woody debris as an integral part of the natural stream habitat, which also influences floodplain inundation. In contrast, the impoundment of streams by dams and the resulting overbank flow can, according to Forest users, have adverse effects on the drainage of grazing lawns and Inclosures and hence on

Forest livestock. Furthermore, some anglers believe that the upstream spawning migrations of sea trout are hindered by the dams, although this is doubtful (e.g. Langford and Hawkins 1997, Langford 2000, 2006). Debris dams at densities of up to four per 100 m (Gregory *et al.* 1985) may delay flood peaks by up to 10 minutes at high flows and 100 minutes at low flows. Over-bank flows and increased sediment deposition also occur at discharge rates less than flood levels where in-stream debris dams are present (Jeffries *et al.* 2003). The number and density of dams varies with land use with the greatest loading originating from deciduous forest (Gregory *et al.* 1993). In the most studied habitat, the Highland Water, debris dams tend to be concentrated in the upper third of the stream (Gregory *et al.* 1993) and an increased density of pools tends to be associated with an increased density of debris dams, although pools are not formed exclusively by such dams (e.g. Gurnell and Sweet 1998).

The flora and fauna

Micro-organisms and algae

There have been few taxonomically based studies of micro-organisms and algae in New Forest streams. Densities of ciliate protozoa were found to be lower than in chalk streams (Baldock and Sleigh 1988), but densities of photosynthetic flagellates, mainly *Synura* spp. reached 148×10^3 cm^{-2}. *Carchesium* spp, *Vorticella* spp. and *Platycola* spp. were the dominant peritrich ciliates (Harmsworth *et al.* 1992). McCollin (1993) sampled 15 sites and recorded 30 species of diatoms (Bacillariophycae) living on stones and plants. *Fragillaria* cf. *pinnata* was the most common species and more abundant than others, where nutrient concentrations and light availabilities were low. Where phosphate concentrations were higher, *Cocconeis placentula* and *Achnanthes miniutissima* were the most common species. The growth and standing crop of *Achnanthes saxonica* on stones were related to water velocity (Moore 1977), although they were also affected by shade. Dominant diatoms on woody debris were *A. saxonica* with *Suirella ovata* var. *minuta*.

Common epipelic species in the Highland Water were *A. minutissima* v. *cryptocephala*, *A. saxonica*, *Cymbella naviculiformis*, *Synedra ulna*, *Opephora martyi*, *Pinnularia biceps* and *P. biceps* f. *peterseni*. Epilithic communities included the *Achnanthes* spp., plus *Gomphonema acuminatum* v. *coronatum*, *G. constrictum* v. *subcapitum*, and *Achnanthes* spp., which accounted for the majority of the standing crop in both epipelic and epilithic communities (Moore 1977). Epihytic and planktonic communities were also dominated by *Achnanthes* spp., with *Gomphonema parvulum*. The epiphytes were mainly on decaying tree branches as macrophytes were scarce in this heavily shaded stream. Diatoms and unicellular algae formed the basis of the diet of the four main herbivores in the Highland water, namely the shrimp *Gammarus pulex*, the mayflies *Ephemera danica* and *Ecdyonurus* sp., and larval brook lamprey *Lampetra planeri*.

Macrophytes

The abundance of in-stream macrophytes in New Forest streams is closely related to the amount of shade, with both species richness and total abundance greater in unshaded reaches (Figure 69). The macrophyte flora (Table 39) of the sandy New Forest streams is regarded as comprising a unique assemblage of species (Haslam

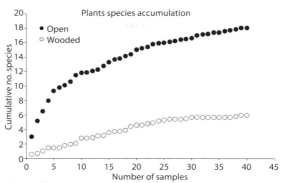

Figure 69
Species accumulation curves for aquatic plants in shaded and unshaded reaches of New Forest streams. The exclusion of light limits both the number and the abundance of species. (From Samuel 2004.)

Table 39
Species of macrophyte recorded in New Forest streams.

Species
Agrostis stolonifera Creeping bent, fiorin *
Alisma plantago-aquatica Water-plantain *
Apium nodiflorum Fool's watercress, water celery *
Callitriche hamulata Intermediate water-starwort *
Callitriche obtusangula Blunt-fruited water-starwort
Callitriche stagnalis Common water-starwort *
Catabrosa aquatica Whorl-grass
Eleogiton fluitans Floating club-rush
Elodea canadensis Canadian waterweed *
Elodea nuttallii Nuttall's waterweed
Glyceria fluitans Flat-grass, floating sweet-grass *
Groenlandia densa Opposite-leaved pondweed
Lemna minor Common duckweed
Ludwigia palustris Hampshire-purselane *
Myosotis scorpioides Water forget-me-not **
Myriophyllum alterniflorum Alternate-flowered water-milfoil
Nuphar lutea Yellow water-lily
Oenanthe crocata Hemlock water-dropwort *
Potamogeton polygonifolius Bog pondweed *
Ranunculus omiophyllus Round-leaved crowfoot **
Ranunculus peltatus Pond water-crowfoot *
Ranunculus trichophyllus Thread-leaved water-crowfoot *
Rorippa nasturtium-aquaticum Summer watercress *
Scrophularia auriculata Water figwort
Sparganium erectum Branched bur-reed **
Veronica scutellata Marsh speedwell

 * indicates from Samuel (2004)
 ** indicates regarded as typical of sandy New Forest streams

and Wolseley 1981, Holmes 1983). Samuel (2004) added eight species to the list given by Langford (1996), making 26 species in total, and included both *Elodea canadensis* and *E. nuttalli*. *Elodea* spp. are sporadically distributed but can become very abundant in some reaches, notably the Ober Water downstream of Markway Bridge (SU 24850385). In the upper reaches of most streams, the commonest macrophyte is bog pondweed *Potamogeton polygonifolius*. Its spearhead-shaped leaves can be seen in both very wet mires and bogs and in stream channels and temporary ponds across the Forest. It is often found where dappled shade prevents the growth of other macrophytes. Among the riparian macrophytes, the marsh St John's-wort, *Hypericum elodes*, appears to be associated with the occurrence of some of the damselfly species along specific streams (Jenkins 1986). Haslam (2006) shows at least 31 plant species associated with clean chalk streams, typically with 10 or 11 species at any one site. In New Forest streams, the number of species at any one site is typically 2–5 (Samuel 2004). In-stream vegetation is also generally more abundant in chalk streams even than in unshaded Forest streams (Samuel 2004, Haslam 2006).

Macro-invertebrates
To date some 296 taxa of macro-invertebrates have been recorded from various studies of the Forest streams (Appendix). Historically, the most commonly studied groups were insects, notably Trichoptera (caddisflies) and Plecoptera (stoneflies) (Langford 1996). By 1940, 20 species of the former and ten species of the latter had been recorded as adults in the Forest. Mayflies were relatively scarce according to early records (Lucas 1932). To date 16 species of stonefly, 20 species of mayfly, 53 species of caddis and 34 species of beetle are listed from the streams, although the list may not yet be complete. The New Forest drainage system typically contains between 10 and 40% of the British species in various freshwater invertebrate groups (Langford 1996), although records of water mites (Hydracarina) and true flies (Diptera) may be affected by the number of specialist taxonomists in the area. The most obvious group of insects to the casual observer is the Odonata (damselflies and dragonflies; see also Chapter 4) (e.g. Welstead and Welstead 1984, Winsland 1994), particularly the large black and yellow golden-ringed dragonfly *Cordulegaster boltonii*, often seen patrolling along the streams, particularly in the wooded reaches. In late May and early June, large numbers of the spectacular blue-green damselfly, the beautiful demoiselle *Calopteryx virgo*, are also visible on certain streams, particularly where a lack of shade allows in-stream vegetation and overhanging bank grasses to flourish. In the open upper reaches of some streams, where in-stream vegetation is present, the keeled skimmer *Orthetrum coerulescens* is more common than golden-ringed dragonfly (Langford, unpublished data).

The southern damselfly *Coenagrion mercuriale* is listed as rare in Britain (Red Data Book category 3) and is an Annex II listed species in the EU Habitats Directive. It is found in the New Forest in a small number of streams and drainage channels, and has been the subject of many studies over more than 40 years (e.g. Goodyear 1967; Welstead and Welstead 1984, Winsland 1994, Jenkins 1995, Watts *et al.* 2007; see also Chapter 4 this volume). The reasons for the discontinuous distribution of the species across the Forest are not known. The most abundant and consistent populations occur along the Crockford Stream (SU 99003505) (Watts *et al.* 2007) draining Beaulieu Heath. This stream also contains the only population of the stonefly *Taeniopteryx nebulosa* in the main Forest drainage system (Langford, unpublished data), although it is similar chemically and physically to other small Forest streams. Among the other aerial insects few are very obvious being mostly small or various shades of brown in colour as adults. The large diving beetle *Dytiscus semisulcatus*, glossy brown with a bold yellow margin to its body, can be found among tree roots, small woody debris or in weed beds in both wooded and open streams. Another diving beetle, *Agabus brunneus*, classed as 'Vulnerable' has been found in Linford Brook in the western area of the Forest, the only site among 26 New Forest streams surveyed (http://www.ukbvap.org.uk, accessed 28/07/2008).

Despite the unusual characteristics of the New Forest drainage system in the region and its biogeographical isolation, there are few rare or protected invertebrate species occurring in the streams. A few relatively rare species occur in cut-off meanders, marginal or floodplain habitats, for example the snail *Omphiscola glabra* and the beetle *Graptodytes flavipes* (Thomas 2006). In the main stream channels no species is classified above 'notable' (see Appendix). Mollusca and Gammaridae are of relatively low abundance in New Forest streams because of the lack of calcium, which they need to construct shells or exoskeletons. The lesser water measurer *Hydrometra gracilenta* was recorded from streams until the 1950s, but not more recently (Kirby 1993). Most other rare or protected aquatic invertebrate species occur in ponds or pools on the Forest (Langford 1996) (see Chapter 16).

Life-history studies of aquatic invertebrates in Forest streams are rare, limited to species inhabiting the gravel interstices, notably the small oligocheate worm *Nais elinguis* (Ladle 1971), the phreaticolous water mite *Neocarus hibernicus* (Gledhill 1969), and the subterranean spring-dwelling crustacean *Niphargus aquilex*.

Fish
Twenty-two species have been recorded in Forest streams of the 55 species found in freshwaters in Britain (Maitland and Campbell 1992, Langford 1996, Quinlan 2000) (Table 40). Brown trout (sea trout), bullheads, brook lampreys, minnows, eels, and stone loach are the most widely distributed. The most numerically abundant species are trout, minnows and bullheads (Langford and Hawkins 1997, Langford 2000). Of the other species, most are found in streams with unshaded reaches (Langford 2000, Quinlan 2000) and are not widespread. Sticklebacks have been found to be most

abundant in the upper Dockens Water (SU 21401200), but are rare elsewhere. In the case of salmon, under-yearlings have usually only been found in the western streams in small numbers (Mann and Orr 1969). Unusually, bullheads were not found in the upper reaches of Dockens Water near Holly Hatch in early surveys (SU 21401200), although they are present downstream (Mann and Orr 1969, Downes 1999, Langford 2000). Recent surveys in 2005–2007 by two of the authors (Jones and Broadmeadow, unpublished data) have still not recorded bullheads at Holly Hatch. The reason for their absence in this reach is unknown. Both the bullhead and the brook lamprey are species protected by the European Habitats Directive (92/43 EEC).

Effects of wood debris on the stream faunas

The published literature on the geomorphological effects of wood debris accumulation in rivers of many countries is extensive (e.g. Montgomery *et al.* 2003). Specific data from New Forest streams are also well documented (e.g. Gregory *et al.* 1985, Gurnell and Sweet 1998, Jeffries *et al.* 2003). In contrast, published data on ecological effects of wood debris are less extensive (see Montgomery *et al.* 2003, Schneider and Winemiller 2008). Typically, woody debris in streams increases cover for some fishes and increases pool areas and the habitat for lentic fish or life-history stages. As noted above, wood provides a suitable substrate for colonisation by microscopic algae in New Forest streams. The effect on invertebrate communities is not clear (Langford 1996), although the species that inhabit wood debris piles are also common in marginal habitats where current velocities are lower than in midstream (Langford 1996). The accumulation of leaves in the wood accumulations provides a suitable habitat for leaf shredder species such as leptophlebiid mayflies. Some invertebrate species feed directly on decaying wood, but no specific studies of this have been made on these in New Forest streams (see Langford 1996, 2000).

More detailed studies on fish (Plate 11), particularly in the Highland Water, have shown that woody debris

Plate 11
Electric fishing in a woody debris dam matrix. Despite the complexity of the dam the matrices can be sufficiently open for stunned fish to be seen and caught as they drift downstream.

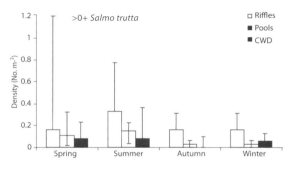

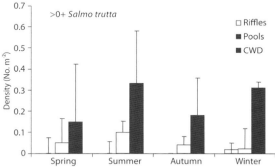

Figure 70
Median and quartile seasonal densities of 0+ and >0+ age groups of *S. trutta* in riffles, pools and CWD matrices in New Forest streams. Samples taken monthly from September 1996 to February 1998, augmented by data from 2000, 2001 and 2003. Highland Water, Bratley Water and Bagshot Gutter data combined. CWD refers to Coarse Woody Debris.

increases pool habitat, which benefits species such as minnows and trout over 1 year old (Langford and Hawkins 1997, Langford 2000, 2006). Where debris dams cause pools to extend over riffles, the area of riffle habitat for under yearling trout and for the EU-protected bullhead decreases. Densities of small trout and bullheads were found to be negatively correlated with amounts of woody debris in a reach, while densities of larger trout and minnows were positively correlated. Seasonal densities of small trout on riffles in the Highland Water averaged from 0.1 to 0.9 fish m⁻², bullheads from 0.8 to 2.8 fish m⁻². In pools older trout averaged from 0.1 to 0.35 fish m⁻², and bullheads 0.1 to 1.4 fish m⁻². Minnows averaged 0–0.2 fish m⁻² in riffles and 0.1 to 0.4 fish m⁻² in pools. Only very large sea trout and eels were more common and abundant in wood piles than in pools or riffles (Langford 2000, 2006) (Figure 70). Furthermore, as trout, minnows, brook lampreys and bullheads all spawn on riffles, potential spawning areas for these species may be lost if debris dams, and hence pool areas, increase. Thus, although there is a current fashion for encouraging wood debris accumulation in streams generally 'to enhance biodiversity", there may be both beneficial and adverse effects on fish and the effects on other biota may be neutral or very small. The use of wood debris as a management tool should therefore only be used if the total ecological effects have been considered.

Effects of shade on stream ecology

Two main categories of stream and reach on the New Forest can be identified by their bankside and riparian vegetation. Along most streams, wooded reaches with relatively little or low riparian vegetation beneath the trees alternate with open lawns or heathland, with bankside vegetation trailing in the water. The lack of shade obviously exposes the stream to direct sunlight and heat. In the unshaded reaches, therefore, maximum summer temperatures can be 8–10°C higher than in fully shaded reaches (Figure 71). The diurnal temperature range can be up to 8°C in open streams but only 1–3°C in heavily shaded streams. On the hottest days in some years, water temperatures may exceed the optimal temperatures for coldwater fish such as trout.

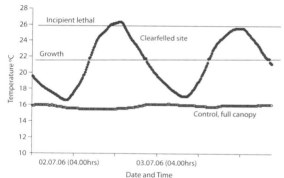

Figure 71
Diurnal temperature variations in the Highland Water following clearfelling over about 200 m of riparian trees compared with a fully shaded reach downstream. Temperatures at which trout growth may cease (22°C) and at which trout may begin to die (26°C) are shown.

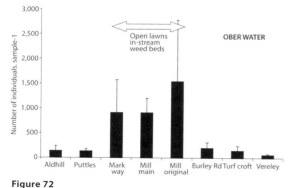

Figure 72
Average numbers of macro-invertebrates collected per sample from shaded and unshaded reaches of the Ober Water. Samples are composite kick samples from midstream and marginal habitats.

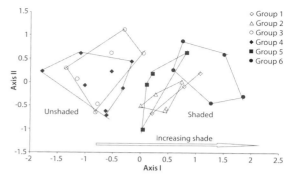

Figure 73
Ordination of macro-invertebrate community samples from shaded and unshaded reaches along the Ober Water. Groups 1, 2, 5 and 6 are from shaded reaches, groups 3 and 4 are from unshaded reaches. The linked symbols indicate similar communities. The separation of unshaded and shaded communities is clear even along one stream. Ordination is a technique for comparing similarity of samples based on the species/taxa present and their abundance in a sample.

Table 40
Fish species found in New Forest streams.

Species
Salmon *Salmo salar* *
Brown (sea) trout *Salmo trutta* **
Chub *Leuciscus cephalus* ***
Minnow *Phoxinus phoxinus* **
Gudgeon *Gobio gobio* *
Bleak *Alburnus alburnus* *
Common bream *Abramis brama* *
Roach *Rutilus rutilus* *
Goldfish *Carassius auratus* *
Rudd *Scardinius erythrophthalmus* *
Dace *Leuciscus leuciscus* *
Grayling *Thymallus thymallus* *
Stone loach *Barbatula barbatula* ***
Bullhead *Cottus gobio* **
Three-spined stickleback *Gasterosteus aculeatus* *+
Perch *Perca fluviatilis* *
Pike *Esox lucius* *
European eel *Anguilla anguilla* ++
Brook lamprey *Lampetra planeri* **
Sea bass *Dicentarchus labrax* +++
Thick-lipped grey mullet *Chelon labrosus* +++
Flounder *Platichthyes flesus*

*	rarely found
**	common and abundant
***	common but most abundant in unshaded streams
*+	not widely distributed but abundant in a few places
++	was common, but has become rarer in recent years, and never abundant
+++	only in brackish lower reaches

Where there are no trees, light encourages weed growth. In-stream water weeds are therefore common and sometimes abundant. Species richness is far greater than that of streams with wooded banks (Figure 69). Some wooded streams such as the Highland Water were devoid of in-stream plants for almost the whole length, though tree clearance in some reaches for planting or stream restoration allowed colonisation (Smith 2006).

Open stream reaches often have more abundant invertebrate faunas (Figure 72), and the species

composition of the invertebrate faunas may be different in shaded and unshaded reaches even along one stream (Figure 73). Where weed beds are present, species of invertebrates that graze on epiphytic algae and diatoms become more abundant and frequent. Furthermore, the streams with open lawns in their catchments also contain more fish species (Langford 2000). Heavily wooded streams contain up to six species (see Table 40), but more open streams can contain 15–16 species, with coarse fish such as chub *Leusicus cephalus*, roach *Rutilus rutilus* and three-spined sticklebacks *Gasterosteus aculeatus* being present and sometimes abundant where shade is absent. The influence of shade is therefore one of the primary features, along with water chemistry, determining the composition of the ecosystem along the streams and can cause both physical and biological discontinuities even at the reach and stream scale.

Table 41
Numbers of species of invertebrates recorded from New Forest streams compared with the numbers in the UK faunal records of established or indigenous species. Data from the authors, RIVPACS lists and Maitland (1977). Numbers of records to 31 July 2008 from known sources. Other records may exist from unknown sources.

Major taxa	Number of spp. in UK	Number of spp. in New Forest	% of UK spp. found in New Forest
Flatworms			
Turbellara/Tricladida	11	4	**36**
Molluscs			
Gastropoda	52	18	35
Bivalvia	27	9	33
Worms and leeches			
Oligochaeta	118	21	18
Hirudinea	14	5	36
Insects			
Ephemeroptera	49	20	43
Plecoptera	34	16	47
Odonata	45	8	18
Hemiptera	62	7	11
Coleoptera	300	34	11
Megaloptera	3	2	67
Neuroptera	4	1	25
Trichoptera	193	49	25
Diptera	1,138	72	7
Crustaceans			
Malacostraca	33	5	15
Water mites			
Hydacarina	322	11	3
Vertebrates			
Agnatha (lampreys)	3	1	33
Teleosti	55	22	40

New Forest streams in a wider context

There are relatively few published spatial studies of the macro-fauna of specific regional or areal stream systems in Britain, despite the long series of routine surveys carried out by statutory authorities over more than 50 years (Langford and Bray 1969, Hildrew 2009). In comparison with national records (Wright *et al.* 2000), the streams of the New Forest contain a good proportion of macro-invertebrate and fish species recorded in Britain (Table 41). The numbers of stonefly and mayfly species were similar to the nearby Moors River in Dorset, which is fed by both chalk and heathland streams (Table 42), even though the number of sites sampled differed markedly. In comparison with a single clean reach of a large lowland river, the Severn near Ironbridge (Langford 1975), there were twice as many species of stoneflies in the Forest streams (24/ 12) but about the same number of mayfly species (24/ 23). In a survey of three Wessex chalk and limestone lowland stream systems, 18 species of mayflies and only four species of stoneflies were recorded (Langford *et al.* 2000). The stonefly fauna is more diverse than in nearby chalk streams, but is similar to those of upland streams in other parts of the UK and to streams of the Ashdown Forest to the east (see Langford 1996 for

Table 42
Comparison of species richness of Plecoptera (Stoneflies) and Ephemeroptera (Mayflies) between selected stream systems. (Full references for the datasets are given in Langford 1996). Data for the Wessex streams are from Langford *et al.* (2000).

Area of survey	Scale of survey	Numbers of species		
		No. sites	Plecoptera	Ephemoptera
New Forest	22 streams	108	16	20
Moors River	Single catchment	28	11	21
North Lincolnshire	24 streams / rivers	50	8	17
Scotland	50 streams/rivers	50	18	17
Ashdown Forest	Riffle sites only	34	13	12
Cow Green Streams	Single catchment	8	23	20
Wessex streams	3 rivers (calcareous)	44	4	18

references), which is also drained by circum-neutral or slightly acidic water.

The abundance of more calciphile taxa such as gammarids or molluscs is much lower in New Forest streams than in chalk streams (Langford 1996, Langford *et al.* 2000). Although the chalk streams of the southern lowlands are commonly perceived as having high biological-diversity, taxon richness at family level at any one site may not be universally greater than in the Forest streams. For example, in the fully shaded Highland Water, standard sampling by the same operator collected between 10 and 30 families. In the partly unshaded Ober Water, the range was 9–36 families, whereas in the Ironbridge reach of the Severn 16–21 families were recorded, and in three Wessex stream systems values were obtained of 18–31 families per sample. The overall abundance of macro-invertebrates is typically lower than in chalk streams and total numbers of individuals per sample varied from 31 to 207 in the Highland Water and from 48 to 2,043 in the Ober Water compared with 262–2,394 in the Wessex chalk streams. The unusually high numbers in the Ober Water were a result of large populations of the small Jenkins' spire shell snail *Potamopyrgus antpodarum* among beds of Nuttall's waterweed at one or two sites (Langford, unpublished data).

Future management and research

The streams of the New Forest have been managed and modified over centuries, either directly through deepening or straightening for drainage or indirectly through the modification of their catchments. The clearance of trees to create open lawns has obviously resulted in changes in both the diversity and composition of the flora and fauna. It is likely that the natural condition of the streams prior to human intervention was not very different from the wooded streams of today, although unshaded areas would exist as a result of natural tree fall or fires. These would typically have been smaller than the open areas of grazing lawns that exist today.

Since 1996, there have been considerable changes in the management of the streams. Woody debris is now retained to encourage overbank flow (e.g. Millington and Sear 2007), trees have been thinned along many stream margins and physical modifications to stream channels in upper and middle reaches have been made to combine potential flood mitigation with the long-term recovery of alluvial floodplain forest and riparian habitats. It was also intended that the reconnection of old meanders and the raising of the stream bed as part of the EU funded LIFE 3 project (see Chapter 17) might provide increased physical diversity in channels, although the rarer invertebrate species were actually found in the unconnected meanders (Thomas 2006). Initial reductions of the stream fauna were caused by the physical alteration of the streams and by displaced silt (Langford 2006). There is now strong evidence of recovery and recolonisation in most reaches (Thomas 2006), although overall biological diversity is unlikely to change from the pre-modification state, being mainly controlled by water chemistry and shade. Tree clearances in some reaches have caused elevated water temperatures and invasion of in-stream plants where none existed previously.

Management of the streams will continue as part of the overall management of the New Forest, especially where this might encourage conservation or restoration of natural or rarer habitats and species. A comprehensive account of the New Forest wetlands shows that there are wide-ranging proposals for future management and conservation of the stream systems (Smith 2006). It is hoped that the management will take into account the unique nature of the drainage system as stated at the beginning of this Chapter.

The streams are the centre of continuing ecological research. Major programmes are focused on the ecological effects of shade, particularly in view of the potential effects of climate change. Forest Research and the University of Southampton are currently studying the effects of shade on water temperatures, invertebrates and fish. Longer-term monitoring of the ecological and geomorphological recovery of the restored reaches of the Highland Water is also in progress, and analysis of the effects of woody debris on fish assemblages is continuing, based at Southampton University.

Acknowledgements

The authors would like to thank all those who have contributed data to this Chapter, including staff of the EA, FBA, IFE and CEH and students of Southampton University, particularly Rachel Downes, Anna Samuel, Cora Nadine Taylor, Alice Walker and James Seabrook. Staff of the Forestry Commission have been extremely helpful and supportive throughout the research programmes on the Forest and have supplied data on stream drainage histories. Particular thanks to Jonathan Spencer, Simon Weymouth, Bruce Rothnie and to local rangers. Historical data also came from Richard Reeves at the 9th Centenary Trust in Lyndhurst. Professor David Sear of the Geography Department of Southampton University has been very helpful with geomorphological discussions. We are grateful for his expertise. Jean Langford compiled and checked the bibliography and copy edited the text several times, for which rigorous and meticulous work the authors extend their grateful thanks.

References

Arbuthnott, A. (1996). *An investigation into the affect of land uses on water quality in New Forest streams; with specific reference to nutrient concentrations.* Dissertation submitted for the degree of BSc., University of Southampton.

Baldock, R. M. and Sleigh, M. A. (1988). The ecology of benthic protozoa in rivers: Seasonal variation in numerical abundance in fine sediments. *Archiv für Hydrobiologie,* 111, 409–421.

Begbie, J. (1934). *Walking in the New Forest*. Alexander Madehose & Co., London.

Brierly, J. (1890). New Forest water. *Proceedings of the Hampshire Field Club*, 1, 71–74.

Brookes, A. (1983). *River channelization in England and Wales: downstream consequences for the channel morphology and aquatic vegetation*. Unpublished Ph.D. Thesis, University of Southampton.

Brown, A. G. (1985). The potential use of pollen in the identification of suspended sediment sources. *Earth Surface Processes and Landforms*, 10, 27–32.

Buttle, J. W., Daniels, D. J. and Beckett, P. J. (1970). *Chemistry: A unified approach*. Butterworths, London.

Cornish, C. J. (1895). *The New Forest and the Isle of Wight*. Selby and Co. Ltd., N.Y. Macmillan.

de Bairacli-Levy, J. (1958). *Wanderers in the New Forest*. Faber, London.

de Crespigny, R. C. and Hutchinson, H. (1899). *The New Forest – Its Traditions, Inhabitants and Customs*. EP Publishing Ltd., British Book Centre Inc., London.

Downes, R. (1999). *A comparison of fish communities, in relation to habitat diversity and riparian cover, in two New Forest streams*. Dissertation submitted for the degree of BSc. University of Southampton.

Everard, C. E. (1957). The streams of the New Forest: A study in drainage evolution. *Proceedings of the Hampshire Field Club and Archaeological Society*, 19, 240–252.

Futter, M. (1985). *Temporal variations and routing of the suspended and dissolved solids loads of the Highland Water (New Forest)*. Unpublished Undergraduate Research Project, Environmental Sciences Centre, University of Southampton.

Gledhill, T. (1969). Some observations of the Phreaticolous water-mite *Neoacarus hibernicus* Halbert (Hydrachnellae, Acari). *Proceedings of 2nd International Congress of Acarology 1967*, 75–80. Akademiai Kiado, Budapest.

Goodyear, K. G. (1967). Observations on some of the scarcer Hampshire and Dorset Odonata. *The Entomologist*, January 1967.

Gregory, K. J. (1992). Vegetation and river channel process interactions. In: *River Conservation and Management* (eds. Boon, P.J., Calow P. and Petts G. E.), pp.255–269. John Wiley & Sons Ltd, Chichester.

Gregory, K. J. and Davis, R. J. (1992). Coarse woody debris in stream channels in relation to river channel management in woodland areas. *Regulated Rivers: Research and Management*, 7, 117–136.

Gregory, K. J., Gurnell, A. M. and Hill, C. (1985). The permanence of debris dams related to river channel processes. *Hydrological Science Journal*, 30, 371–381.

Gregory, K. J., Davis, R. J. and Tooth, S. (1993). Spatial distribution of coarse woody debris dams in the Lymington Basin, Hampshire, UK. *Geomorphology*, 6, 207–224.

Gurnell, A. M. and Gregory, K. J. (1987). Vegetation characteristics and the production of run-off: analysis of an experiment in the New Forest, Hampshire. *Hydrological Processes*, 1, 125–142.

Gurnell, A. M. and Sweet, R. (1998). The distribution and magnitude of large woody debris accumulations and pools in relation to woodland stream management. *Earth Surface Processes and Landforms*, 23, 1101–1121.

Harmsworth, G. C., Sleigh, M. A. and Baker, J. H. (1992). The abundance of different peritrich ciliates on stone surfaces in contrasting lowland streams throughout the year. *Journal of Protozoology*, 39, 58–65.

Haslam, S. M. (2006). *River plants*. Forrest Text. Cardigan, Ceredigion.

Haslam, S. M. and Wolseley, P. A. (1981) *River Vegetation: Its identification, assessment and management*. Cambridge University Press. Cambridge.

Hildrew, A. G. (2009). Sustained research on stream communities: a model system and the comparative approach. *Advances in Ecological Research*, 41, 175–312.

Holmes, N. T. H. (1983). *Focus on Nature Conservation: Typing British Rivers according to their flora*. Shrewsbury, Nature Conservation Council.

Jeffries, R., Darby, S. E. and Sear, D. A. (2003). The influence of vegetation and organic debris on flood-plain sediment dynamics: case study of a low-order stream in the New Forest, England. *Geomorphology*, 51, 61–80.

Jenkins, D. K. (1986). A population study of *Coenagrion mercuriale* (Charp.) at a New Forest site using a modified "Pollard Walk". Part 1. *Journal of the British Dragonfly Society*, 2, 17–20.

Jenkins, D. K. (1995). A population study of *Coenagrion mercuriale* (Charpentier) in the New Forest. Part 6. Mark/recapture programme. *Journal of the British Dragonfly Society*, 11 (1), 10–16.

Kirby, P. (1993). A review of the scarce and threatened Hemiptera of Great Britain. *UK Conservation, No. 2*. Joint NCC Committee, Peterborough, UK.

Ladle, M. (1971). Studies on the biology of oligochaetes from the phreatic water of an exposed gravel bed. *International Journal of Speleology*, 3, 311–318.

Langford, T. E. (1975). The emergence of insects from a British river warmed by power station cooling-water. Part 11. The emergence patterns of some species of Ephemoroptera, Trichoptera and Megaloptera in relation to water temperature and river flow upstream and downstream of the cooling-water outfalls. *Hydrobiologia*, 47 (1), 91–133.

Langford, T. E. (1996). Ecological aspects of New Forest streams, draining one of Britain's unique areas. *Freshwater Forum* 6, 2–38.

Langford, T. E. (2000). *Fish and wood in New Forest streams*. Thesis for the degree of PhD, University of Southampton.

Langford, T. E. (2006). Woody debris, restoration and fish populations. In: I. J. Winfield, *Fisheries on the Edge*. pp. 6–20. Proceedings of the Institute of Fisheries Management Conference, 2005, Salford, UK.

Langford, T. E. and Bray, E. S. (1969). The distribution of Plecoptera and Ephemeroptera in a Lowland Region of Britain (Lincolnshire). *Hydrobiologia*, 34 (2), 243–271.

Langford, T. E. and Hawkins, S. J. (1997). The distribution and abundance of three fish species in relation to timber debris and meso-habitats in a lowland forest stream during autumn and winter. *Limnetica*, 13 (2), 93–102.

Langford, T. E., Somes, J. R. and Bowles, F. (2000). *Effects of physical restructuring on channels on the flora and fauna of three Wessex rivers*. Pisces Conservation Ltd., Pennington, Lymington, UK.

and heathland sites, is the input of nutrients to these ponds from dung (as highlighted by Bratton (1990), Chatters (1996) and Tubbs (1997)).

These analyses confirmed that ponds with a similar set of environmental variables shared a similar macro-invertebrate community. The composition of the wetland plant community from these 72 ponds was analysed using the same classification procedure. A greater number of distinct pond types could be identified using invertebrate, rather than the floral communities, suggesting that macro-invertebrates are responding to more subtle differences in environmental conditions between ponds (Pond Conservation and Environment Agency 2002). Therefore, whilst macrophytes may enable a coarse classification of temporary pond habitats, macro-invertebrate community composition offers a more detailed description upon which to base management decisions.

The National Pond Survey methodology and the Predictive Score for Multimetrics (PSYM) developed by Ponds Conservation, provide a standardised detailed methodology upon which to assess both the flora and macro-invertebrate composition of temporary pond communities. However, a provisional classification, such as given in Table 45, may provide enough

Table 45
Provisional classification of temporary ponds in the New Forest based on macro-invertebrate composition (Ewald 2008).

Pond Group	Habitat / Geology	pH	Shade/ Conductivity/ Turbidity	Area/ Depth/ Isolation	Hydroperiod	Grazing	Characteristic species
1	Grassland habitats on gravels.	Neutral	Open habitat. High due to nutrient input from dung.	Very small surface area, very shallow. Isolated.	Very short, less than 5 months of the year.	Heavily grazed but not heavily poached.	Lowest species diversity. Ponds in this group may contain *Chirocephalus diaphanus*, but the occurrence of this species in any one year will be variable
2	Heathland sites on clays.	Low	Open habitat.	Relatively large and often in a complex with other ponds.	Relatively short hydroperiod.	–	Higher invertebrate diversity than group 1. *Hydroporus gyllenhalii*, a species tolerant of low pH[1]. *Graptodytes flavipes*, a New Forest specialist water beetle[2]. *Agabus nebulosus*, a species tolerant of temporary pond conditions[3]. *Limnephilus auricula*, a widespread and common caddis of temporary pools[4].
3	Heathland sites on sands.	Low	Open habitat. Low in conductivity.	Small in area and isolated.	–	Lightly grazed.	Sanderson's type 1 floral assemblage. Macro-invertebrate species diversity is low with a similar assemblage to pond type 2; *Hydroporus gyllenhalii* and *Graptodytes flavipes* still present, but joined by few other species, and only those which are mobile e.g. *Sigara nigrolineata*[5].
4	Pre-dominantly grassland but some heathland overlaying base-poor clays, sands and gravels.	–	Open habitat.	Relatively large but not very deep.	Moderate, neither very long nor very short.	Heavily grazed but not heavily poached.	Sanderson's type 2 floral assemblage. Highest macro-invertebrate species diversity; characterised by temporary pond species when the pond first fills, e.g. *Chirocephalus diaphanus* and in suitable years *Triops cancriformis*[6]. Colonised by more mobile species as the hydroperiod continues into the spring e.g. *Hesperocorixa sahlbergi*[5].
5	Heathland and grassland, overlaying a mixture of base-rich clays and gravels.	Near neutral	Open habitat. Turbid	Largest surface area.	Relatively long hydroperiod.	Heavily grazed and poached.	Relatively low macro-invertebrate species diversity. Species present require a long hydroperiod e.g. *Cloeon dipterum*[7], *Planorbis leucostoma*[8] and *Sigara striolatum*[5].
6	Grasslands on gravels and sands	Neutral	Open habitat.	–	Very ephemeral. They may not hold water every year.	Heavily grazed but not heavily poached.	A subset of the type 3 ponds identified by Sanderson. They have the potential to contain important temporary pond species e.g. *Chirocephalus diaphanus* and *Triops cancriformis*[9], but due to the brevity of the hydroperiod coinciding with suitable conditions for these species, they are often overlooked.

Table 45 ... continued

Pond Group	Habitat / Geology	pH	Shade/ Conductivity/ Turbidity	Area/ Depth/ Isolation	Hydroperiod	Grazing	Characteristic species
7	Woodland ponds on base-poor clays and sands	–	Least shaded wooded sites. Low conductivity. Low turbidity.	Isolated.	Very long hydroperiod.	Not heavily poached.	High invertebrate diversity. Species that require a long period of inundation are able to colonise, e.g. *Planorbis leucostoma*[8], *Cloeon dipterum*[7] and *Limnephilus centralis*[4].
8	Woodland sites on base-poor clays and sands	Low	Shaded. Turbid.	Deep	Long hydroperiod.	–	Sanderson's type 5 floral assemblage. Macro-invertebrate diversity relatively high. Characterised by species tolerant of low pH; *Hydroporus gyllenhalii*[1] and *Limnephilus vittatus*[4].
9	Woodland ponds on a mixture of base-rich clays and sands	Near neutral	At least 50% open water.	Within a complex of other ponds. Convoluted shallow margins.	Relatively short hydroperiod.	Poached.	Sanderson's type 2 floral assemblage. Species invertebrate richness relatively low, but heterogeneity of habitat allows shade and open water species to co-exist. *Omphiscola glabra*, *Lymnaea truncatula*[8], *Anacaena globulosus*[1], *Glyphotaelius pellucidus*[4] and *Hirudo medicinalis*[10].
10	Woodland ponds on a mixture of base-rich clays and sands	Low	Shaded. Turbid.	–	–	–	Ponds would share a similar macro-invertebrate community to ponds in Group 9 and presumably at one point did so, but the surrounding habitat has been planted with conifers. Species richness is less and no species were identified as characteristic of this habitat type. Ponds in this group have the potential for restoration.
11	Woodland sites on gravels and clays.	Low	Heavily shaded.	–	–	–	Few wetland plant species, clumps of *Sphagnum* spp. in the drawdown zone. They are species poor, but the species present are tolerant of anaerobic conditions, for example *Trichostegia minor*[4] or low pH e.g. *Hydroporus gyllenhalii* [1]

– Environmental variable is not useful in the categorisation of this pond type.
1 Friday (1988); 2 Bratton (1990); 3 Balfour-Browne (1950); 4 Wallace et al. (1990); 5 Savage (1989); 6 Williams (1987); 7 Elliott et al. (1988); 8 Macan (1977); 9 Hall (1976); 10 Ausden and Dawes (2000).

information upon which to base management strategies and as a tool to prioritise ponds for future survey.

Species research

Other than a handful of studies already mentioned, little investigation has been made of temporary pond communities in the New Forest; most work has concentrated on individual species. The following section reviews research on two flagship species, the tadpole shrimp *Triops cancriformis* and the fairy shrimp *Chirocephalus diaphanus*, associated with temporary ponds in the New Forest.

Triops cancriformis (tadpole shrimp)

Triops cancriformis is the best known temporary pond species in the UK, often described as one of the true 'living fossils' (Futuyma 1990 in Zierold *et al*. 2007) as it appears to be morphologically unchanged since the

Devonian Period (Tasch 1963). It is a rare species in Britain and classed as RDB endangered (Bratton 1991). It has been recorded from a single site in the UK, in the New Forest, since 1935 (Ewald 2001, 2008; Fox 1949, Hampshire and Isle of Wight Wildlife Trust unpublished, Hobson and Omer-Cooper 1935), but records as early as 1816 may refer to this site (Leach 1816 unpublished, records kept by Hampshire and Isle of Wight Wildlife Trust). Other sites in the UK appear to have lost their populations, probably as a result of cessation in grazing (Maitland 1995), and one in Scotland that was lost to the sea (Balfour-Browne 1909). However, *T. cancriformis* has since been rediscovered in the same locality in Scotland by a site ranger, whilst he was conducting a Natterjack toad survey (BBC 2004). This highlights the fact that populations may not develop in a pond for several years, waiting for ideal conditions, and that populations at low densities can easily be overlooked.

Laboratory studies have identified that this species requires a hatching temperature of between 15°C and

20°C (Hempel-Zawitkowska 1967). Field studies in the New Forest supported these results. In 1999, the pond where *Triops cancriformis* occurs in the New Forest first filled in mid-September. Temperatures were between the required hatching temperatures and *T. cancriformis* were present in the pond a few weeks later. The following year the pond filled later in the year (by 10 October), by which time the temperature was below the minimum required for hatching and *T. cancriformis* did not appear that year (Ewald 2001).

It is not understood why this species is apparently restricted to a single site in the New Forest when other seemingly suitable ponds are located nearby. Translocations, funded by WWF, were undertaken in 1975 to two new sites in the New Forest (Hall 1976), one of which appears to have been successful (Hall 1977). However, no adults have been seen laying eggs in this pond (which has a very short hydroperiod) so its viability as a population is unknown (Ewald, pers. obs.).

Chirocephalus diaphanus (fairy shrimp)

The second archetypal temporary pond species for which research work exists is the fairy shrimp *Chirocephalus diaphanus*. It is listed as RDB vulnerable (Bratton 1991) and is known from 72 10-km squares nationally (Bratton and Fryer 1990). In the New Forest it has been recorded from seven 10-km squares and is present in 10 to 15 ponds each year depending on weather conditions (Ewald 2008). The national breeding programme population was established with stock from a New Forest pond (P. Wisniewski, pers. comm.).

The species is confined to temporary ponds because it is apparently defenceless against predators (Bratton and Fryer 1990) and has the potential to reach maturity within three weeks (Hall 1953). Studies have looked at different aspects of their environment and the life history traits of *C. diaphanus*, many of which have been based on the New Forest populations (Ewald 2008, Hall 1953, 1959a,b,c, 1961, Khalaf and Hall 1975, Lake 1969, Taylor 1965). In summary, *C. diaphanus* is tolerant of a wide range of temperatures (5°C–26°C, Nourisson 1964) and has been known to survive at temperatures above 30°C (Mura 1991) and at low temperatures (e.g. Hall (1961) observed the species under ice), although their survival and reproductive ability is affected at these extremes (Lake 1969). Water depth has also been identified as a significant factor limiting egg hatching (Hall 1959c). However, the impact of predation on this species has not been investigated, until now (Ewald 2008).

Protection and conservation status

Temporary ponds in the New Forest fall short of the Habitats Directive definition of Mediterranean temporary ponds (European Commission 1992), although the statement for the New Forest SAC acknowledges that they support elements of the floral assemblage associated with that habitat (JNCC 2008).

In fact, Macabendroth (2004) has found that the New Forest ponds contain slightly fewer invertebrate species than the Mediterranean temporary ponds (as defined in the SAC) on the Lizard Peninsula, but that the New Forest ponds show greater heterogeneity. Several sites within the New Forest are included within the 'Oligotrophic to mesotrophic standing waters with vegetation of the *Littorelletea uniflorae* and/or of the *Isoëto-Nanojuncetea*' definition (European Commission 1992), although this is only a small percentage of the total number of ponds (Ewald, pers. obs.).

Despite the lack of Annex 1 status, the importance of the temporary ponds has been acknowledged in the New Forest SAC management plan (Wright and Westerhoff 2001), which highlights the conservation importance of both the plant and animal species that they support. The citation for the New Forest SSSI also includes temporary ponds as a reason for notification because of the nationally important assemblages of rare and scarce invertebrates (Natural England 1996). In addition the Hampshire Biodiversity Action Plan (Hampshire Biodiversity Partnership 1998) requires an individual habitat action plan to be written because of the importance of ephemeral pools and their conservation value in maintaining the county's biodiversity. However, few documented management prescriptions exist for these ponds, and it is worth considering here some of their requirements and the key threats that they currently face.

Habitat management

In most cases, the management prescription for temporary ponds will be non-intervention (Biggs *et al.* 2001), the ideal being numerous ponds across a range of environmental conditions. The New Forest is unique in the UK because it provides this pond heterogeneity within a mosaic of habitats. Data collected on Coleoptera occurring within the New Forest marl pits (number of sites surveyed =14, total beetle species = 87) showed that pond complexes contained the highest number of species. Isolated marl pit ponds contained an average of 18 beetle species, whilst those within a complex of ponds, as for example at Crockford Bridge, had on average of 26 species per pond (Ewald 2008).

As already mentioned, continuity of grazing is important for the temporary ponds on the New Forest lawns. It ensures that at least 25–75% of the habitat will remain open at the end of the summer (Wright and Westerhoff 2001). It also provides both areas of bare, poached mud, important for specialist plant and animal species (Chatters 1996), and a supply of dung, whose nutrients form the basis of the temporary pond food chain (Kuller and Gasith 1996, Tubbs 1997, Williams 1987).

Grazing is also important for other temporary ponds, including the base-rich marl sites. *Bidessus unistriatus* is one of the rarest beetles in Britain, currently known from only three sites, one of which is in the New Forest (Foster 2006). The shallow, neutral poached pools on the edge of this pond are thought to be important for its survival. In fact it was lost from a second site in the New Forest because the site became very heavily overgrown with scrub (Foster 2006). A survey (2007) for Coleoptera in New Forest marl pits, showed that sites which had been cleared of scrub for a number of years (greater than 5), or those which appeared to have always maintained at least one pond that was open within a complex of ponds, had the greatest number of beetle species. Within one complex, ponds that were open contained 20% more species than those that were shaded (Ewald 2008).

It is important, though, to consider heterogeneity within individual ponds and not just between sites. One temporary pond in the New Forest is a site for both *Hirudo medicinalis* (medicinal leech) and *Omphiscola glabra* (the mud snail). As this is one of only six ponds in the New Forest known to hold *H. medicinalis* (Reeves 1998), a species that requires high temperatures (Ausden and Dawes 2000), the decision was made to clear willow scrub from half of the pond (M. Noble, pers. comm.). Two years later, the number of juvenile leech in the pond had doubled and continues to be high (Ewald, pers. obs.). However, the pond is also a site for *Omphiscola glabra*, which in many of the New Forest sites appears to prefer ponds with a layer of leaf litter sediment (M. Willing, pers. comm.; Ewald 2008). This species is also rare in the UK, with a scattering of sites in the New Forest. Thus, the fact that the site remains partly shaded provides heterogeneity, benefiting both species.

Invasive species: New Zealand pigmyweed *Crassula helmsii*

Invasion by alien species is recognised as a significant global threat to the diversity of native flora and fauna (Glowka *et al.* 1994, Hobbs and Huenneke 1992, Vitousek *et al.* 1997). The threat is also recognised in the UK, at both national (Clement and Foster 1994, DEFRA 2003, Williamson 1999) and local scales (Hampshire Biodiversity Partnership 1998, Wright and Westerhoff 2001). One such invasive alien weed, New Zealand pigmyweed *Crassula helmsii* has been identified as a major threat to UK freshwaters (Dawson and Warman 1987, Huckle 2007, Leach and Dawson 1999). It is a perennial plant with both aquatic and terrestrial growth forms and is tolerant of a wide range of environmental conditions (Leach and Newman 2000). It was first recorded as 'naturalised' in a pond in Essex in 1956 (Dawson and Warman 1987) and in the New Forest in 1976 (Crutchley and Wicks 2001).

In a survey by Hampshire and Isle of Wight Wildlife Trust (HWT) in 1999, it was found that 39% of water bodies surveyed within or adjacent to the New Forest SAC contained *Crassula helmsii* (Crutchley and Wicks 2001). A fourfold increase in its distribution was recorded in 10 years, from 21 sites in 1990 to 76 sites in 1999 (Crutchley and Wicks 2001). It is easily spread as tiny fragments of stem and in some circumstances it forms extremely dense stands of vegetation (Stone 2002), which can lead to severe oxygen depletion (Newman 2004).

Despite concerns, few experiments have been conducted to investigate what impact *Crassula helmsii* has on native flora and fauna. There are anecdotal accounts of its impact on notable flora in the New Forest (Crutchley and Wicks 2001). At Hatchet Pond Triangle in 1986, *C. helmsii* was recorded along with pillwort *Pilularia globulifera*, but the latter had disappeared by the 1999 survey. Both Hampshire-purslane *Ludwigia palustris* and slender marsh-bedstraw *Galium constrictum* were recorded from Hill Top Pond in 1976, but by 1986 *C. helmsii* was abundant and only *L. palustris* remained. By 1999, only *C. helmsii* was present (Crutchley and Wicks 2001). Langdon *et al.* (2004) have shown that *C. helmsii* can suppress the germination of native plants by up to 83%; however, there is no significant loss of plant species. They also found that the developmental stage of great crested newts *Triturus cristatus* at hatching was unaffected whether eggs were laid on *C. helmsii* or on another plant. Whilst smooth newt *Lissotriton vulgaris* eggs were at a later developmental stage on hatching when they were laid on *C. helmsii*, this may have had no effect on overall population numbers.

In a supplementary study, *Crassula helmsii* had no significant effect on macro-invertebrate species richness, species diversity or community composition when comparing four ponds with and four ponds without heavy infestations (>75% cover). However, there was a significant increase in the diversity of molluscs in ponds with *C. helmsii*, possibly because of the greater surface area provided by *C. helmsii* from which they could graze algae. There was no significant decline or increase in any other taxonomic group between the ponds. It is worth noting that it was difficult to find enough ponds with which to perform a comparative study. This was because, although the number of ponds with *C. helmsii* has increased since the HWT survey, presumably spreading outward from areas of infestation by the action of grazing ponies, the density of *C. helmsii* at many sites had declined, kept in check it would seem by the grazing animals (Ewald 2008).

In the light of these results, more investigation is needed on the impact of *Crassula helmsii* on the conservation value of temporary ponds in the New Forest SAC and on how grazing may suppress *C. helmsii* (Dawson and Warman 1987).

What effect will climate change have on New Forest temporary ponds?

In the UK, human-induced climate change is likely to result in increases in average annual temperature, with greatest warming in summer and autumn. The onset of temperature rise in spring is expected to be one to three weeks earlier and the onset of winter temperature declines one to three weeks later (Hulme *et al.* 2002). Annual rainfall may decrease, but seasonal differences are likely to lead to less rainfall in the summer months and a greater risk of storm events in the winter (Fowler et al. 2005; Hulme et al. 2002). Cloud cover and relative humidity are expected to decrease, with a corresponding increase in solar radiation (Hulme et al. 2002). The New Forest falls within the UK South East region, where average daily temperatures are expected to increase by between 3°C and 5°C by 2080. Summer precipitation is predicted to decrease by 15–60% and winter precipitation to increase by 15–30% (Hulme et al. 2002).

Temporary ponds have a delicately balanced hydrological regime and may therefore be under increased threat from climate change (Bailey-Watts et al. 2000, Graham 1997). Temporary ponds are subject to predictable changes on a seasonal and annual basis, i.e. in any one year, there will be a dry phase, followed by an autumnal through to spring wet phase. Species within temporary ponds are adapted to respond to these changes (Wiggins et al. 1980, Williams 1997, Williams 2006). However, in some years temperatures may be below or above the physiological tolerances of species normally found within temporary pools, or there may be no rainfall at times when these temperatures persist. In these unsuitable years, species may not be reproductively successful but they have bet-hedging strategies to allow them to recover and replenish the population in the next suitable year (Cohen 1966). Climate change is likely to increase both within- and between-year variation in precipitation and temperature and hence alter the hydrological regimes permanently beyond the tolerances of specialist species and perhaps beyond the abilities of species to recover (Williams and Biggs 1998).

The impact of changing climatic conditions on pond communities and the sensitivity of temporary pond species to change was illustrated by field observations of New Forest temporary ponds, both within and between years. In year one of an investigation (2004/2005) in the month when the pond filled, mean temperatures were 11.3°C, sunshine hours were 107.0 hours and rainfall was 129.6 mm. In the second year (2005/2006) temperatures were higher, 17.1°C, but sunshine hours were similar (105.6 hours) and rainfall was less, 98.0 mm (Met Office 2004/2005), affecting when the pond filled: at the end of September in year 1 and the end of October in year 2 (Ewald 2008). Temporary ponds in the New Forest experienced a reduction in water levels between years one and two, as a result of a reduction in rainfall and an increase in temperature which increased evaporation rates (Hulme et al. 2002).

Investigation showed that the communities from different pond types (Table 45) responded differently to changes in climatic conditions. Woodland ponds (groups 7–11) remained stable between years; retaining the same macro-invertebrate community composition despite changes in climatic conditions. Ponds in open habitats (groups 1–6) such as those on the New Forest lawns, including species such as Chirocephalus diaphanus, were less stable and changed in community composition between years. Species diversity in these ponds was also significantly less in year 2 compared with year 1. The results would suggest that the open exposed ponds, which have the highest biodiversity value, may be most at risk from changes in climate.

Changes in community composition may result from the environmental tolerance limits of individual species being exceeded or disruption of the complex interactions between species. Laboratory experiments investigated the impacts of temperature on the life history traits of two species characteristic of the grassland pools in the New Forest: Chirocephalus diaphanus and one of its predators, Heterocypris incongruens. Reared in the absence of the predator, hatching success and fecundity for C. diaphanus were greatest at 20°C, followed by 10°C. Despite hatching early and growing quickly initially, most individuals were killed by temperatures of 25°C. Therefore, modest temperature increases beyond those currently experienced would benefit C. diaphanus, but a marked increase would have a negative impact on their performance (Ewald 2008). However, the hatching success of the predator H. incongruens was greatest at 25°C and rates of predation were significantly higher at 20°C compared with 10°C. The predator benefited more from an increase in temperature than the prey, such that the optimal temperature for C. diaphanus survival, in the presence of H. incongruens, is only 10°C. This is at the lower limit of the temperature range currently experienced by C. diaphanus in the field.

Predicting the impacts of climate change on invertebrate communities in temporary ponds will clearly be complex, but the results from this study suggest that large increases in temperature will have adverse effects on prey, whilst even small increases in temperature will be very detrimental where such changes increase the rate of predation and/or increase predator growth rates, to a greater extent than those of the prey.

Management recommendations

The temporary ponds of the New Forest are an important habitat type, both in terms of the species they contain and the contribution they make to the biodiversity of the New Forest. They also provide important study systems to assess the impact of environmental change. Although there is no immediate need for management intervention, a long-term management plan for these ponds would ensure that heterogeneity is maintained and that overall numbers of temporary ponds do not decline further.

There are currently gaps in our knowledge, particularly with regard to species distributions, of both rare and common taxa. Even when the distribution and status of rare species are known, it is often difficult to determine management prescriptions because of a lack of knowledge about species requirements. More work is required to assess the impact of potential threats, for example invasive alien species and climate change, in order to implement effective conservation strategies. Continued survey and a programme of monitoring would help to answer these questions. Although single species surveys are obviously extremely important, a community level approach will ultimately provide more useful insights into the condition and status of temporary pond communities.

References

Ausden, M. and Dawes, S. (2000). *Medicinal leech progress report June 1999 to December 1999*. UK Medicinal Leech BAP Steering Group.

Bailey-Watts, T., Lyle, A., Battarbee, R., Harriman, R. and Biggs. J. (2000). Lakes and ponds, In Acerman, M. (ed.) *The hydrology of the UK: a study of change*, pp. 180–203. Routledge, London.

Balfour-Browne, F. (1909). Notes on the rediscovery of *Apus cancriformis* in Britain. *Annales of Scottish Natural History*, 118.

Balfour-Browne, F. (1950). *British water beetle species*, volume II. The Ray Society, London.

BBC. (2004). Ancient creatures found in firth. http://news.bbc.co.uk/1/hi/scotland/3714524.stm

Biggs, J., Fox, G., Nicolet, P., Whitfield M. and Williams, P. (2001). Dangers and opportunities in managing temporary ponds. In Sutcliffe, D. and Rouen, K. (eds.) *European Temporary Ponds: a threatened habitat. Freshwater Forum*, 17, 71–80.

Biggs, J., Williams, P., Whitfield, M., Nicolet, P. and Weatherby, A. (2005). 15 years of pond assessment in Britain: results and lessons learned from the work of Pond Conservation. *Aquatic Conservation – Marine and Freshwater Ecosystems*, 15, 693–714.

Boycott, A. E. (1936). The habitats of fresh-water mollusca in Britain. *Journal of Animal Ecology*, 5,116–186.

Bratton, J. H. (1990). Seasonal pools, an overlooked invertebrate habitat. *British Wildlife*, 2, 22–29.

Bratton, J. H. (1991). *Invertebrates: Red Data Books*, vol. 3. JNCC, Peterborough.

Bratton, J. H., and Fryer, G. (1990). The distribution and ecology of *Chirocephalus diaphanus* Prevost (Branchiopoda, Anostraca) in Britain. *Journal of Natural History*, 24, 955–964.

Buckley, J. (2001). The conservation and management of amphibians in UK temporary ponds, with particular reference to natterjack toads. In Sutcliffe, D. and Rouen, K. (eds.) *European Temporary Ponds: a threatened habitat. Freshwater Forum*, 17, 54–62.

Chatters, C. (1996). Conserving rare plants in muddy places. *British Wildlife*, 7(5), 281–286.

Clement, E. J. and Foster, M. C. (1994). *Alien plants of the British Isles: a provisional catalogue of vascular plants (excluding grasses)*. Botanical Society of the British Isles, London.

Cohen, D. (1966). Optimizing reproduction in a randomly varying environment. *Journal of Theoretical Biology*, 12, 119–129.

Collinson, N. H., Biggs, J., Corfield, A., Hodson, M. J., Walker, D., Whitfield, M., and Williams, P. J. (1995). Temporary and permanent ponds – an assessment of the effects of drying out on the conservation value of aquatic macroinvertebrate communities. *Biological Conservation*, 74,125–133.

Crutchley, S. and Wicks, D. (2001). *Australian swamp stonecrop (Crassula helmsii) in the New Forest: an assessment of current distribution and potential for eradication*. Hampshire and Isle of Wight Wildlife Trust, Curdridge, Hampshire.

Dawson, F. H. and Warman, E. A. (1987). Crassula helmsii (T-Kirk) Cockayne – is it an aggressive alien aquatic plant in Britain? *Biological Conservation*, 42, 247–272.

DEFRA. (2003). Review of non-native species policy: Report of the working group. Department for Environment, Food and Rural affairs, London.

Elliott, J. M., Humpesch, U. H. and Macan, T. T. (1988). *Larvae of the British Ephemeroptera: a key with ecological notes*. Freshwater Biological Association, Ambleside, Cumbria.

European Commission. (1992). *On the conservation of natural habitats and of wild fauna and flora*. Council Directive 92/43/EEC 21 May 1992.

Ewald, N. C. (2001). *Report to identify and study the biotic and abiotic factors which affect the presence of Triops cancriformis in temporary ponds in the New Forest, Hampshire*. Bsc(Hons) thesis, Farnborough College of Technology, Farnborough.

Ewald, N. C. (2008). *The impact of climate change on temporary pond macroinvertebrate communities*. DPhil thesis, University of Sussex, Brighton, Sussex.

Foster, G. N. (2006). *The status of the one-grooved diving beetle Bidessus unistriatus (Goeze, 1777) (Coleoptera, Dytiscidae) in Britain – an update*. Report to the Environment Agency, The Aquatic Coleoptera Conservation Trust.

Fowler, H. J., Ekstrom, M., Kilsby, C. G. and Jones, J. I. (2005). New estimates of future changes in extreme rainfall across the UK using regional climate model integrations. 1. Assessment of control climate. *Journal of Hydrology*, 300, 212–233.

Fox, H. M. (1949). On *Apus* – its rediscovery in Britain, nomenclature and habits. *Proceedings of the Zoological Society of London*, 119, 693–702.

Friday, L. (1988). A key to the adults of British water beetles. *Field Studies*, 7, 1–151.

Fryer, G. (1966). *Branchinecta gigas* Lynch, a non-filter-feeding raptory anostracan, with notes on the feeding habits of certain other anostracans. *Proceedings of the Linnean Society of London*, 177, 19–34.

Glowka, L., Burhenne-Guilmin, F. and Synge, H. (1994). *A guide to the Convention on Biological Diversity*. IUCN, Cambridge and Gland.

Graham, T. B. (1997). Climate change and ephemeral pool ecosystems: potholes and vernal pools as potential indicator systems. In *Impacts of Climate Change and Land Use in the Southwestern United States*. World Wide Web poster session. http://geochange.er.usgs.gov/sw/

Gray, J. and Taylor, D. W. (1988). Evolution of the fresh-water ecosystem – the fossil record. *Palaeogeography, Palaeoclimatology, Palaeoecology*, 62, 1–214.

Hall, R. E. (1953). Observations on the hatching of eggs of *Chirocephalus diaphanus* Prevost. *Proceedings of the Zoological Society of London*, 123, 95–109.

Hall, R. (1976). *Conservation of the Notostracan crustacean Triops cancriformis. Report on the year October 1975 – October 1976*. World Wildlife Fund, Godalming.

Hall, R. (1977). *Conservation of the Notostracan crustacean Triops cancriformis. Report on the year December 1976 – December 1977*. World Wildlife Fund, Godalming.

Hall, R. E. (1959a). Delayed development of eggs of *Chirocephalus diaphanus* Prevost. *Hydrobiologia*, 13, 160–169.

Hall, R. E. (1959b). The development of eggs of *Chirocephalus diaphanus* Prevost at a low temperature. *Hydrobiologia*, 13, 156–159.

Hall, R. E. (1959c). The development of eggs of *Chirocephalus diaphanus* Prevost in relation to depth of water. Hydrobiologia 13:79–84.

Hall, R. E. (1961). On some aspects of the natural occurrence of *Chirocephalus diaphanus* Prevost. *Hydrobiologia*, 17, 205–217.

Hampshire and Isle of Wight Wildlife Trust. unpublished. *Notes on the wetting and drying patterns of a temporary pond in the New Forest.* Paper notes by various authors. Hampshire and Isle of Wight Wildlife Trust, Curdridge, Hampshire.

Hampshire Biodiversity Partnership. (1998). *Biodiversity Action Plan for Hampshire. Volume 1.* Hampshire County Council.

Hempel-Zawitkowska, J. (1967). Natural history of *Triops cancriformis* (Bosc.). *Zoologica Poloniae*, 17, 173–239.

Henderson, P. A. (1990). *Freshwater ostracods: synopsis of the British fauna (New Series).* vol. 42. Universal Book Services, Oegstgeest, Netherlands.

Hobbs, R. J. and Huenneke, L. F. (1992). Disturbance, diversity and invasion – implications for conservation. *Conservation Biology*, 6, 324–337.

Hobson, A. D. and Omer-Cooper, J. (1935). *Apus cancriformis* in Great Britain. *Nature*, 135, 972.

Huckle, J. (2007). *The Invasive Alien Species Project: Crassula helmsii.* Fact Sheet 1. English Nature and University of Liverpool.

Hulme, M., Jenkins, G. J., Lu, X., Turnpenny, J. R., Mitchell, T. D., Jones, R. G., Lowe, J., Murphy, J. M., Hassell, D., Boorman, P., McDonald, R. and Hill, S. (2002). *Climate change scenarios for the United Kingdom.* The UKCIP02 Scientific Report. Norwich, Tyndall Centre for Climate Change Research, School of Environmental Sciences, University of East Anglia.

JNCC. (2008). Special Areas of Conservation: Habitats Accounts. Freshwater Habitats: 3170 Mediterranean temporary ponds. http://www.jncc.gov.uk/

Khalaf, A. N. and Hall, R. E. (1975). Embryonic development and hatching of *Chirocephalus diaphanus* Prevost (Crustacea-Anostraca) in Nature. *Hydrobiologia*, 47,1–11.

Khalaf, A. N. and Macdonald, L. J. (1975). Physicochemical conditions in temporary ponds in the New Forest. *Hydrobiologia*, 47, 301–318.

Kuller, Z. and Gasith, A. (1996). Comparison of the hatching process of the tadpole shrimps *Triops cancriformis* and *Lepidurus apus* Lubbocki (Notostraca) and its relation to their distribution in rain-pools in Israel. *Hydrobiologia*, 335,147–157.

Lake, P. S. (1969). The effect of temperature on growth, longevity and egg production in *Chirocephalus diaphanus* Prévost (Crustacea: Anostraca). *Hydrobiologia*, 33, 342–351.

Langdon, S. J., Marrs R. H., Hosie C. A., McAllister H. A., Norris K. M. and Potter J. A.. (2004). *Crassula helmsii* in UK ponds: Effects on plant biodiversity and implications for newt conservation. *Weed Technology*, 8, 1349–1352.

Leach, J. and Dawson, F. H. (1999). *Crassula helmsii*: an unwelcome invader. *British Wildlife*, 10, 234–239.

Leach, J. and Newman, J. R. (2000). *Myriophyllum aquaticum, Crassula helmsii, Hydrocotyle ranunculoides* and *Azolla filiculoides.* In P. Bradley (ed.) *Exotic and invasive species: should we be concerned?* Proceedings 11th Conference of the Institute of Ecology and Environmental Management, 6 April 2000, pp. 62–71. Institute of Ecology and Environmental Management.

Macan, T. T. (1977). *A key to the fresh and brackish-water Gastropods.* Vol. 13, Freshwater Biological Association, Ambleside, Cumbria.

Maitland, P. S. (1995). *Species Action Plan: tadpole shrimp Triops cancriformis (Bosc 1801) (Crustacea, Notostraca).* Triops Conservation Group, London.

McAbendroth, L. (2004). *The ecology and conservation value of Mediterranean temporary ponds.* DPhil thesis, University of Plymouth, Plymouth.

Met Office. (2004/2005). *Monthly summaries.* http://www.metoffice.gov.uk/

Mura, G. (1991). Life-history and interspecies relationships of *Chirocephalus diaphanus* Prevost and *Tanymastix stagnalis* (L.), (Crustacea, Anostraca) inhabiting a group of mountain ponds in Latium, Italy. *Hydrobiologia*, 212, 45–59.

Natural England. (1996). *New Forest SSSI notification.* http://www.naturalengland.org.uk/

Newman, J. R. (2004). *Information Sheet 11: Australian Swamp Stonecrop.* Centre for Ecology and Hydrology, Wallingford, Oxon.

Nicolet, P. (2002). *The classification and conservation value of wetland plant and macroinvertebrate assemblages in temporary ponds in England and Wales.* DPhil thesis, Oxford Brookes University, Oxford.

Nicolet, P., Biggs, J., Fox, G., Hodson, M. J., Reynolds, C., Whitfield, M. and Williams, P. (2004). The wetland plant and macroinvertebrate assemblages of temporary ponds in England and Wales. *Biological Conservation*, 120, 261–278.

Nourisson, M. (1964). Existence d'un intervalle de température favorable an développement des œeufs asséchés de *Chirocephalus stagnalis* Shaw. *Comptes rendus l'Académie des sciences de Paris*, 253,1994–1996.

Pond Action. (1998). *A guide to the methods of the National Pond Survey.* Pond Conservation, Oxford.

Pond Conservation, and Environment Agency. (2002). *A guide to monitoring the ecological quality of ponds and canals using PSYM.* Environment Agency Midlands Region.

Reeves, R. (1998). *New Forest medicinal leech survey 1998 interim report.* Hampshire and Isle of Wight Wildlife Trust, Curdridge, Hampshire.

Sanderson, N. (2001). A provisional classification of the flora of New Forest temporary ponds. In Westerhoff, D. and Wright, R. (eds.) *New Forest SAC management plan.* English Nature, Lyndhurst.

Savage, A. A. (1989). *Adults of the British aquatic Hemiptera Heteroptera: a key with ecological notes.* Freshwater Biological Association, Ambleside, Cumbria.

Stone, I. (2002). War against *Crassula helmsii* – one year on. *Enact*, English Nature, 10, 9–10.

Tasch, P. (1963). Evolution of the Branchiopoda. In: *Phylogeny and evolution of Crustacea* (eds. Whittington, H. B. and Rolfe, W. D. I.) , pp. 145–162. Museum of Comparative Zoology, Cambridge.

Taylor, E. W. (1965). *An investigation of the physicochemical adaptations fitting Chirocephalus diaphanus for life in temporary ponds*. DPhil thesis, University of Southampton, Southampton.

Tubbs, C. R. (1986). *The New Forest*. New Naturalist Series. Collins, London.

Tubbs, C. R. (1997). The ecology of pastoralism in the New Forest. *British Wildlife*, 9, 7–16.

Vitousek, P. M., Dantonio, C. M., Loope, L. L., Rejmanek, M. and Westbrooks, R. (1997). Introduced species: A significant component of human-caused global change. *New Zealand Journal of Ecology*, 21, 1–16.

Wallace, I. D., Wallace B. and Philipson, G. N. (1990). *A key to the case-bearing caddis larvae of Britain and Ireland*. Vol. 51. Freshwater Biological Association, Ambleside, Cumbria.

Wiggins, G. B. (1973). A contribution to the biology of caddisflies (Trichoptera) in temporary pools. *Royal Ontario Museum Life Science Contributions*, 88, 1–28.

Wiggins, G. B., Mackay R. J. and Smith, I. M. (1980). Evolutionary and ecological strategies of animals in annual temporary pools. *Archiv für Hydrobiologie*, 58, 97–206.

Williams, D. D. (1987). *The ecology of temporary waters*. Croom Helm Ltd., Beckenham, Kent.

Williams, D. D. (1997). Temporary ponds and their invertebrate communities. *Aquatic Conservation-Marine and Freshwater Ecosystems*, 7, 105–117.

Williams, D. D. (2006). *The biology of temporary waters*. Oxford University Press, Oxford.

Williams, P. and Biggs, J. (1998). *Seasonal ponds: indicators of climate change*. Pond Conservation, Oxford

Williams, P., Biggs, J., Fox, G., Nicolet, P. and Whitfield, M. (2001). History, origins and importance of temporary ponds. In Sutcliffe, D. and Rouen, K. (eds.) *European Temporary Ponds: a threatened habitat. Freshwater Forum*, 17, 7–15.

Williams P.J., Briggs, J., Barr, C. J., Cummins, C. P., Gillespie, M. K., Rich, T. C. G., Baker, A., Beaseley, J., Corfield, A., Dobson, D., Collin, A. S., Fox, G., Howard, D. C., Luursema, K., Rich, M. M., Samson, D., Scott, W. A., White, R. and Whitfield, M. (1998). *Lowland Pond Survey 1996: Final Report*. Department of the Environment, Transport and the Regions, London.

Williamson, M. (1999). Invasions. *Ecography*, 22, 5–12.

Wood, P. J., Greenwood, M. T. and Agnew, M. D. (2003). Pond biodiversity and habitat loss in the UK. *Area*, 35, 206–216.

Wright, R. and Westerhoff, D. (2001). *New Forest SAC management plan*. English Nature, Lyndhurst.

Zierold, T., Hanfling, B. and Gomez, A. (2007). Recent evolution of alternative reproductive modes in the 'living fossil' *Triops cancriformis*. BMC *Evolutionary Biology*, 7, 161–173.

Plate 12
Dartford warbler
Sylvia undata.
Photo: David Kjaer

Plate 13
LEFT: New Forest Keeper
climbing to a
sparrowhawk's nest to
ring chicks *Accipiter nisus*.
RIGHT: New Forest
Keepers ringing
sparrowhawk chicks.
Photos: Isobel Cameron /
Forest Life picture library,
Forestry Commission

◀ **Plate 14**
Roydon river, providing good foraging for bat species such as barbastelle.
Photo: C. Mainstone

◀ **Plate 15**
Bechstein's bat *Myotis bechsteinii* in mist net.
Photo: P. Hope

◀ **Plate 16**
Barbastelle bat *Barbastellus barbastella*.
Photo: P. Hope

▲ **Plate 17**
**Adder *Vipera berus*
dragging its prey into the
long grass at the New
Forest Reptile Centre.**
Photo: Forest Life picture
library, Forestry
Commission

◄ **Plate 18**
**Male and female sand
lizards *Lacerta agilis*,
male showing breeding
coloration. This species
has recently been
reintroduced to the
New Forest.**
Photo: Isobel Cameron /
Forest Life picture library,
Forestry Commission

◄ **Plate 19**
Southern damselfly
Coenagrion mercuriale.
Photo: Phill Watts

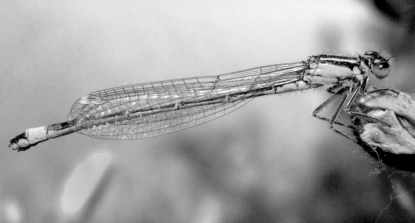

◄ **Plate 20**
Blue-tailed damselfly
Ischnura elegans.
Photo: Phill Watts

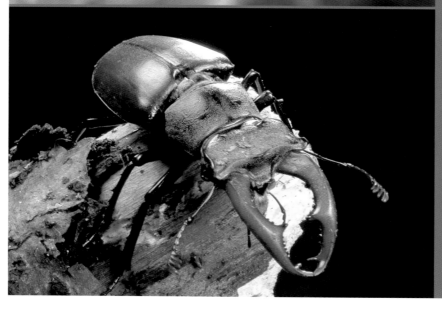

◄ **Plate 21**
Stag beetle
Lucanus cervus.
Photo: IACR, Rothamsted

◀ **Plate 22**
Noble chafer
Gnorimus nobilis.
Photo: Matt Smith

◀ **Plate 23** LEFT
Silver-studded blue
butterfly *Plebeius argus.*
Photo: Jim Asher

◀ **Plate 24** RIGHT
Small pearl-bordered
fritillary *Boloria selene.*
Photo: Jim Asher

◀ **Plate 25** LEFT
New Forest cicada
Cicadetta montana.
Photo: J. A. Grant

◀ **Plate 26** RIGHT
Wood cricket *Nemobius
sylvestris*, a nationally
scarce insect, for which
the population occurring
in the New Forest is the
largest in the UK.
Photo: Niels Brouwers

◀ **Plate 34**
A group of ancient beech trees that are exceptionally rich in lichen species, on the edge of a small glade at Lyndhurst Hill. In total these two trees support four RDB lichen species and three BAP species. The white streak on the largest tree proved to be a new species for the New Forest, *Anisomeridium robustum*. Such well lit but sheltered, leaning and twisted ancient beech trees are typically rich in rare and declining species.
Photo: Neil Sanderson

◀ **Plate 35**
A lichen mosaic in a rain track on an ancient beech in Mark Ash Wood, with the Critically Endangered RDB species *Enterographa elaborata* (paler thallus, long apothecia), along with *Enterographa hutchinsiae* (darker thallus, medium length apothecia), *Enterographa crassa* (dark thallus, short apothecia) and *Pyrenula chlorospila* (dark thallus, round perithecia). These lichens form a very specialist community of rain tracks on old beech.
Photo: Neil Sanderson

Plate 36 LEFT
Bearded tooth fungus
Hericium erinaceum.
Photo: A. Newton

Plate 37 RIGHT
Coral tooth fungus
Hericium coralloides.
Photo: A. Newton

Plate 38 LEFT
Nail fungus
Poronia punctata.
Photo: A. Newton

Plate 39 RIGHT
Zoned rosette fungus
Podoscypha multizonata.
Photo: A. Newton

Plate 40
Knothole yoke-moss
Zygodon forsteri on beech
root, near Rufus Stone.
Photo: P. Creed

◀ **Plate 41**
Looking towards Vales Moor and Strodgemoor Bottom, from Picket Plain, illustrating a typical mosaic of heathland, grassland and woodland communities.
Photo: A. Newton

◀ **Plate 42**
July regrowth on a recently burned heath, providing nutritious forage for ponies.
Photo: Clive Chatters

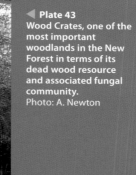

◀ **Plate 43**
Wood Crates, one of the most important woodlands in the New Forest in terms of its dead wood resource and associated fungal community.
Photo: A. Newton

◄ **Plate 50**
Pony and foal grazing in Long Slade Bottom.
Photo: Forest Life picture library, Forestry Commission.

◄ **Plate 51**
Red deer stag
Cervus elaphus.
Photo: Isobel Cameron / Forest Life picture library, Forestry Commission

◄ **Plate 52**
Fallow deer stags
Dama dama.
Photo: Isobel Cameron / Forest Life picture library, Forestry Commission

◀ **Plate 53**
Wood accumulation in the Highland Water, New Forest, winter 1997.
Photo: T. Langford

◀ **Plate 54**
Pond at Pilley Bailey, invaded by New Zealand pigmyweed *Crassula helmsii*.
Photo: A. Newton

◀ **Plate 55**
Hatchet Pond, botanically one of the most notable sites in the New Forest, and also an important habitat for invertebrates.
Photo: A. Newton

◀ **Plate 56**
Eyeworth pond.
Photo: A. Newton

◀ **Plate 57**
Valley mire.
Photo: Isobel Cameron / Forest Life picture library, Forestry Commission

◄ **Plate 58**
Burning of heathland
undertaken to manage
vegetation structure
and composition.
Photo: Dave Morris,
Forestry Commission

◄ **Plate 59**
Heather baling of
heathland.
Photo: Dave Morris,
Forestry Commission

◄ **Plate 60**
Heather baling and
burning of heathland (in
background), Rockford,
undertaken to manage
vegetation structure
and composition.
Photo: New Forest
National Park Authority

17 The contribution of the LIFE II and III projects to wetland conservation in the New Forest

Tim Holzer and Maxine Elliott

A Vision

"Retaining its [the New Forest's] integrity as an irreplaceable complex of wildlife habitats will continue to be the goal of the naturalists and conservationists who are involved. If the commitment to management for wildlife were great enough, perhaps restoration of its vanished features is not beyond possibility." (Derek Ratcliffe: March 2001, from Tubbs (2001)).

This statement by the late Derek Ratcliffe recognises the inherent and highly valued nature conservation importance of the New Forest and a strong desire to protect such interests. However, it also appears to invite interested parties to demonstrate just how committed they are by posing the ultimate challenge of restoring features that are not just damaged, but have gone altogether.

The conservation and restoration of wetland habitats in the New Forest represents a particularly significant challenge. In addition to the logistical difficulties involved of recreating or restoring complex natural processes, there are difficulties in working within such a sensitive environment where the restoration itself can result in at least short-term damage, and where the long-term implications of wetland restoration appear to be in conflict with other legitimate interests and activities.

High risk of project failure has been a driving force responsible for the evolution of a new approach to the conservation of wetland habitats in the New Forest under two successive initiatives, referred to as the LIFE II and LIFE III projects. The LIFE acronym comes from the European Union funding body *'L'Instrument Financier pour l'Environnement'*, of which LIFE-Nature is a component part. This fund assists nature conservation projects, targeting habitats and species populations, particularly Natura 2000 sites (Special Areas of Conservation (SAC) and Special Protection Areas (SPA)).

Each discrete tranche of LIFE funding has provided the opportunities and financial assistance to greatly increase the pace of practical conservation on the ground. However, highly ambitious programmes of conservation work have also succeeded on account of significant improvements to the consultation processes and stakeholder engagement.

The LIFE II project: 'Securing Natura 2000 Objectives in the New Forest'

The first of the two New Forest LIFE projects was one of the largest and most complex multi-agency projects ever funded by LIFE-Nature. It was a partnership project comprising English Nature, Forestry Commission, Hampshire County Council, Hampshire Wildlife Trust, National Trust, New Forest Committee, Ninth Centenary Trust, RSPB, Verderers of the New Forest and the Wiltshire Wildlife Trust. The five year project ran from 1997 to 2001 and had a budget of £5.2 million, 50% of which came from the LIFE-Nature funding body.

The LIFE II project aimed to draft a Management Plan for the 13 habitats and three species that comprised the features of the SAC, which extends over 29,000 ha. The Management Plan represents a fundamentally important tool for the successful management of such a large and complex area of habitats where the integration, consistency and consensus of management activities is paramount (Wright and Westerhoff 2001). The project also had ambitious targets to restore around 4,000 ha of degraded habitat, wetland components of which included bog woodland, mire, wet heath and ephemeral ponds. Land purchase featured amongst the key objectives in order to further facilitate sympathetic management.

The completion of a comprehensive mire-by-mire survey was particularly informative in characterising the condition of this wetland habitat type and resolving the extent and nature of damage, principally from historic drainage operations. Excellent progress was made through LIFE II on the delivery of conservation measures for non-wetland habitat types, primarily where management techniques were already in wide use across the Forest (e.g. tree and scrub removal from heath). However, progress with the restoration of wetland habitats (primarily the mires) was slow. Strong resistance to the reversal of historic drainage resulted in a failure to meet restoration targets, where around 170 ha of the targeted 500 ha received works to restore hydrological attributes. This highlighted the need for a specific approach to resolve differences of opinion between various New Forest interest groups. Future progress on the restoration of such wetland habitats would be strongly influenced by an ability to demonstrate that the long-term viability of livestock grazing would not be compromised. Indeed, given the importance of livestock as a management tool for many SAC habitats, including wetlands, the long-term viability of livestock grazing was in the interests of both conservation and Commoning alike.

This issue had been recognised in formulation of the LIFE II project, where the New Forest Verderers were able to introduce a pony premium scheme (with categories for ponies, mares, stallions, colts and mature stallions). This scheme provided financial incentives to commoners in return for improving the quality of the pony stock on the Forest. Increased sale value of the stock would also improve the economics of this activity and further assist in securing the long-term viability of grazing. However, this scheme was insufficient to allay all of the concerns relating to the perceived impact upon grazing habitat from wetland restoration.

In spite of difficulties experienced under the LIFE II project, significant conservation achievements for wetland habitats (primarily mires) were made, and the debate over the principles of wetland restoration in the New Forest was greatly advanced. The foundations for tackling this difficult issue were laid and there was strong support for a second bid to Europe and the LIFE III tranche of funding in order to pursue wetland conservation goals.

The LIFE III project: 'Sustainable Wetland Restoration in the New Forest'

The success of a bid for funding under the LIFE III programme can be attributed to a number of factors. Firstly, the LIFE-Nature funding body was impressed by the achievements of LIFE II, particularly in terms of successfully managing a large, diverse and potentially cumbersome partnership. Attention was drawn to the difficulties frequently encountered when trying to bring together wide and potentially diverging interests for a common purpose. Success in this area still represents something of a novelty and the development of best practice models was being strongly encouraged. The aspirations of a LIFE III partnership to tackle precisely this issue appealed to LIFE-Nature. A strong focus on SAC Priority habitats (bog woodland and alluvial forest), where restorative actions also have novelty value, was similarly instrumental in a successful bid. LIFE III ran from 2002 to 2006. It involved six partners including English Nature, Environment Agency, Forestry Commission, Hampshire County Council, The National Trust and RSPB and cost £2.9 million, 40% of which was funded by LIFE-Nature.

Restoration of alluvial forest brought with it new challenges, particularly where historic damage comprised extensive deepening, straightening and rerouting of the river channel and separation of it from its flood plain. Particularly problematic was the 'loss' of significant volumes of mineral material from the system where dredged material had been spread too

thinly to be recovered, and where increased flow energy had apparently caused large amounts of eroded material to be flushed from the system altogether. Whilst such works have historically been confined largely within the Inclosures (woodland enclosed for the purposes of silviculture), upstream migration of erosion extended the damage onto the Open Forest and into mire systems that had been the focus of much attention under LIFE II.

Taking a holistic, catchment-based approach to restoration of alluvial forest therefore extended remedial works up into mire systems, creating a tangible and necessary link between works under the two LIFE projects. The long-term sustainability of earlier mire work very much depended on comprehensive mends throughout the system.

The importation of very large volumes of mineral material required to backfill drains and raise river bed levels, together with the resulting changes in hydrological conditions, undoubtedly caused greatest concern for partners and stakeholders (see also Chapter 15). Smaller-scale pilots or demonstrations helped to build confidence that restoration on such a scale was possible and desirable. The resulting effect on flood plain functionality was visually dramatic during the onset of winter rainfall, as river channels began to make regular contact again with their flood plain. Restoration of such physical and hydrological processes enabled the SAC habitat to self-mend and thereafter perpetuate conditions that limit the requirement for further intervention, contributing to the sustainable approach to the restoration works advocated by the project.

The success of managing such extensive works relied heavily upon effective communication and consultation. This was achieved through the creation of a Water Basin Management Forum comprising representatives from around 20 interest groups, local experts and, importantly, an independent chair. Meeting three or four times each year, round-table and in the field, proved invaluable in achieving the necessary progress on the ground and has been heralded as a consultation model.

It is a tribute to the success of effective consultation through both LIFE projects, but particularly that achieved through the Water Basin Management Forum in LIFE III, that so much wetland habitat was restored to favourable or unfavourable-improving condition (see Chapter 12 for definitions) between 1997 and 2006 (Table 46).

Table 46
Wetland habitat restoration works under LIFE Projects 1997 to 2006.

Habitat	LIFE II	LIFE III	Comment
Alluvial Forest	0 ha	261 ha, 10 km river length	Major hydrological restoration and vegetation management. Required the importation of over 28,500 tonnes of mineral material otherwise lost from the system from previous drainage works
Bog Woodland	1.5 ha	18 ha	Hydrological restoration and vegetation management
Valley Mire	170 ha	184 ha	Hydrological restoration and vegetation management
Ephemeral Ponds	3	0	Mostly vegetation management
Wet Grassland	0 ha	141 ha	Mostly vegetation management with some hydrological restoration

Table 47
Selected wetland management interventions proposed in the New Forest for the period 2006–2016, focusing on ecological and nature conservation issues. Adapted from the Wetland Management Plan (Smith 2006).

Ecological and nature conservation issues	Proposed actions
Condition status of habitats	• Restoration of wetland habitats to achieve 95% SSSI favourable condition status by 2010
Drying of mires	• Mire restoration
Drainage and canalisation resulting in loss of flooding regime resulting in habitat degradation	• Restoration of rivers and associated floodplain function
Invasion of pest and exotic species	• Removal of exotics and pest species • Increase knowledge of distribution of pest species
Dead wood removal and debris dams	• Remove cut timber and brash, especially conifer fellings from the floodplain
Coppice of alder/sallow stands in riverine woodland	• Undertake coppicing and pollarding work in selected locations
Trapped pre-Inclosure riverine and bog woodland	• Restoration of natural flood regime, selective felling and scrub removal, reintroduction of grazing
Effect of river restoration on fish species	• Monitoring • Planning timing of works to avoid migration and spawning periods • Use of sediment mats in sensitive location to avoid smothering of downstream gravels
Effects of debris dams on fish	• Monitoring of debris dams to ensure that passage of migratory fish is unimpeded
Effect of channelisation on macro-invertebrate communities	• Restoration of hydraulic connectivity and channel variation • Survey and monitor existing and future works
Decline in breeding wader populations	• Implementation of initiatives from Progress Project • Ongoing wetland habitat restoration • Continued survey and monitoring
Low flows placing stress on fish populations	• Continue mire restoration • Support Catchment Abstraction Management • Strategy process, developed by Environment Agency • Support/help with initiatives to improve water quality

New Forest Wetland Management Plan 2006 to 2016

Continuing on with the successes of LIFE II and III, work beyond the projects has formed the basis of a comprehensive management plan specific to wetland habitat within the New Forest SAC (Smith 2006). Drafted by the Forestry Commission in consultation with the LIFE partners and members of the Water Basin Management Forum, this document brings together a significant amount of information on factors influencing habitat characteristics and condition with the many issues that influence restoration. It distils and presents the experiences from the LIFE projects together with highly informative and illustrative case studies. More specifically, it represents the foundation for wetland conservation efforts in the New Forest to 2016 (Table 47).

Conclusion

Although the New Forest LIFE projects are unlikely to have restored habitats otherwise thought to have vanished, they have made a highly significant contribution to the restoration of wetland habitats hitherto in the process of vanishing. The Water Basin Management Forum and a 10-year catchment-based wetland habitat management plan together represent a worthy model for continuing such conservation efforts, as well as tackling the objectives and requirements of new conservation drivers such as the Water Framework Directive.

Detailed reporting on the LIFE II and III projects can be found in New Forest Life Partnership (2006) and at: http://www.newforestlife.org.uk/life2/life2index.htm.

References

New Forest Life Partnership (2006). *Sustainable wetland restoration in the New Forest*. Technical final report. LIFE Project Number LIFE02NAT/UK/8544. Hampshire County Council, Winchester, Hampshire.

Smith, J. (2006). *New Forest Wetland Management Plan 2006–2016*. Forestry Commission, Lyndhurst, Hampshire.

Tubbs, C. R. (2001). *The New Forest. History, ecology and conservation*. New Forest Ninth Centenary Trust, Lyndhurst.

Wright, R. N. and Westerhoff, D. V. (2001). *New Forest SAC Management Plan*. English Nature, Lyndhurst.

18 Biodiversity in the New Forest: a National Park perspective

Stephen Trotter and Ian Barker

Introduction

This chapter outlines the role of the recently established National Park, and reflects on some of the key strategic issues for wildlife conservation in the New Forest from a National Park perspective.

The previous chapters in this book provide a wealth of evidence demonstrating the significance of the wildlife interest in the New Forest. Within a small land area of only around 55,000 ha, the New Forest can justifiably lay claim to being one of the UK's key hotspots for wildlife on the basis of its richness of wild species and habitats (see also Chatters 2006, 2007). These contributions have also highlighted how little we know of our wildlife, despite the high profile of the area amongst naturalists and ecologists. Major gaps exist in survey coverage and our understanding of whether land management practices are maximising the quality and quantity of biodiversity that remains.

Table 48
The special qualities of the New Forest (New Forest National Park Authority 2008).

The New Forest National Park's landscape is unique; it is a 'living' and working remnant of medieval England with an overwhelming sense of continuity, tradition, and history. It is the survival of not just one special quality but a whole range of features that brings a sense of completeness and integrity.

These features include:
- the New Forest's outstanding natural beauty: the sights, sounds and smells of ancient woodland with veteran trees, heathland, bog, autumn colour and an unspoilt coastline with views of the Solent and Isle of Wight
- an extraordinary diversity of plants and animals of international importance
- a unique historic, cultural and archaeological heritage from royal hunting ground to shipbuilding, salt-making and 500 years of military coastal defence
- a historic commoning system that maintains so much of what people know and love as 'the New Forest' forming the heart of a working landscape based on farming and forestry
- the iconic New Forest pony together with donkeys, pigs and cattle roaming free
- tranquillity in the midst of the busy, built-up south of England
- wonderful opportunities for quiet recreation, learning and discovery in one of the last extensive, gentle landscapes in the south including unmatched open access on foot and horseback
- a healthy environment: fresh air, clean water, local produce and a sense of 'wildness'
- strong and distinctive local communities with real pride in and sense of identity with their local area.

It is also important to remember that the New Forest is significant for a range of other special qualities in addition to its wildlife interest. The relatively unspoilt natural beauty, tranquillity and landscape character of the area are seen as being particularly important. A summary of the National Park's special qualities has recently been compiled by the National Park Authority following consultation with the public (see Table 48). A key point is that many of these attributes are related and frequently have interdependent relationships; individual elements should not be considered in isolation for management and conservation purposes, including the wildlife interest. The list has been produced as a tool to help focus conservation efforts on some of the key issues.

The New Forest has been highly valued, cherished and loved by many people for generations. Consequently, and as a result of a number of perceived and real threats to its special qualities over the years, the modern conservation movement has been prominent in 'defending' the New Forest since at least 1865 (Briscoe Eyre 1870, New Forest Association 2004).

For many years the administrative arrangements within the Forest seemed to be adequate to tackle the challenges facing the New Forest. These mostly related to internal land management issues and the balance between commoning interests and those of the Crown. However, more recently it had become apparent that these arrangements would not be sufficient to protect and conserve the Forest from a range of new pressures. In particular, those pressures arising from both social and economic change had the potential to cause serious impacts and potential damage to the special qualities of the Forest. Critically, the challenges were not only internal but also came from external threats. No single organisation had a holistic perspective or the powers to address these strategic planning issues across the whole of the New Forest (and not just the central core). Additionally, even though the Forest is a relatively intact landscape (at least compared to the rest of lowland England), its small size meant that it could not isolate itself from developments in the outside world and, as well as concentrating on the internal details of land and species management, the New Forest must look beyond its boundaries.

These considerations led, in 2005, to the designation of the New Forest National Park and the creation of a new National Park Authority, specifically to address the wider issues. This was despite the view held by some in the Forest that this might be an additional layer of bureaucracy in an already congested administrative landscape.

National Park designation in the New Forest

National Park designation provides the highest level of protection for landscape in UK legislation. The National Park Authority's role is to ensure that the two purposes of national park designation are achieved, in other words to act as the National Park's guardian. These purposes, common to all national parks, are:

- to conserve and enhance the natural beauty, wildlife and cultural heritage of the Park; and
- to promote opportunities for the understanding and enjoyment of the Park's special qualities by the public.

In doing this, the Authority also has a duty to seek to foster the social and economic wellbeing of local communities within the National Park.

The National Park Authority was formally established on 1 April 2005 and took on its full statutory powers and responsibilities on 1 April 2006, as the:

- local planning authority, responsible for spatial planning, minerals and waste planning, development control and enforcement and other related regulatory functions within the National Park;
- access authority and relevant authority for the National Park under the Countryside and Rights of Way Act 2000, dealing, for example, with applications for restrictions and closures. The Authority has also taken on joint responsibility for the New Forest Access Forum, in partnership with Hampshire County Council.

It is required to:

- produce a Management Plan for the National Park; and
- administer a Sustainable Development Fund.

Apart from these statutory functions, the National Park Authority also has wide powers to take forward the twin purposes of the National Park.

As a relative newcomer in the history of the New Forest, the organisation of the Authority and the way it works differs slightly from that of other national park authorities. It has relatively few staff because its role will focus on developing the strategic and policy framework for the National Park and advising on and facilitating the work of existing organisations, such as the Forestry Commission, to deliver national park purposes. Project work and action on the ground aims to support the work of partners who contribute to delivering national park purposes, to fill gaps in the coverage of existing providers and in so doing to avoid duplication.

The Authority's funding comes from central government (Defra) rather than local taxpayers. This reflects the fact that unlike local councils, its responsibilities extend well beyond its boundaries, as it is working with others to look after the National Park for the whole nation.

A key mechanism for achieving the Park's purposes will be the National Park Management Plan. Initial versions of this plan brought together several strategic planning and development control documents (i.e. combining the Local Development Framework Core Strategy and revised Development Control policies). As it continues to be developed, the National Park Plan will be for the National Park as a whole and for all those with a stake in it, not just for the National Park Authority. It is intended to provide the long-term strategic policy framework for the National Park and to guide the work of the Authority and all the other organisations, partners and stakeholders that can contribute to the delivery of the national park purposes.

The Government also sets out its expectations of National Parks, in consultation with Natural England and the National Park Authorities. These highlight the areas on which the Government particularly expects progress to be made in the period to 2012. They include the statutory duties and Defra's current *Strategic Priorities,* often enshrined in Public Service Agreements (PSAs), and *Departmental Strategic Objectives* such as:

- putting in place climate change mitigation and adaptation measures;
- contributing to the delivery of the Natural Environment PSA, retaining local landscape character, promoting landscape restoration and sustainable tourism, supporting implementation of the Water Framework Directive, delivery of agri-environment scheme outcomes, and biodiversity outcomes (including contributing to Defra's targets of bringing 95% of Sites of Special Scientific Interest into favourable condition by 2010, and reversing the decline of farmland birds);
- promoting the principles of sustainable development.

The National Park's approach to conservation

Conservation is a value-driven activity that is about people and their relationship with a place; it involves making choices about what we feel it is important to conserve. The Authority has a clear approach to 'conservation' in the New Forest. This accepts and embraces change as an inevitable process and recognises that the key to conserving and enhancing the special qualities is to manage, as far as possible, the direction and rate of change. By managing the process of change, we aim to transfer from the present to the future those significant features, characteristics and attributes that make the New Forest special and distinctive.

The important first step is to define exactly what is significant so that we can be clear about our priorities and work. This is the reason for attempting to define the special qualities (see Table 48) and refine our understanding of them. Further work is underway to define the detail beneath this headline list, including the development of a Biodiversity Action Plan. It is also about recognising that we aim to take a balanced and holistic approach across the wide range of qualities. That said, owing to the recognition in legislation of its international significance, nature conservation must be the clear priority for the National Park as, arguably, it is the most significant and foremost attribute of the New Forest.

What sustains the richness of the natural environment?

It is important to try to understand the factors that have created the New Forest's high value for nature conservation – and indeed what sustains this – if we are to devise strategies and policies to conserve the biota effectively.

A number of authors (e.g. Tubbs 1986, 2001; Chatters 1996, 2006, 2007; Vera 2000; Rose 1996) have identified some key drivers that are associated with and help to sustain the richness of the 'core' Open Forest. These include:

- The location, climate, geology and biogeography of the area (Tubbs 1986).
- The long and continuous history of extensive pastoral management that to some degree mimics the perception of what a natural system might look like (Vera 2000; see Chapter 13). Grazing, as a result of active commoning and the presence of four species of deer, acts as a proxy for the role of herbivores that are no longer present in modern-day ecosystems in the UK.
- Many of the fundamental drivers of keystone ecological processes that have often been lost elsewhere in the lowlands still appear to operate (albeit in a modified form) in the New Forest. Many are related to the actions of a mixture of large free-roaming herbivores, for example processes such as the creation of mud and bare ground, temporary water bodies and ponds, shifting dynamic habitat mosaics (although also strongly anthropogenically controlled in some places) of scrub, heath and woodland and so on.
- Long-established and sustained land management practices (e.g. heath burning and cutting) that seem to promote structural habitat diversity and maintain the open habitats (Tubbs 1986, 2001; Chatters 1996, 2006, 2007).
- The integrity of many habitat systems in which the ecological stress of low nutrient levels and low productivity is combined with grazing and ecological disturbance (Chatters 1996, 2006, 2007).
- The extensive nature of relatively unimproved and protected habitats at a landscape scale, and the comparatively low levels of internal fragmentation (including the minimal amount of fine-scale nature reserve manipulation as a land management tool, because of the scale of the landscape and relatively functional state of natural processes) (Chatters 1996, 2006, 2007).
- An apparent resilience to short-term incidents of disturbance and change, possibly owing to the inherent stability of species-rich communities. Even when change is dramatic, observers often report that the Forest seems to bounce back with new features of value and interest for conservation (Tubbs 1986, 2001, Chatters 2007).
- Low levels of disturbance and pollution (Tubbs 2001, Rose 1996).

Challenges and issues for the National Park

As noted by other chapters in this book, despite the general survival of these factors, there is evidence of an ongoing deterioration in the quantity and quality of the wildlife species present in recent decades. This probably reflects the wider changes in the UK countryside, driven to a considerable extent by the subsidy regime of the Common Agricultural Policy. However, the impacts of intensive farming practices have not been anywhere near as pronounced or damaging in the Forest as in many other lowland areas. Recent losses appear to have been the result of some subtle and not-so-subtle changes in the 'drivers' and management pressures on the New Forest. Some of the following changes, amongst others, may have had an impact on the biota of the New Forest:

- Drainage (and 'cultivation') for 'improving' the productivity of forestry and grazing (Tubbs 2001, Wright and Westerhoff 2001).
- Coniferisation and internal fragmentation of habitat blocks (Tubbs 1986, 2001; Sanderson 2007).
- Changes in the types of machinery and technology employed.
- Invasive 'problem' species (as addressed during the LIFE II and III projects; see Chapter 17).
- Changes in grazing intensity (Tubbs 1986, Oates 1996), and potentially changes in grazing type, for example in the ratios between cattle, ponies and deer.
- Recreational disturbance and associated impacts (Sharp et al. 2008).
- Increased diffuse pollution (e.g. atmospheric pollution from vehicles, sewage, nitrification, pesticides, veterinary products, light, noise, etc.).
- Ongoing shrinkage of the grazed area and loss of active management of peripheral commons (Cox and Reeves 2000).

However, these impacts have not obliterated or irreversibly damaged the interest across the whole Forest. Even areas of the Forest that were ploughed for food production during the Second World War have reverted to relatively diverse communities when given the chance (presumably because of the minimal use of inorganic fertilisers?). Some of these drivers continue to act on the Forest in combination with several external pressures.

External drivers

A number of critical external drivers are likely to affect the conservation of wildlife in the New Forest. Few, if any, of the new threats are likely to bring enhancements unless there is concerted and determined action by a range of partners and organisations to manage the impact of the changes. Some impacts may be completely preventable, if we anticipate them early enough; for others we may not be able to prevent them and we will have to concentrate on minimising their impact on the New Forest and help species to adapt as best they can.

Socio-economic change

Commoning, and the many related activities that have given rise to the special qualities of the area, are generally a function and product of the poverty and deprivation that the area has traditionally suffered, until recent decades. There are still pockets of relative rural deprivation but this is now, predominantly, an affluent area with major shifts in the socio-economic composition of local communities. The rural population involved in land management is now a minor proportion of the total population. For example, the population of the National Park is around 34,000 (New Forest National Park 2008), and there are in the region of 550 registered Commoners (Verderers 2008), with probably no more than 1500–2000 people involved in active commoning. The rural economy is also small and marginal in comparison to the mainstream economy. The trend towards a more urban-based population is likely to continue.

The financial returns from keeping livestock have similarly been under pressure. A recent study has shown how Commoners are losing money on their animals despite the efforts of Forest Friendly Farming initiatives and agri-environment scheme income (Ivey 2007). Increasingly, commoning is becoming as much a lifestyle choice as it is an economic necessity formed from the need to supplement an individual's income. Land and house prices are a significant barrier to new young Commoners becoming active and independent of their parents.

The National Park needs a strategy to sustain the land management processes that have caused the New Forest to develop and maintain its interest – principally commoning and pastoralism, but also other land management such as the work undertaken by the Forestry Commission and other landowners. Importantly we must design systems and processes to ensure that local people and land managers continue to have a stake in sustaining the wildlife of the New Forest. A Commoning Review (New Forest Commoning Review Group 2007), led by the Commoners themselves, has made some recommendations that should help to provide a sustainable future for active commoning (see Table 49).

If the fragile links that maintain the local social networks and structures start to fail, we could see the collapse of pastoralism in the medium to long term,

Table 49
Summary of the New Forest Commoning Review Recommendations (New Forest Commoning Review Group 2007).

	Open Forest grazing needs and conservation, financial returns and young people
2.1	Support the continuation of current schemes which provide direct support to Commoners for grazing their stock on the Open Forest, ensuring any benefits are available to young Commoners.
2.2	Support the continuation of locally tailored farm advisory support services to ensure that Commoners can utilise agri-environment and farm support schemes.
2.3	Support the continuation of existing schemes where these can demonstrate added value and business efficiencies to commoning enterprises i.e. New Forest Pony Publicity Group, Forest Friendly Farming Business Grant Scheme, Forest Friendly Farming Training Grant Scheme, New Forest Marque and New Forest Farmers and Producers Markets.
2.4	Explore opportunities to review the Defra Single Payment Scheme.
2.5	Consult with major landowners to investigate and develop opportunities for the use of land for back-up grazing and affordable homes for Commoners.
2.6	Provide financial and technical resources to support regular campaigns to reduce the speed of motorists travelling on the Forest.
2.7	Reduce collection costs of fallen stock on Forest roads.
2.8	Encourage Defra to consider a special derogation for the New Forest for the identification of horses.
2.9	Support the continuation of the Stallion Scheme, including raising awareness of the scheme with the general public.
2.10	Encourage Commoners to breed and register full-bred New Forest ponies.
2.11	Support the continuation of the current level of the Forestry Commission annual burning programme, providing resources if necessary to complete within the required time period.
2.12	Provide further assistance to investigate and develop markets for the bi-products of bracken cutting.
2.13	Work with the Forestry Commission to implement a programme for the reinstatement of lost forest lawns.
2.14	Assist in the defence of encroachments on the Open Forest, including raising awareness of the problem with local landowners and developers.
2.15	Assist with the upkeep of forest fencing used in the rounding up of Forest stock.
2.16	Assist with the further development of Beaulieu Road Sale Yard to meet modern standards.
2.17	Support the setting up and continued support of a young Commoners' group.

Table 49 … continued

Planning, housing and back-up land
3.1 Review the current Commoners' Dwellings Scheme with respect to: • Faster application process with improved transparency. • Greater flexibility within selection criteria, whilst keeping firm principles. • Further research and definition of the needs of Commoners both in terms of domestic living and commoning activity. • Affordability in terms of land and construction costs. • Post application guidance – e.g. guidance with ratable value, IHT issues.
3.2 Support the acquisition of land and holdings which can be tied to commoning through a range of schemes.
3.3 Develop a range of full/part ownership and rental schemes between Commoners and local estates, landowners and relevant authorities with land holdings.
3.4 Develop partnerships between authorities to make the best use of sites for communing.
3.5 Support the development of schemes to allow freehold properties to be entered into trust for future commoning generations.
3.6 Investigate whether there are opportunities to bracket Commoners' holdings with farms in terms of inheritance tax.
3.7 Review current planning policies to ensure that they: • Support the upgrading of existing facilities to ensure that Commoners holdings can remain viable. • Support the provision of agriculturally orientated buildings used in connection with commoning activity. • Recognise the relationship between ancillary rural trades and the viability of commoning enterprises.
3.8 Commission further research to identify the amount, use and nature of back-up land and to ensure planning policy wherever possible, protects land used regularly for back-up land from other uses.
Education and awareness raising including conflicts between recreation, commoning and conservation
4.1 Employ a clear set of guidelines to educate and inform the public about commoning.
4.2 Identify a range of audiences who need to be approached e.g. • Visitors and tourists. • Residents of the New Forest area. • Local businesses that operate in the New Forest area and need to have regard for the different conditions that apply to it (e.g. driving schools, delivery companies, estate agents). • Local businesses that provide services to the area's visitors (e.g. camp sites, hotels, restaurants). • Local school and college students, as well as those engaged in life-long learning. • People who drive within or across the Open Forest. • Young Commoners who need to be encouraged about the importance of what they do. • Management and conservation organisations with a remit in the New Forest.
4.3 Focus the messages on a range of subject areas appropriate to the audience being addressed, e.g. • How to behave in the New Forest (as in general countryside advice, and things that are specific to the New Forest). • How to deal when in contact with Commoners' stock. • The rights and responsibilities of Commoners and those who come in contact with them. • How to drive in the New Forest. • The rights and responsibilities of people whose land abuts the Open Forest.

with a knock-on impact for nature conservation and the environment. This is essentially what happened to the most of the lowland commons in the UK; many heaths and woodlands were enclosed and cleared, but in others the social systems that supported commoning broke down and disintegrated. It is no accident that the quality of the New Forest is high and that the commoning systems survives – the two go hand in-hand. Even though there may sometimes be differences and heated discussion on points of detail, strategically the interests of nature conservation and Commoners are very closely aligned.

A major priority for the National Park is to provide a framework within which commoning can survive and thrive and to create the conditions for a living landscape, where a sustainable core of people in local communities have a stake in the environment and a role in delivering biodiversity.

Different chapters of this book have made a case for the application of management regimes to meet the needs of particular groups of species. Any management comes at a cost and somebody has to fund it. The existing contribution from central government is probably inadequate and under constant pressure from other calls on government expenditure. We will need to ensure that land managers have the resources to deliver agreed and balanced management for the Forest in a sustainable way. Alternative funding streams to support land management will be required in future. Visitors and tourism currently bring in around £100 million per annum to the New Forest, supporting in the region of 2,500 jobs (NFDC / NF Visitor Survey 2005). Only a small percentage of this income supports land management directly, despite the tourism industry being largely dependent on the special environmental qualities of the National Park. One of the important challenges will be to develop better mechanisms for visitor income to help fund land management.

Climate change

The impacts of climate change as currently forecast are likely to have major and fundamental impacts on the landscape of the National Park and its wildlife. These are summarised in Table 50.

It seems probable that because of the likely speed and severity of change, many of our most precious and rare species near the southern limits of their distribution may not be able to adapt and are likely to become extinct locally as their viable 'climate space' moves north and westwards. Theoretical modelling suggests that other species, such as the wild gladiolus or Bechstein's bat, near the northern limit of their range, may do well and expand their range into newly favourable 'climate space' if suitable habitat exists (Monarch Project 2006).

Some non-indigenous species are already colonising the South coast and more new arrivals are likely. Consequently there are likely to be winners and losers as the climate changes, and we will probably observe significant changes in the composition of communities and habitats across the New Forest. At present the level of scientific knowledge about how species will respond has a high degree of uncertainty. It is difficult (and probably risky) to predict how species interactions will be affected or what the outcomes

Table 50
A summary of likely climate change in the New Forest and south-east England in the coming decades. (Sources: South East Climate Change Partnership 2004, Hossell and Rowe 2006).

All figures are derived from the UKCIP02 scenarios (Hulme *et al.* 2002). Where a range is given this relates to the low emissions (assuming large cuts in present emissions) and high emissions ('business as usual') scenarios, but also reflects geographical variation within the south-east.

Winter represents the average for December, January and February; summer represents the average for June, July and August.

The climate changes projected to the 2020s are similar across all scenarios. This is because we are already committed to some climate change as a result of past greenhouse gas emissions. Climate changes beyond the next few decades depend on future emissions, but even the low emissions scenario represents an acceleration of climate change when compared to the 20th century.

Relative to the baseline period of 1961 to 1990, the main climate changes projected for the South East by the 2050s are:
- Increase in winter temperatures of 1.0–2.0°C.
- Increase in summer temperatures of 1.5–3.5°C.
- Increase in winter precipitation by 0–20%.
- Decrease in summer precipitation by 10–40%.

Under the high emissions scenario, by the 2080s, summer temperatures may be more than 4.5°C higher on average, with many more very hot days. Summer precipitation may be less than half that of the baseline period. Winters will become more reliably warm. Winter precipitation will increase, but become more variable, with some winters being particularly wet. Winter rainfall intensities will increase. Summer will become more reliably dry, although temperatures may vary more widely from year to year. Cloud cover and relative humidity are likely to reduce, particularly in summer. Soils will become drier, especially in summer and autumn. Wind speeds may increase in winter, but this is only predicted with low confidence.

In terms of extreme events, by the 2050s, under the medium-high emissions scenario, for England and Wales:
- A dry summer, similar to 1995, will occur on average one year in three.
- A warm dry year, similar to 1999 (37% drier than average), will occur on average three years in four.

Winter	On average winters are predicted to become wetter and milder with less frost / ice / snow cover leading to increased flood risk. Greater night-time than day-time warming in winter. This could result in: • Longer growing seasons. • Increased flood risk. • Increased soil erosion and pollutant leaching.
Summer	On average, summers will be much hotter and longer but with lower rainfall. Greater warming in summer and autumn than in winter and spring. Greater day-time than night-time warming in summer. This could result in: • Increased tourism and leisure. • Enhanced yields of crops / new crops being viable. • Changes in species and habitats. • Increased risk of drought and increase in heathland / grassland / woodland fire risk. • Increase in low river flows and water quality problems. • Reduction in soil moisture. • Increased tree stress and loss.
Sea level	Sea level is predicted to rise by around 841 mm by 2115, leading to increased risk of coastal erosion and flooding and loss of important coastal habitats Increased risk to coastal power stations and industry.
Wind speed	Possible higher wind speeds leading to more frequent risk of damage to essential infrastructure and an increased likelihood of large insurance claims. Winter depressions become more frequent including deepest ones.
Rainfall	Extreme rain events may happen twice as often by the 2080s leading to an increase in flood risk and risk of damage to essential infrastructure / increased likelihood of large insurance claims. By the 2020s: • Winters could be 5–15% wetter (winters 10–30% wetter by the 2080s). • Summers could be 15–30% drier (summers 25–55% drier by the 2080s). • Heavy rainfall episodes in winter become more common. • Summers as dry as 1995 (37% drier than average) become more common. • Snowfall totals decrease significantly.

Table 51
Potential climate change impacts on biodiversity in the New Forest National Park. After Hossell and Rowe (2006).

	Threats?	Opportunities?
Biodiversity	• Uncertainty over how individual species will respond but those at the edge of their range are at risk – changes may be subtle at first and affect habitat composition. • There will be winners and losers. • Species may be lost more quickly in adverse conditions than others colonise. • Species may be unable to migrate due to barriers of roads, development / unsuitable habitat, resulting in local extinction. • Changes and greater variation in hydrology e.g. lower water tables in summer. • Biodiversity is strongly influenced by land-use; changes in land-use management driven by climate e.g. in agriculture, tourism and forestry may impact nature conservation. • Loss or erosion of some habitats e.g. valley bogs, wet heathland. • Effect on stream temperatures and invertebrates / fish ecology. • Increase in drought stress to trees and bogs and other vulnerable species. • Increase in damage to trees in extreme events and early frosts. • Fish migration and spawning impeded by low flows. • Increased erosion risk to soft coastal habitats and coastal squeeze. • Risk to species requiring sub-zero period to break seed dormancy. • Risk of expansion of invasive species (e.g. bracken). • Increased visitor pressure on natural environment. • Increased incidence of fire in hot dry summers. • Reduction in extent and location of wet heath and some mires. • Timing and phenology may be upset and inter-related species may be out of synchrony.	• Flora and fauna with pronounced southern distribution become more widespread – some species will gain and others will lose. • Expansion of some habitats and development of new community types. • Spread of species new to the UK. • To use agri-environment mechanisms to integrate land management to aid nature conservation. • To develop ecological networks and green infrastructure to enable species to migrate and use spatial planning for integrating nature conservation with other land uses. • To ensure that existing habitats are managed in better condition and hence more resilient to changing climate.
Coast	• Rising sea levels and possible increased storminess will increase coastal erosion and damage coastal infrastructure. • Natural assets such as beaches, wetlands, mudflats, salt marshes and dunes may be lost and their flora and fauna will be affected – silting of estuaries? • Deterioration in water quality and increase in algal blooms. • Increased run-off and leaching from land? • Protecting or relocating coastal assets may be too costly, therefore in some cases managed retreat may be the best option • Retreating from coastal areas in some locations, may not be viable, and protecting them will be very expensive. • Properties in high risk areas will lose value, and may become uninsurable or unsaleable, resulting in losses for individuals and lending institutions. • Replacement of existing sea defences (e.g. Lymington–Keyhaven sea wall has a limited life of approx. 50 years at current rate of sea-level rise) unlikely to be affordable.	• Increased tourism on the coast may boost local economy. • Increased marine activity, water sports, surfing, etc., but pressures could arise from increased tourism and activity in the coastal fringe.
Agriculture and commoning	• Higher carbon dioxide concentrations and a longer growing season will enhance growth of some crops and offer the potential for growing new crops if practices adapt to changes in timing of seasons – may also result in pressure to intensify agriculture. • Potential increase in pests and diseases, including species new to the region. • Increased need for irrigation and on-farm storage, owing to reduced summer rainfall and higher temperatures. • Potential loss of competitive advantage for some sectors of south-east agriculture, e.g. current livestock management may become less viable than areas further north due to drought and impact on grass growth and increased heat stress; changes in needs for buildings and their design; need for more shade in fields. • Intense rainfall in winter may increase direct and indirect damage to crops and soils, causing soil erosion, accessibility problems, blocked drains and damage to rural roads. • Decreased soil quality and increased erosion owing to increased run-off from winter rainfall. • Possible increase in wind, heat and storm damage during severe events. • Lack of winter chilling. • Other issues as important in decision making e.g. CAP reform, economics etc and it is difficult to predict how farmers will respond. • Some loss of land on coast.	• Longer and earlier growing season. • Increased growth rates and yields (but not quality?). • Potential for new crops. • Reduced frost damage should increase productivity. • Potential increased growth rate (e.g. for forest trees). • Increased visitor numbers to the region in warmer weather means a larger market, particularly for local specialities. • Changes to food and drink consumption patterns, including ice creams, cold drinks and salads in summertime.

Table 51 ... continued

	Threats?	Opportunities?
Landscapes	• Increasingly arid landscape that may change in character, and the typical New Forest landscapes may be degraded in some aspects (the outcome of the balance between increasing wetness in winter and summer drought is not clear). • The small-scale intricate pattern of traditional pastures may not be conducive to the extended grazing systems that would be best suited to taking advantage of a longer grass-growing season. • Flow rates in streams and rivers will reduce in summer and increase in winter – major temperature, erosion and ecological issues in summer and winter.	• With the dynamic nature of the New Forest new landscapes will evolve of equal beauty?
Forestry	• Plantations and woodlands could be affected by soil moisture deficits. • There may be greater susceptibility to fungal diseases particularly for conifers. • Changes to natural structure and species composition of woods.	• Higher carbon dioxide concentrations could increase growth rates and productivity.

might be. We should, however, be prepared to see massive changes in the wildlife populations of the New Forest over the next 100 years (see Table 51). Beyond the 2050s–2080s, there would seem to be critical and currently unanswered questions about the survival and sustainability of several New Forest specialities such as:
• low-lying coastal habitats and their associated species, as sea levels rise and retreat squeezes up against the coastal defences at places such as the Keyhaven–Lymington Marshes;

• wetland areas, valley bogs and peat;
• heathland flora and fauna;
• ancient trees and woodland and their associated species.

What should the strategic response be to these changes? Some potential questions and actions (after Hossell et al. 2000, Hossell and Rowe 2006, Walmsley 2006, Hopkins 2007) to help biodiversity adapt to climate change are outlined in Table 52 below.

Table 52
Some strategic issues and potential responses to climate change.

1 Management should aim to maintain New Forest habitats, natural processes and species populations in as 'favourable condition' as possible – to promote resilience and give existing species and habitats the best chance of survival.

2 Reverse the anthropogenic degradation of recent decades by restoring processes and management of damaged areas.

3 Maximise and expand the area available to semi-natural habitats and species and adopt a landscape-scale approach to 'growing the Forest'.

4 Move the focus away from the conservation of individual species towards enabling landscape scale processes to function. (In the coming years we can expect an increasing demand for projects and resources to 'save' the most desirable and threatened species which will be hard to resist. However, the conditions which led to the presence of current species have changed, and preventing change will probably be unsustainable no matter how much funding is invested. Is a change in our thinking required?).

5 We need to be much more open and look forward to the emergence of new assemblages of species, new communities and new landscapes (which we have not yet seen or enjoyed) – but which could be of equivalent significance and value. Do we need to review our concepts of what constitutes an appropriate species, and indeed whether the label of 'native' species has any meaning in future? We need to be prepared to accept the new arrivals.

6 Do we need to recognise that what really makes the New Forest special is the functioning and operation of relatively natural processes. Is it really 'naturalness' and an element of 'wildness' that we value? If so, we need to make a leap of faith and manage the landscape in such a way that natural or semi natural processes can operate and function. That probably requires a semi-natural style of management with minimal intervention (i.e. free-ranging extensive grazing). Can we then accept, enjoy and value the species that arrive within this regime?

7 Provide opportunities for species to move northwards – by reversing the fragmentation of the countryside north and west of the New Forest. Identifying opportunities for habitat creation in the agricultural landscape and promoting management that makes those landscapes more permeable to species movement and dispersal. Ideally this would involve the 'growing the Forest' approach – should we be encouraging opportunities for a network of land grazed animals? Can we explore mechanisms to do this such as encouraging part time / hobby commoning in other areas using the New Forest system as an exemplar? This will also require biodiversity needs to be genuinely integrated with development (i.e. a serious investment in green infrastructure).

8 This provides the exciting opportunity for the New Forest to act as a reservoir of species from which other areas might be re-populated with species.

9 This will help some species but others are likely to lose out. One of the interesting problems may well be what can we do to help the heathland and bog species move northward – if this is deemed desirable. We really do not understand enough about these issues and we may need to develop new techniques and mechanisms to assist natural dispersion processes to operate.

Development and further fragmentation

Some 1.7 million people live around the National Park and 34,000 people live within it. The South East and South West Plans have identified the need for an additional 80,000 houses in South Hampshire and 30,000 in Dorset by 2026. The direct impacts of new housing or industrial growth are likely to be minimal within the National Park, owing to the planning controls in this newly protected landscape and a considerable amount of growth has already taken place in the New Forest during the post-war period. Beyond the boundaries, development pressure may reduce the opportunities for connecting and 'de-fragmenting' the countryside, unless appropriate natural 'greenspace' is designed and integrated into development.

However, the proposed growth beyond the Park boundary is likely to have a number of direct and indirect impacts on the National Park situated, as it is, between the two expanding conurbations of South Hampshire and Bournemouth. Apart from traffic and direct pollution impacts, the most significant effects on wildlife in the New Forest are probably those arising from recreation and visitor pressure. These have not yet been fully quantified in the New Forest but research on other areas of lowland heath (see Haskins 2000 and Underhill-Day 2005) has highlighted the following impacts:

- trampling of vegetation and soil compaction;
- nutrient enrichment;
- increased frequency of arson and wildfire;
- disturbance of ground nesting birds and other species, especially by dogs.

A recent study by Sharp, Lowen and Liley of Footprint Ecology (2008) on behalf of the National Park, Natural England and New Forest District Council has analysed the patterns of visitor use in the National Park and estimates that the number of visitor days could rise by an additional 1.2 million or 12% if the predicted housing growth takes place. A recreational management strategy is in preparation for the National Park to identify, resolve and address some of the issues for the New Forest.

What does the National Park want to do?

The key conclusion is that continued pastoralism would seem to offer the optimal mix for biodiversity conservation and the maintenance of physical and ecological processes in the New Forest. Whilst current management may not be perfect and may not provide the ideal structure for each and every species, it certainly does appear to deliver the requirements for the survival of a broad suite of special plants, animals and fungi. The effective conservation of this special and precious place is inextricably linked to the mixture of herbivores and especially the Commoners' animals. Nature conservationists may, from time to time, have issues with some of the detailed practices of modern day commoning, but taken overall, the two groups share virtually identical interests for the future. That is why the National Park has placed the support and promotion of commoning activity as one of its top priorities in the first years of its existence.

Table 53 summarises some of the activities that the National Park would like to facilitate and implement. These focus on using the key mechanisms at our disposal, encouraging and coordinating all those with

Table 53
A summary of potential actions.

1	Develop and implement more appropriate conservation and protection through spatial plans and planning policies for the National Park • A new Park Plan by 2009.
2	Support the key ecological drivers e.g. grazing and commoning / appropriate forestry activity. • Improve our understanding of the Forest through surveying the areas that have not been adequately investigated and how natural processes operate. • Invest resources in rural businesses via a new Leader scheme. • Secure a better share of subsidy payments for the New Forest. • Undertake and implement the Commoner-led commoning review. • Work to improve the targeting of Stewardship. • Work to improve the supply of affordable housing to Commoners and other key workers. • Investigate a partnership approach to land purchase /management for adaptation to climate change to meet strategic aims? • Influence policy makers and plans beyond our boundaries. • Reduce the number of animal accidents.
3	Work to expand the core New Forest. • Explore opportunities for expanding the commons and exporting the New Forest system? • Follow natural processes – get away from focusing too much on species. • Find mechanisms to assist species to move northwards. • Raise the profile of coastal issues.
4	Build on the tremendous success of LIFE II and LIFE III + Pathfinder projects (see http://www.newforestlife.org.uk/). Continue to identify new funding and resources for sustaining and improving land management and implementation of the SAC management plan, to deliver favourable condition to 95% of the protected habitats.
5	Produce a Biodiversity Action Plan, with partners, which aims to influence policy makers and plans beyond our boundaries, seek to promote better public understanding and involvement by reconnecting the public with nature.

a role to help advance the cause of nature conservation, secure additional funding and resources for more survey and action and to use the planning tools at our disposal to promote sustainable and appropriate development.

References

Briscoe Eyre, G. E. (1870). *The New Forest: its common rights and cottage stock-keepers.* Reprinted in 2006 in *Briscoe-Eyre's New Forest* by The New Forest Ninth Centenary Trust, Lyndhurst.

Chatters, C. (1996). Conserving rare plants in muddy places. *British Wildlife*, 7, 281–287

Chatters, C. (2006). The New Forest – National Park status for a medieval survivor. *British Wildlife*, 18, 110–119.

Chatters, C. (2007). *The New Forest National Park.* Halsgrove Publishing, Wellington, Somerset.

Cox, J. and Reeves, R. (2000). *A review of the loss of commonable grazing land in the New Forest.* A report to the Commoners' Defence Association, Hampshire Wildlife Trust and the New Forest Association

Haskins, L.E. (2000). Heathlands in an urban setting – effects of urban development on heathlands of south-east Dorset. *British Wildlife*, 4, 229–237.

Hopkins, J. (2007). British wildlife and climate change 2. Adapting to climate change. *British Wildlife*, 18, 381–387.

Hossell, J. and Rowe, K. (2006). *Headline indicators on the impact of climate change on South Eastern protected landscapes.* ADAS report to SEEDA and the South East Protected Landscape Partnership.

Hossell, J. E., Briggs, B. and Hepburn, I. (2000). *Climate change and UK nature conservation: a review of the impact of climate change on UK species and habitat conservation policy.* Final report to MAFF/DETR.

Ivey, J. (2007). *The costs of keeping ponies and cattle on the New Forest.* A report for the New Forest Commoners' Defence Association and the New Forest National Park Authority.

Monarch report (2006) see http://www.branch.org.uk

New Forest Association (1994) *An agenda for the New Forest's future.* http://www.newforestassociation.org.uk.

New Forest Commoning Review Group (2007). New Forest Commoning Review. http://www.newforestnpa.gov.uk/index/livingin/commoningreview.htm. New Forest National Park Authority, Lymington, Hampshire.

New Forest National Park Authority (2008). New Forest National Park Authority website. http://www.newforestnpa.gov.uk

Oates, M. (1996). The demise of butterflies in the New Forest. *British Wildlife*, 7, 205–216.

Rose, F. (1996). The habitats and vegetation of present day Hampshire. In Brewis, A., Bowman, P. and Rose, F. (eds.) *The Flora of Hampshire*, pp. 21–30. Harley Books, Colchester.

Sanderson, N. A. (2007). *New Forest Inclosure habitats: habitat fragmentation and landscape history.* Report to Hampshire and Isle of Wight Wildlife Trust.

Sharp, J., Lowen, J. and Liley, D. (2008). *Changing patterns of visitor numbers within the New Forest National Park, with particular reference to the New Forest SPA.* Report by Footprint Ecology on behalf of the New Forest National Park Authority, Natural England and New Forest District Council.

South East Climate Change Partnership (2004). *Meeting the challenge of climate change.* Summary of the South East Climate Threats and Opportunities Research Study (SECTORS) Project: A study of climate change impacts and adaptation for key sectors in South East England. South East Climate Change Partnership, Guildford, Surrey. See http://www.seccp.org.uk/

Tubbs, C. R. (1986). *The New Forest.* Collins, London

Tubbs, C. R. (2001). *The New Forest. History, ecology and conservation.* New Forest ninth Centenary Trust, Lyndhurst.

Underhill-Day, J. C. (2005). *A literature review of urban effects on lowland heaths and their wildlife.* Report Number 624. English Nature, Peterborough

Vera, F. W. M (2000). *Grazing ecology and forest history.* CABI publishing, Wallingford.

Verderers of the New Forest (2008). Verderers of the New Forest website: http://www.verderers.org.uk

Walmsley, C. (2006). *Changing wildlife, challenging choices.* Conference on climate change. Institute of Ecology and Environmental Management.

Wright, R. N. and Westerhoff, D. V. (2001). *New Forest SAC Management Plan.* English Nature / LIFE partnership, English Nature, Lyndhurst.

19 Managing the New Forest's Crown lands

Jane Smith and Libby Burke

Introduction

The Crown lands cover around 26,756 hectares of the New Forest, and comprise a mosaic of heathland, mires, grassland (referred to locally as lawns), Ancient and Ornamental (A&O) woodland, forestry Inclosures and agricultural land. The Crown lands of the New Forest have been managed by the Forestry Commission, on behalf of the Secretary of State, since 1924.

The Forestry Commission was formed in 1919, with the aim of renewing national timber stocks that had been dangerously depleted during the Great War. The organisation, originally set up along quasi-military lines, remained focused on maintaining Britain's self-sufficiency in raw materials through World War II and beyond. It continues to produce valuable and renewable timber stocks for the nation from its sustainably managed woodlands. However, in recent years its mission has diversified, so that now it is also engaged in landscape design and habitat restoration, wildlife conservation, animal welfare and public health and recreation. It also has roles in fire safety, archaeological conservation, rural employment, the local economy, industry and education. It is among the key guardians of the New Forest's unique 'commoning' culture, which has survived for more than 1,000 years. In short, the Commission sits at the very heart of Forest life.

In order to understand why the Crown lands are managed as they are today and the issues involved, it is important to appreciate the historic legacy and the associated conflicts that have led to the current position. The history of land use and management in the New Forest is long and complex (Table 54) and has helped to create and maintain the valuable mosaic of habitats found in the Forest today. On the other hand, specific events (such as the introduction of various Government Acts of Parliament) have led to the decline and degradation of heathland, wetland and ancient woodland habitats.

Guiding principles and context

The direction of the Forestry Commission derives from Government policy. The New Forest is unique in also being governed by a 'Minister's Mandate'. This commits the Forestry Commission to producing a management plan for the Crown lands of the New Forest. The plan in turn must conform with national guidance on the area's internationally important environmental status as a Special Area of Conservation, along with national and regional forest policy. In this context, the National and regional forestry policy (e.g. the Strategy for England's Trees, Woods and Forests and the South-East

England Regional Forestry Framework) provide broad aims within which local policies are developed.

The New Forest is also unique in being governed by a set of statutes referred to as the New Forest Acts (Table 54). The New Forest Acts of 1877, 1949, 1964 and 1970 dictate how certain elements of the Forest should be managed. As a result, certain activities require the cooperation and consent of the Verderers of the New Forest, particularly relating to management of areas where common rights are exercisable, notably the heathlands and grasslands and unenclosed pasture woodlands. On that basis the Forestry Commission is responsible for creating the master plan for managing the Crown lands of the New Forest (26,756 hectares), which must take into account every external and internal influence affecting the area.

The management plan's general aim is to achieve a suitable balance between conservation, recreation and timber production. High priority is also given to conserving the New Forest's natural and cultural heritage. Opportunities for community engagement, public access and recreation, rural development and increasing public awareness must also be taken into account.

The Crown lands divide into three distinct parts: the Inclosures, the Ancient and Ornamental (A&O) Woodlands and the Open Forest. Each is considered separately below.

Inclosures

Parcels of William the Conqueror's former 'New Forest' hunting grounds were first enclosed for timber production as far back as the 1700s. They appeared in a landscape of wood and heathland worked by people whose way of life had existed possibly since Neolithic times. Their perimeter fences served to keep browsing deer and commoners' livestock away from young trees.

During World War I the demand for raw materials led to an extreme shortage of timber. Complaints were made about many private landowners who were not thought to be managing their woods properly. The crisis not only led to the establishment of the Forestry Commission, but also to a move away from broadleaved trees to faster-growing conifer crops, as frequently seen today in the New Forest's Inclosures. However, by the late 20th century, national priorities had changed to favour nature conservation. The Commission therefore began working to restore some of the wildlife habitats destroyed or damaged by the previous headlong rush to produce timber.

Management of the enclosed 8500 hectares of land within the Inclosures is now set out in a series of Forest Design Plans. First drawn up in 2001, these set out a long-term vision for the direction of future management, together with a detailed prescription for the next 20 years. However, it is not just foresters who

Table 54
Selected events of note in relation to the history of management of the Crown lands (adapted from Forestry Commission 2008).

Date	Historic significance
1079 The designation of the New Forest as a royal 'forest' by King William I.	Forest managed exclusively for deer and other game. Removal of all fences and introduction of Forest Laws. Common rights granted as recompense.
Act of 1542.	Creation of the post of Surveyor General of the King's Woods to increase the commercial function of Crown woodlands. This new office was under the direction of the Exchequer with responsibilities for timber and 'profit of the king'.
1698 Act of the Increase and Preservation of Timber in the New Forest.	First large-scale afforestation through the creation of Inclosures. Conflicts with commoners over loss of grazing and imposition of Forest Laws. By end of 18th century, Forest poorly managed and timber supplies declining.
1808 Act of the Increase and Preservation of Timber in Dean and New Forests.	Confirmed allowances of 1698 Act resulting in Inclosure of 6000 acres at any one time in a rolling programme.
1845.	Opening of Southampton and Dorchester railway, bringing artists, naturalists and other recreational users to the New Forest.
1846–52.	First drainage schemes to improve Forest for grazing.
1851 Deer Removal Act.	Culling of deer in return for Crown enclosing 10,000 acres of open forest. Forest Laws of fence month and winter heyning still imposed, which together with loss of grazing led to large-scale revolts among commoners and gentry. Large-scale introduction of conifers and drainage works.
1877 New Forest Act.	No further creation of Inclosures permitted other than that granted under previous Acts. No further enclosure of Ancient & Ornamental woodland allowed. "Re-creation" of Court of Verderers to administer common rights and pastoral interests remote from Crown influence. Introduction of ornamental trees into Forest by Victorians.
The First World War and inter-War Years.	Forest intensively managed for timber production. Large tracts of land acquired for airfields, firing ranges and food supply.
1920s–30s.	Further drainage of the Open Forest.
1924.	Forestry Commission takes over responsibility for management of New Forest from the Crown. National forest policy ensures that afforestation is vigorously pursued.
The New Forest Act 1949.	Revived Verderers Court and clarified responsibilities between Verderers and Forestry Commission. Act set out requirement for Forestry Commission to maintain drainage and scrub control for grazing interests. Led to significant drainage between 1965–1986. Creation of Verderers Inclosures in return for compensation payments. Enclosure of small areas of Ancient and Ornamental woodland allowed to secure future regeneration.
The New Forest Act 1964.	Alteration of perambulation boundary and addition of fencing and cattle grids to help control livestock movement and prevent accidents. Provision for creation of campsites. Obligation for Forestry Commission and Verderers to give due regard to nature conservation interests. Permission to carry out silvicultural maintenance to preserve Ancient & Ornamental Woodland.
The Ministers Mandate 1971.	In recognition of the unique environment of the New Forest, permission was granted to allow forest management to diverge from national policy of large scale conifer planting.
1959, 1971, 1987.	Designation and extension of New Forest Site of Special Scientific Interest.
The Ministers Mandate 1991.	Places obligation on the Forestry Commission to conserve the natural and cultural heritage and places a high priority on maintaining the Forest's traditional character.
Countryside and Rights of Way Act 2000 (CROW).	Legislative requirements place duty on organisations and individuals to promote the interests and sustainability of the Forest and to achieve favourable status of habitats.
The New Forest National Park Establishment Order 2005.	New Forest designated a National Park.
2005.	New Forest receives full status as a Special Area of Conservation (SAC), under the Habitats Directive.

make the decisions. The Commission's keepers, ecologists and recreation team also play an integral role. Decisions about the wide-ranging and sometimes conflicting management needs of wildlife conservation, public access and forestry also involve many other organisations and individuals.

Today, the Commission forms a connecting body that links all statutory and other organisations with interests in the environment, wildlife, history, culture,

business or recreational use of the area. Consultation is key in managing the area's internationally famous, and scientifically important, habitats. So too is soliciting the opinions of individuals, both residents and visitors alike.

The Commission's biggest ever public consultation exercise was carried out in the New Forest in 2000. Called *'New Forest – New Future'*, it sought over a 24-month period to engage local communities, voluntary groups and statutory organisations in discussions about the future management of more than 100 Inclosures. This process established a Forest Design Plan Forum, with its members representing the wide-ranging interests and activities taking place in the area. The Forum assisted Commission staff with the creation of the first series of draft Forest Design Plans. These aimed to reconcile the often conflicting needs of nature conservation, commoning, timber production and recreation, and set out a prescription for the management of each forest Inclosure. The draft proposals were then put to local communities for comment and discussion. Initial scepticism about whether local opinions could really have any influence was laid to rest, as drafts were revised to more closely match local need.

As an example, at Dibden Inclosure, the draft plan called for mature conifers to be felled to allow for the restoration of an area of lowland heath, an internationally endangered and important habitat. Nearby residents expressed concerns that doing so would take away the woodland they enjoyed walking in every day. Forest planners therefore revised the proposals to produce a mosaic of woodland and heathland, so that both people and wildlife would benefit from the plans in the long term.

'New Forest – New Future's' range of displays, talks and guided walks proved hugely successful in explaining the proposed management plans and at giving people opportunities to influence work on the ground. It now forms the model for all consultations in the Forest. As design plans come up for their five-year reviews, the Forum and nearby communities are again involved in the consultation process. Each set of proposals is individually tailored to the site or sites that it covers. However, the general aims of them all are to:

- restore or re-create New Forest habitats;
- maintain or enhance existing habitats for nature conservation;
- manage public access to safeguard vulnerable habitats;
- create a suitable mosaic of woodland, heathland, native grassland and wetland;
- grow timber for future generations;
- protect archaeological sites; and
- enhance the New Forest landscape.

No matter how good a plan might be, it must be implemented properly if its objectives are to succeed. So before work begins on any site, an operational site assessment is completed to ensure it is being accurately implemented. These assessments also identify key features such as archaeological sites, fragile or rare habitats and wildlife sites so that they can be protected while contractors are on site. They also assess how to minimise disruption to visitors and keep them safe, deciding where safety signage should be placed to keep people well away from the working zone.

The New Forest Inclosures produce an average of 50,000 tonnes of timber annually. The bulk of this comes from plantations that are being thinned partway through their economic life, or from areas being clear-felled either at maturity or where another habitat is being restored. All timber produced in Forestry Commission woodlands is certified as coming from sustainably managed forests, and carries the internationally recognised Forest Stewardship Council (FSC) logo. Forest operations rotate through the Inclosures on a five-year cycle.

Ancient and Ornamental (A&O) woodlands
The New Forest is perhaps most famed for its towering beeches and oaks. These immense trees help create the area's unique character. They stand majestically in ancient pasture woodlands. Around their bases the understorey vegetation is browsed by deer, ponies and cattle. Pigs are also turned out into the woods in autumn to fatten up on acorns and beech mast, a time-honoured practice called 'pannage' (see Chapter 14). Acorns are poisonous to ponies; the pigs help to remove them and protect the ponies from harm.

Pasture woodlands are a traditional form of agroforestry that has persisted without a break here in the Forest for hundreds of years. Elsewhere in Britain the practice has largely died out, although attempts to restore some former pasture woods through reintroduction of grazing animals are now underway. Minimum intervention is the guiding rule in these historic woods, with the natural cycle of regeneration, growth, senescence, decay and death largely continuing uninterrupted. Foresters intervene to trim branches or fell damaged, diseased or dying trees, and clear the network of tracks and paths that run through the woodlands when public safety is an issue.

These woods are a key refuge for a host of rare lichens that grow on the trunks and branches (see Chapter 9). Each winter, gangs of forest craftsmen pollard thickets of holly to prevent them shading out these encrusting organisms. The New Forest ponies have learnt to come at the gallop when they hear the chainsaws; the holly trimmings are a welcome supplement to their meagre winter diet. There is also a regular programme of removal of 'alien' species. *Rhododendron* is a particular problem with its heavy shade and toxic leachates. This and other non-native species, such as Turkey oak, are being gradually removed from the Forest.

Open Forest
Management out on the Open Forest continues largely as it has for many centuries. The network of unfenced grasslands, heathlands, lawns and mires covers around 12,300 hectares. It requires an extensive management programme in order to maintain its historic character and its value as grazing for commoners' ponies and livestock. Late winter sees controlled burning of gorse and heather taking place out on the heathlands. This encourages new growth and forms a mosaic of different-aged vegetation. This in turn attracts the widest possible range of wildlife, from sun-loving sand lizards and ground nesting birds such as woodlark and nightjar, to invertebrates such as silver studded blue butterflies and emperor moths. The burning also helps

create effective firebreaks that help protect heaths, woods and adjacent properties from spreading wildfires.

Summer sees teams of forest craftsmen out managing the bracken. This tall fern can swamp other plants with its vigorous growth while its underground rhizomes are quick to colonise the forest's precious heathlands if left unchecked. Tractor-mounted swipes or hand cutting or spraying the bracken prevents other plants being smothered and reduces its vigour. The cut fronds are turned into a valuable garden mulch, which is sold at local garden centres and nurseries. Self-seeded pine and birch trees will gradually encroach across heathland and grassland if left unchecked, shading out the natural vegetation. In autumn and winter, dozens of people help the Commission's rangers pull up the young saplings to protect these habitats.

Volunteering

Perhaps one of the best indicators of the overall success of the Commission's strategy is the organisation's growing number of volunteers. During the past five years more than 500 people have given up their time to become involved in the practical management of the New Forest. Volunteer ranger duties range from clearing non-native trees to helping with the annual pony round up. They patrol the forest offering help and advice to the throngs of visitors who come to the area every year. Many have been engaged in the survey work crucial to the Commission's management public recreation and wildlife conservation. Some now lead their own parties of walkers on long explorations of the heaths and woodlands. They bring a great deal of enjoyment to people as well as providing them with the significant health benefits to be had from outdoor exercise. The success of many arts and wildlife projects, and public entertainment events also depends on the volunteers' involvement. Children too are engaged in conservation projects, as well as work to prevent vandalism and arson in vulnerable woodland areas. These people come from every age group and background conceivable. Along with their peers in the forest design plan forum, they represent the entire community's support for and involvement in every aspect of the Commission's work.

The Crown Lands Management Plan 2008–2013

The development of the latest Management Plan for the Crown lands of the New Forest was concluded following wide consultation during 2008, and covers the period 2008–2013. It can be considered as a component part of the Special Area of Conservation (SAC) Plan (Wright and Westerhoff 2001), which was produced as part of the LIFEII Project (see Chapter 17). The Plan essentially contributes to the implementation part of the SAC Plan, which demonstrates how landowners intend to maintain and enhance the nature conservation interest of the SAC.

The principles on which the work of the Forestry Commission is based essentially remains unchanged from previously, but the Plan does, however, reflect changes in national, regional or local policy, for instance in relation to the National Park, which was designated since the SAC Plan was written in 2001. Another new development reflected in the Crown lands Plan is the commitment of the Forestry Commission to a Public Service Agreement Target to improve 95% of the New Forest Site of Special Scientific Interest (SSSI) to favourable condition by 2010.

The Crown Lands Management Plan covers the background, management objectives, policies and actions for each of the key subject areas that fall under the responsibility of the Forestry Commission, notably: Inclosures, Ancient and Ornamental woodlands, heathlands, archaeology and cultural heritage, recreation and community, and estates. The first three of these are considered further below, based on the information provided in the Plan itself (Forestry Commission 2008).

Inclosures

Although the Inclosures were initially established to provide a timber resource, they now provide a much wider range of benefits to society and are increasingly recognised for their nature conservation and recreation value, in addition to their ability to yield quality timber. The Inclosures were generally established on former heathland or ancient woodland sites and remnants of these former habitats still survive within the modern day Inclosures. Where recognisable, these remnant heathland and woodland habitats are often of international importance, representing important examples of Annex 1 habitats as identified by the European Habitats Directive. Of particular significance are the 400 hectares of pasture, riverine and bog woodland communities that were incorporated into the 18th and 19th century Statutory Inclosures. Restoration of such habitats forms an important part of the Plan's proposed activities, although sustainable timber production also remains a central objective.

Objectives of the Plan relating to Inclosures are as follows:

1. To transform Inclosure woodland in accordance with Forest Design Plans to enhance the special nature conservation and landscape qualities through appropriate habitat restoration and management.
2. To manage sustainable timber production from the Inclosures through the generation of reliable production forecasts and provision of a regular supply of good quality timber to the market place.
3. To work in partnership with stakeholders in the revision of Forest Design Plans.
4. To carry out targeted monitoring to ensure that our Inclosure woodland is being managed in a sustainable way and meeting our management objectives in relation to UK Woodland Assurance Standard.
5. To encourage the use of Inclosures by recreational users of the Forest.

Specific policies and actions that will be taken towards meeting these objectives include the on-going removal or control of non-native trees and shrub species where they present an invasive threat. Such species include *Rhododendron*, Turkey oak, red oak, sycamore and western hemlock. There will be a policy of opening Inclosures to grazing, in accordance with the Fencing Plan, but where Inclosures remain fenced, appropriate measures will be taken to exclude livestock. Restoration of mires, riverine woodland and associated floodplain habitats will be continued. Reference is made to the need to manage Inclosures to take account of Biodiversity Action Plan (BAP) habitats and species, including management of the deadwood resource. The Plan also refers to the continuation of timber production and restocking, in accordance with Forest Design Plans. The Plan also includes a commitment to undertake appropriate and targeted monitoring, to ensure that management prescriptions are achieving their objectives.

Ancient and Ornamental (A&O) woodlands

The A&O woodlands owe their features to both natural processes and the influence of people through the centuries. Many of the habitats found in these woodlands are of European importance. Although the ancient beech and oak stands form the core of the A&O woodland, other types of woodland are intermingled with these stands in a complex mosaic (see Chapter 13). Some woodland types are associated with particular soils, while others may be the natural precursors of the beech and oak woods or degenerate forms of them.

The general structure of the A&O woodlands includes the presence of numerous large trees, large quantities of dead wood, small and moderate gaps in the canopy and a pattern made up of groups of trees of similar ages that collectively span the whole age-range of the main tree species of beech and oak. Their structure has developed under the influence of natural processes, such as storm, drought, mortality in old age and natural regeneration, acting on the mature woodlands inherited from previous centuries. However, their structure has also been extensively influenced by people through the ages. The effects of past pollarding of oaks, beech and holly can still be seen, as can the cohort of trees and shrubs that established in the late 19th century when deer browsing was much reduced. The absence of low branches and a distinctive browse line (see Chapter 13) reflects the grazing by populations of horses, deer and cattle. This grazing is a major factor in producing the structure of a high forest canopy interspersed with open glades, arranged in a mosaic of different habitat types. The degree of grazing pressure is important in determining the vegetation composition and structure; too much grazing leads to a lack of regeneration, while under-grazing results in a rapid regeneration of trees and shrubs. This subsequently impacts negatively on the ground flora as well as affecting light availability and microclimate. This can be unfavourable for established lichens and bryophytes.

Objectives of the Plan relating to A&O woodlands are as follows:

1. To maintain the unique character of the A&O woodlands by preserving the traditional structure, habitats and landscapes.
2. To ensure that any intervention that takes place in A&O woodland is purely for the benefit of conserving or restoring important habitats, landscapes or maintaining traditional forest Rights.
3. To support and encourage the pastoral traditions of the A&O woodlands.
4. To carry out focused monitoring to ensure the health and wellbeing of the A&O woodlands.

Specific policies and actions that will be taken towards meeting these objectives include maintenance of the current configuration of the A&O woodlands, with no tree felling to influence age structure, although actions may be taken to stimulate regeneration where appropriate. Some expansion and contraction of woodland area is deemed acceptable, so long as the ratio of woodland habitat to grazing land on the Open Forest is maintained. As in the Inclosures, there is a commitment to systematically remove non-native trees, shrubs and other exotic or pest species, including *Rhododendron*, sycamore, Turkey oak and sweet chestnut, where deemed appropriate.

Removal of larger stands of Scots pine will continue, except where they form important landscape features or provide shelter to groves of ancient trees. Other proposed interventions include management of deadwood, bracken control and pollarding of trees.

Heathland

Heathland and grassland covers around 12,306 ha of the New Forest Crown land, and is found both on the Open Forest and within restored areas of Inclosures. In the context of the Plan, the term 'heathland' covers a variety of different vegetation/habitat types, including:

- Dry heath – 714 ha
- Bracken – 803 ha
- Gorse – 347 ha
- Humid heath – 4,498 ha
- Wet heath – 1692 ha
- Valley mire – 1444 ha
- Wet lawn –911 ha
- Lowland acid grassland – 1864 ha
- Partially improved grassland – 12 ha
- Ponds – 21 ha

Grazing by horses and cattle is an integral part of New Forest heathland management. The heathland, mires and grasslands have been grazed by commoning stock for centuries, which has led to the unique landscape and habitats so characteristic of the Open Forest. Many of the traditional heathland management techniques that have been practised historically are still applied today. In the past 10 years heathland management and restoration has progressed significantly, owing to funding from the New Forest LIFE II (1997–2001) and LIFE III projects (2002–2006) (see Chapter 17). For example, LIFE II enabled restoration work to commence on some 4,000 ha of heathland habitats within the Crown lands that were in unfavourable condition, whereas LIFE III concentrated on the restoration of a variety of wetland habitats (Chapter 17).

To make management more efficient and effective, the New Forest heathlands are divided up into 10 management units. Work programmes are devised for each management unit annually. Much of the current work is focused around the condition of SSSI units (see Chapter 12), and the requirements of the New Forest Act 1949 to keep the open Forest 'sufficiently free of coarse herbage, scrub and self-sown trees'. While grazing by livestock exerts a measure of control over scrub and broadleaved tree species, it is ineffectual against Scots pine. Grazing animals also make an important contribution to the management of bracken and gorse brakes, but further interventions are required to ensure sufficient control of bracken and gorse, and to maintain favourable condition of heathland habitat (Wright and Westerhoff 2001). Without such additional measures, principally cutting and burning, Scots pine and scrub would quickly become dominant over large parts of the Forest habitats, with consequent loss of nature conservation value.

As noted by Wright and Westerhoff (2001), since 1949 the Forestry Commission has carried out an annual programme of controlled burning of heathland, which initially covered 800–1,200 ha annually, but averaging 400 ha a year since 1965. Forestry Commission staff produce a relatively cool burn that removes the standing vegetation but does not kill the more sensitive plants. Typically burning is carried out from 1 November to 31 March when the soil is still moist yet the vegetation is dry enough for the fire to carry well. The area burned is strictly confined to limit the fragmentation of animal populations. In addition, the Forestry Commission cuts the heathland using a tractor-mounted swipe, to make fire breaks. Relatively uniform heather stands or areas containing dense bracken are also sometimes cut, for example on sites too dangerous to burn.

In the 1960s and 1970s the Forestry Commission used to cut and bale heather for sale in the road building industry, but the practice subsequently ceased. However, cutting has taken on a new significance in the Forest with the recent use of heather bales for mire restoration under the LIFE II programme (Chapter 17). Cutting is carried out using mowing/swiping with a tractor-mounted machine or hand-cutting with chainsaws, brush cutters, bow saws or loppers. Mechanised harvesting only takes place on sites where suitable machinery can operate safely.

Cutting is primarily used for controlling pine and birch colonisation, gorse, willow and general scrub management. On average 36 hectares are cut each year. A significant advantage of cutting is that it is far less reliant on precise weather conditions than burning. However, it is a relatively costly operation, although costs may be offset to some extent by sale or effective use of by-products (Wright and Westerhoff 2001).

Objectives of the Plan relating to heathland are as follows:

1. To maintain and restore heathland habitats in order to support and enhance the important nature conservation interest and landscape character of the Open Forest.
2. To support the traditional depasturing of commoning stock through appropriate and targeted heathland management techniques and maintenance of access.
3. To develop the economic returns from heathland by-products to help fund and sustain heathland management activities.
4. To carry out targeted monitoring to inform heathland management decisions and to ensure that heathland management objectives are being achieved.

Specific policies and actions that will be taken towards meeting these objectives include continuation of work programmes to restore Open Forest heathland SSSI units to favourable condition using appropriate techniques, and restoration of wetland in accordance with the Wetland Management Plan (Smith 2006; see Chapter 17). A commitment is also made to recover lost heathland habitats from within Inclosures, and to continue the heathland cutting and burning programme. Trees invading heathland will be controlled using techniques such as swiping, forage harvesting or hand pulling, in addition to burning, and control of *Rhododendron* and bracken will also continue to be undertaken.

References

Forestry Commission (2008). *The Crown Lands Management Plan 2008–2013.* The Forestry Commission, Lyndhurst, Hampshire. http://www.forestry.gov.uk/forestry/INFD-7A3F82

Smith, J. (2006). *New Forest Wetland Management Plan 2006–2016.* Forestry Commission, Lyndhurst, Hampshire.

Wright, R. N. and Westerhoff, D. V. (2001). *New Forest SAC Management Plan.* English Nature, Lyndhurst.

20 Synthesis: status and trends of biodiversity in the New Forest

Adrian C. Newton

Introduction

The preceding chapters provide an overview of biodiversity in the New Forest, focusing on the current status and trends in species of conservation concern, and the habitats with which they are associated. A brief overview is also provided of current management approaches and future challenges. The aim of this chapter is to integrate some of the information presented by previous authors, and thereby to identify any cross-cutting issues that emerge, with the aim of informing future management decisions. The chapter does not claim to provide a comprehensive, integrated analysis of biodiversity in the New Forest, but rather offers a personal perspective on some of the issues raised by other authors. Similarly, no attempt is made to provide a detailed, critical evaluation of current management approaches. Rather, some suggestions are made regarding how such approaches might develop in future, based on an exploration of available evidence.

The chapter first assesses the importance of the New Forest for biodiversity, and then considers current trends in the status of particularly notable species and habitats, with the aim of identifying any common issues or themes. Information needs are then highlighted. The implications of current biodiversity trends for management of the New Forest are also considered, with reference to some of the management approaches that are currently being employed. It should be emphasised that no attempt is made here to identify a consensus of opinion among the contributors to this volume. As became clear during the conference on which this book is based, the New Forest provides a rich topic for debate, and is the subject of a wide variety of opinions, some of which are strongly held! The comments provided here represent an individual perspective, which is offered in the hope of encouraging further dialogue. Such debate has perhaps been something of a tradition in the Forest.

Importance of the New Forest for biodiversity

Many authors have suggested that the New Forest is of exceptional importance for biodiversity. Chatters and Read (2006), for example, describe the Open Forest as being *'one of the richest places for wildlife in Europe and one of the best wetlands in the world'*. Ratcliffe (in Tubbs 2001) describes the New Forest as *'the most important single wildlife area in southern Britain'*. In the light of evidence presented in the chapters of this volume, can these claims be sustained? The answer is a resounding 'yes'.

The most comprehensive assessment of the conservation importance of the New Forest is provided by the SAC Management Plan (Wright and Westerhoff 2001), which provides the following description: *'The New Forest candidate SAC is one of the most important sites for wildlife in the United Kingdom, and is widely recognised as being of exceptional importance for*

Table 55
Comparative evaluation of New Forest habitats of nature conservation importance. This highlights the comparative status of some of the features for which the New Forest has been designated in terms of their international and national context.

Vegetation type	Internationally important	Nationally important	Significance of the New Forest for site feature
Pasture woodland	Yes *	Yes	Outstanding
Riverine woodland	Yes	Yes	Outstanding
Bog woodland	Yes *	Yes	Outstanding
Inclosure woodland	No	Yes	
Dry heath	Yes	Yes	Outstanding
Wet heath	Yes	Yes	Outstanding
Mire	Yes *	Yes	Outstanding
Dry grassland	No	Yes	Outstanding
Wet grassland	Yes *	Yes	Outstanding
Temporary ponds	Yes *	Yes	Outstanding
Permanent ponds	Yes *	Yes	Outstanding
Streams	No	Yes	Outstanding

Internationally important refers to SAC/SPA/Ramsar designations. **Nationally important** refers to the SSSI designation. The national significance of the habitats given in the final column summarises the national evaluations for key habitat groups undertaken by English Nature.
* Does not include all plant communities within this vegetation type. Adapted from Wright and Westerhoff (2001).

Table 56
Importance of the New Forest for different groups of species.

Species group	Internationally important*	Nationally important*	Significance of the New Forest at national scale**	Number species of conservation concern	Estimated total number of species recorded in the New Forest	New Forest species richness expressed as a % of total number of species in Britain	Comments made by Tubbs (2001)
Birds	Yes	Yes	Outstanding; particularly important for breeding waders, raptors, heathland and woodland communities	37*	Approx. 100[†]	17%	Generally rich; exceptionally rich in woodland birds
Mammals other than bats	No	Yes	Species present of conservation importance include dormouse, otter and water vole	3*	19*	35%	Small mammals generally scarce
Bats	No	Yes	High species richness; may contain significant populations of Bechstein's and barbastelle bat, two of the rarest bats in Europe	13	13	81%	Outstandingly rich; possibly the most important area in Britain
Reptiles and amphibians	Yes	Yes	One of the most important areas in the UK. High species richness; particularly notable species include smooth snake, sand lizard and great crested newt	12	12/13	92%	All but one of native British species present
Fish	No	Yes (probably)	Fairly high species richness, possibly of national importance	>2*	22	88%	–
Invertebrates	Yes	Yes	Nationally significant	544*	5,000–10,000[†]	17–33%[†]	>50% of all British insects present
Dragonflies and damselflies			A national hotspot for diversity	9	31	69%	73% of British species present (breeding)
Saproxylic beetles			One of the richest parts of Britain, and of European significance	53	326[#]	55%[#]	Exceptionally rich
Butterflies and moths			Outstanding national importance	72 RDB and 192 NN	1,488 (of which 33 are butterflies)	66%	55% of British species recorded
Other invertebrates			Exceptionally rich invertebrate fauna, at least in woodlands	403* including Coleoptera, Hymenoptera, Diptera, Orthoptera, Hemiptera, Crustacea	1,539 Coleoptera[†], 22 Orthoptera[†], 296 taxa of macro-invertebrate recorded from Forest streams		47.5% of British Coleoptera recorded and >67% of British Orthoptera. Largest British assemblage of Diptera known
Vascular plants	Yes	Yes	Nationally and internationally important, but perhaps not of exceptional importance at the international scale	72 RDB, 43 nationally rare or scarce	Approx. 540*	36%	At least 46 internationally or nationally rare species present
Lichens	Yes	Yes	Outstanding international importance	64 RDB, plus 78 other species of conservation interest	421	18%	Outstanding
Fungi	Yes	Yes	Of the highest importance nationally, and of high international importance, at least for some fungal groups (e.g. beechwood saprotrophs)	89*	2600	22%	Outstanding
Bryophytes	Yes	Yes	One of the best areas in lowland England for bryophytes	33*	326*	32%	Outstanding

Internationally important refers to SAC/SPA/Ramsar designations. **Nationally important** refers to the SSSI designation.
** Based on information in preceding chapters, and the national evaluations for selected groups undertaken by English Nature reported by Wright and Westerhoff (2001). *Based on information provided by Wright and Westerhoff (2001). † Data from Tubbs (2001). ‡ Data from http://www.newforestexplorersguide.co.uk/. # SQI species only (see Chapter 5). RDB, Red Data Book; NN, Nationally Notable.

nature conservation throughout the European Union. It supports a complex mosaic of wildlife habitats, formerly common in lowland western Europe but now rare and fragmented. The major components are the extensive wet and dry heaths with their rich valley mires and associated wet and dry grasslands, the ancient pasture and enclosed woodlands, the network of clean rivers and streams and frequent permanent and temporary ponds. Outstanding examples of thirteen habitats of European interest are represented together with two priority habitat types, namely bog woodland and riverine woodland.'

The reasons for designation of the New Forest SAC include a range of both habitats and species (Appendix), many of which are considered in preceding chapters. As described in Chapter 1, part of the New Forest is also designated as a Special Protection Area (SPA) on account of its bird populations. The New Forest is also designated as a Ramsar site, because it possesses the largest concentration of intact valley mires of their type in Britain. The justifications for such designations provide powerful evidence of the importance of the biodiversity of the New Forest, at both national and international scales (Table 55). However, as is made clear by Tubbs (2001) and by Wright and Westerhoff (2001), it is not just the presence of such habitats that is important, but their occurrence in an intimate mosaic.

With respect to individual groups of species, the preceding chapters again repeatedly emphasise the conservation importance of the New Forest. For all of the species groups considered, the New Forest is of national importance, and for many, it is also of international importance (Table 56). The species richness of many groups is high, sometimes exceptionally so. For example, more than two thirds of the British species of reptiles and amphibians, butterflies and moths, fish, bats, dragonflies and damselflies are found in the New Forest (Table 56). Even for those groups that are less well represented, at least one sixth of all British species have been recorded in the area. In every group considered, the New Forest is home to species of national conservation concern, and in some groups, the numbers of such species is very substantial; for example 155 vascular plants, 264 butterflies and moths, and 142 lichens (Table 56).

Status and trends in the biodiversity of the New Forest

One of the observations that stimulated the production of this book was the comment made by Colin Tubbs in his classic account of the area, that 'the biodiversity of the New Forest is now diminishing rapidly' (Tubbs 2001, p.365). Is this suggestion supported by the evidence presented in the preceding chapters? This question is considered below with respect to both habitats and species. Reference is also made to the threats (or threatening processes; Balmford et al. 1998) responsible for causing the decline and loss of species and habitats. Effective biodiversity conservation

depends on a thorough understanding of such threats. Here, the principal threats to biodiversity in the New Forest are briefly considered, based on the evidence presented in previous chapters.

Trends in habitat condition

Chapter 12 presents an overview of the current condition of habitats in the New Forest, based on the Common Standards Monitoring (CSM) approach conducted by Natural England. As is made clear in current management plans for the New Forest (Forestry Commission 2008, Wright and Westerhoff 2001), the CSM forms the basis of habitat monitoring in the Forest. Formal monitoring using this approach has only been undertaken in recent years (principally the last decade), and therefore the data have limited value for assessing recent trends in habitat condition. However, the results do provide an indication of the current status of habitats in the New Forest.

Current results indicate that 463 units (out of 576) are in unfavourable condition (including 366 unfavourable recovering, 75 declining, 20 no change, and 1 partially and 1 totally destroyed). This represents 80% of units, or 68% expressed as a percentage of the total area (see Chapter 12). For 114 of the 463 units in unfavourable condition, no information was provided on the reasons for the condition being unfavourable. For those units for which data are available, the reasons for the condition being unfavourable provide an insight into the main threats currently affecting New Forest habitats. Results indicate that the threats differ between habitat types. In dry heathland and grassland habitats, the principal threat is overgrazing, although inappropriate scrub control is also a significant factor (Table 57). In wet heathland, wet grassland and mire habitats, the principal threat is drainage. In woodland habitats, inappropriate forestry or woodland management practices are the principal threat, although drainage is also a significant factor accounting for unfavourable condition. In none of the habitats is public access or disturbance cited as a significant factor (Table 57).

Trends in species

One of the issues repeatedly raised by the authors of preceding chapters is the lack of systematic survey and monitoring data. As a result, it is difficult to ascertain the trends in abundance of individual species or species groups with any precision. However, the available evidence indicates that at least 170 species have been lost from the New Forest in recent decades. This estimate is necessarily uncertain; many species are difficult either to locate or to identify, and might be rediscovered by future survey work (see, for example, Chapter 9). On the other hand, this estimate might be conservative, as information on many species groups (particularly the most speciose) is lacking. The number of species that have been extirpated varies between different groups; losses of butterflies and moths are particularly high, but significant losses also appear to have occurred in lichens, saproxylic beetles and fungi (Table 58). A number of other species appear to be

Table 57
Assessment of threats to habitats in the New Forest, based on results of Common Standards Monitoring (CSM) assessments (see text), accessed in August 2008. The threat data represent the reasons cited for unfavourable condition given in the CSM assessments. Values presented are percentages of the total area classified as in 'unfavourable condition' (including unfavourable recovering, unfavourable declining, unfavourable no change, and partially or totally destroyed). The values are based on the assumption that the adverse conditions listed affect the whole unit area, but excluding the 114 units for which no information was provided. Only the main threats are included (i.e. affecting 20% of one or more habitats), although 'Public access/ disturbance' is also included for comparison.

	Habitat type			
Threat	Dry heathland and dry grassland	Wet heath, wet grassland and mire	Pasture, riverine and bog woodland	Inclosure woodland
Forestry and woodland management	3.17	0.73	35.3	45.4
Overgrazing	39.7	0.02	1.79	–
Inappropriate scrub control	34.2	11.5	10.5	–
Drainage	0.19	43.6	17.3	30.2
Public access/disturbance	0.72	–	–	0.42

Table 58
Declines and losses of different species groups in the New Forest, and associated causes (threats). Based on information presented in preceding chapters, except where indicated by asterisk, which indicates that the information was sourced from Wright and Westerhoff (2001).

Species group	Trends	Threats
Birds	At least three species lost during the last century. While some species (such as nightjar and woodlark) are stable or increasing, others (such as Dartford warbler, snipe, curlew and redshank) are declining.	Species losses attributable to habitat loss and possibly climate change. Causes for declines in species often unclear, but may include inappropriate habitat management (e.g. Dartford warbler, sparrowhawk), disturbance from human recreation (e.g. ground-nesting birds), climate change, nest predation (e.g. Montagu's harrier).
Bats	No evidence of species losses. Insufficient data to determine trends.	Some forest management interventions may be negative (e.g. tree felling and holly pollarding). Possible disturbance from recreation.
Reptiles and amphibians	One extinction of a native species (natterjack toad). Sand lizard lost but reintroduced.	Common toad declines may be caused by fungal disease. Inappropriate heathland management (burning) responsible for loss of sand lizard. Main threat to reptiles is inappropriate heathland management.
Fish	No evidence of losses. Insufficient data to determine trends.	History of catchment modification and drainage likely to have had negative impacts on fish populations, but evidence limited. Current management interventions including woody debris accumulation in streams and physical modifications to stream channels can have both positive and negative effects. Tree clearances in some reaches have caused elevated water temperatures and invasion of instream plants where none existed previously.
Invertebrates		
Dragonflies and damselflies	One extinction. Some evidence of historic declines in some species; others appear stable.	Drainage actions and scrub development responsible for species loss.
Saproxylic beetles	At least five species believed to be extinct; 27 further species not reported in past 25 years. Insufficient data to determine trends, although some species appear to have declined.	Extinctions caused by scrub clearance, and forestry / commoning activities involving the felling of large, old trees.
Butterflies and moths	General decline of many species in recent decades; 124 species believed to have been lost.	Increased levels of herbivore grazing and browsing, particularly in the Inclosures, leading to a loss of structural diversity and food sources. Greater intensity of management for grazing (burning, reseeding, scrub clearance). Direct destruction of habitat caused by forestry operations (e.g. conifer planting, surfacing of rides in Inclosures). Economic pressures driving land use at the Forest margins (e.g. urban development, pony paddocks, lack of support for traditional woodland management).

Table 58 ... continued

Species group	Trends	Threats
Other invertebrates	Insufficient data to determine trends. Some extinctions are likely to have occurred as many rare species have not been recorded for a long time, e.g. New Forest cicada may now be extinct. Groups such as Orthoptera appear to have undergone significant declines.	Changes to the grazing regime and management of the heaths and woodlands are likely to have had a detrimental affect on many insect species and their habitats. Increase in grazing intensity since the 1960s is a particular issue, especially in Inclosures. The intensification of farmsteads within the Forest and the loss of small rotationally managed fields must also have been negative in the Forest, as throughout the wider countryside. "Improvement" of sandy footpaths and tracks for access to bicycles and horses by resurfacing them with compacted gravel and clay reduces nesting sites. Removal of large carrion reduces habitat availability. Inappropriate ride management and widespread scrub clearance likely to have negative impacts.
Vascular plants	One species known to have gone extinct in the middle of the 20th century: summer lady's-tresses *Spiranthes aestivalis*, which was exterminated by over-collecting and drainage damage*. Little evidence of declines in species, although few monitoring data available and impacts of human activity largely uncertain.	Invasion by exotic water plants (e.g. New Zealand pygmyweed *Crassula helmsii*) is probably a major threat to flora associated with ponds. Other invasive species such as *Rhododendron* similarly pose a threat to terrestrial vegetation. In the 20th century, forestry practices involving creation of new plantations and planting up of ancient woodland undoubtedly caused enormous damage. Management practices and laissez-faire attitudes to grazing within the Inclosures during the second half of the 20th century led to negative impacts on flowering plants.
Lichens	Few monitoring data available. Most uncommon species appear to be stable. However, some are clearly declining and some extinctions appear to have occurred. A total of 13 species were recorded from New Forest woods in the 19th century and have not yet been refound, and may therefore be extinct. In addition, four leafy species recorded since 1967 appear to have been lost and a further four are declining and rare.	The spread of holly, and hence increased shade, in the past 150 years is the most significant issue. Pollution is another significant factor, especially of sulphur and nitrogen. This may be responsible for difficulties in colonising rather than direct poisoning of the mature thalli. Death of trees has also caused loss of colonies.
Fungi	Few monitoring data available. Little evidence of declines. Extinctions hard to evaluate although 18 species of conservation concern have not been seen in the past 50 years* and may be extinct.	Substantial losses of semi-natural woodland through felling and establishment of exotic conifers in the 20th century must have had a major deleterious impact on fungi. Other threats include deadwood removal, and possibly also commercial collecting and climate change.
Bryophytes	Four species of liverwort have apparently become extinct.* Most species generally stable.	Some species threatened by scrub invasion.*

declining, although again, the lack of robust monitoring data limits the conclusions that can be drawn.

The preceding chapters identified a range of different causes of the decline or loss of species, which vary among different groups (Table 58). The widespread damage to ancient woodland habitats caused by forestry operations in the 20th century appears to have had a significant negative impact on groups such as vascular plants, fungi and some invertebrates. Another key issue has been the increase in grazing and browsing pressure in recent decades, particularly in the Inclosures, which accounts for the losses of many invertebrates, especially the Lepidoptera. As for the assessment of habitat condition (see above), inappropriate habitat management interventions are widely cited, including scrub control, tree felling and heathland burning (Table 58). The loss or decline of some species may be the result of

processes occurring in the wider countryside, including agricultural intensification and land use change in areas adjacent to the New Forest (Table 58).

Information needs

As noted above, there is an urgent need for improved information regarding the status and trends of biodiversity in the New Forest. There is some evidence that Tubbs (2001) was right to suggest the biodiversity of the New Forest is diminishing. However, this suggestion is difficult to evaluate without improved survey and monitoring data. The current distribution of most species in the New Forest is inadequately known, and even less information is available regarding trends in abundance of individual species, even for those of international conservation concern for which the area was designated. It is widely recognised that effective conservation management depends on adequate monitoring, so that management interventions can be amended and adapted in response to available evidence (Sutherland 2000). Although the CSM approach provides a valuable source of information, it does not capture trends in individual species, and as indicated in Chapter 13, it appears to provide results that are poorly related to more quantitative and repeatable monitoring approaches.

Much of our current knowledge of species in the New Forest depends on the dedication and hard work of naturalists, many of whom collect information in an entirely voluntary capacity. These efforts deserve much greater support from those agencies and organisations responsible for managing the New Forest. There is scope to improve the coordination and targeting of survey effort. There is also a need to improve the management of biodiversity information. Although the Biodiversity Information Centres in Hampshire and Wiltshire have an important role in compiling and managing biodiversity data (often submitted from volunteers), the information is typically incomplete and out of date. There is arguably a case for a biodiversity information system to be developed explicitly for the New Forest. There is also a need to ensure that existing information can be readily accessed by those responsible for management decisions on the ground, so that such decisions can be informed by current knowledge. It is hoped that this book will encourage greater coordination and collaboration among those with an interest in the New Forest, to improve the collection, management and dissemination of biodiversity information.

Management responses

Given the importance of the New Forest for biodiversity, as indicated at the beginning of this chapter, the current status and trends of both habitats and species should be the focus of significant concern. There is a clear need for management action to address this situation.

A striking conclusion from the evidence presented above is that inappropriate management currently represents the principal threat to biodiversity in the New Forest. This provides a marked contrast to the National Park perspective (see Chapter 18, and New Forest National Park Authority 2008a), which currently focuses on the potential threats of climate change and increasing recreation pressure, despite the fact that there is currently little evidence that either of these factors are negatively affecting New Forest biodiversity to any great extent (although they clearly have the potential do so in future). To a large degree, the declines and losses of species that have occurred, and the currently unfavourable condition of much habitat, is the legacy of decades of mismanagement that occurred during the 20th century, as chronicled in detail by Tubbs (2001). Substantial progress has been made in amending and improving management approaches, including the restoration of degraded

habitats undertaken during the LIFE projects (see Chapters 17 and 19), and as reflected in current management plans (Forestry Commission 2008, Wright and Westerhoff 2001). Such efforts undoubtedly merit recognition and support. However, the evidence presented in this book highlights some of the challenges that remain, if further losses of biodiversity are to be avoided.

A detailed evaluation of current management approaches is beyond the scope of this chapter. Instead, some cross-cutting issues that have emerged from the preceding chapters are briefly considered here.

Grazing pressure

Is the New Forest overgrazed? This issue has long been the subject of debate. As noted in Chapter 7, for example, many entomologists believe that grazing pressure is too high. Many forest ecologists might say the same thing (Chapter 13). On the other hand, it is widely recognised that many of the distinctive characteristics of the New Forest, and the survival of many of its species, depends directly on the maintenance of large herbivore populations. It is for this reason that recent management plans (Wright and Westerhoff 2001, New Forest National Park Authority 2008a) have placed the maintenance of the pastoral economy, and the tradition of commoning, as a principal objective.

Despite the importance of grazing to the maintenance of many species, overgrazing has clearly contributed to biodiversity loss. The high losses of invertebrate species, especially Lepidoptera, have largely been attributed to an increase in grazing pressure in recent decades, particularly within the Inclosures (Chapters 6 and 7). Such losses should not be dismissed as a minor concern, reflecting the advocacy of an individual species group by enthusiasts. Rather, they are an indicator of a decline in the condition of the New Forest as an ecological system. Declines in the invertebrate fauna must have had a negative impact on the other species that depend on them, such as insectivorous birds and bats. What Putman (Chapter 14) refers to as the 'unique' characteristic of the New Forest, namely the lack of small mammals and the birds and mammals that predate them, is the result of an impoverished insect fauna caused by high grazing pressure (Putman 1986). Declining availability of invertebrate food resources could also be a factor in the recent declines in wading birds (Chapter 1), although this has not been examined to date.

What, then, is the optimum grazing pressure in the New Forest? The most detailed analysis of this question is that provided by Putman (1986), based on almost a decade of research into the behaviour and impacts of large herbivores. Estimates of forage offtake per day per individual cow or pony were related to measurements of forage productivity, to determine the potential stocking density of the Forest for livestock. This approach was used to estimate the total carrying capacity for ponies across the New Forest. Values were

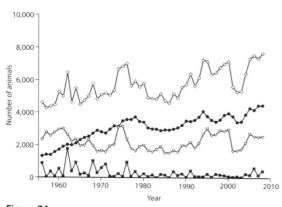

Figure 74
Numbers of stock depastured in the New Forest. Data from the New Forest Verderers (http://www.verderers.org.uk/stock_depastured.pdf). Symbols: pigs, filled squares; cattle, open triangles; ponies, filled circles; total, open diamonds.

found to vary with season, reaching a maximum of 2,840 in July. As Putman (1986) emphasises, the values provided by this analysis should be viewed with a great deal of caution, because of the uncertainties associated with estimating the amount of forage available to animals, the influence of range use and behaviour on animal densities, and the productivity of different vegetation types. In addition, this estimate is based on an agricultural approach, focusing on the capacity of New Forest vegetation to support stock, rather than defining the stocking density that would be desirable for maintaining biodiversity.

Despite such caveats, this figure of 2,840 provides a rough indication of how many ponies the New Forest might support. Interestingly, this number has been exceeded every year since 1972 (Figure 74). The number of ponies depastured on the Forest has increased steadily since the early 1950s, reaching values of more than 4,200 in each of the years 2005–2007. Such numbers are higher than at any time in the past (Tubbs 2001). Pony numbers are particularly significant in terms of overall grazing pressure on the Forest, because ponies consume more vegetation than ruminants such as cattle and deer (Tubbs 2001). For example, Tubbs (1991, 2001) suggested that one pony may be the equivalent of at least two cattle or three deer in terms of forage intake. In the early 1980s, when livestock numbers were substantially lower than at present, Putman (1986) concluded from his analyses of the New Forest that 'it is apparent that, at least in some habitats and in some areas, grazing really is excessive – by *whatever* criteria' [original emphasis]. This suggestion is borne out by the data on habitat condition presented above.

The SAC Management Plan avoids defining either upper or lower limits for grazing animals in the New Forest, rightly pointing out that there is 'no ecologically derived justification for the upper and lower stocking levels seen in the past' (Wright and Westerhoff 2001). Instead, the Plan suggests that 'all that can be usefully stated is that within the historical

upper and lower stocking levels, experience shows that as far as grazing goes, the individual habitats are maintained in favourable condition' (Wright and Westerhoff 2001). This avoids the fact that some habitats are not currently in favourable condition (as noted above), and fails to address the fact that livestock numbers are currently higher than ever before and are continuing to increase. However the Plan does accept that overstocking can occur, and is an issue that has to be addressed and managed.

Overall limits to numbers of livestock can be set by the Verderers. Currently (2003–2013) there is a Countryside Stewardship Scheme in place, which is a 10 year agreement between Defra and the Verderers, under which Defra makes available payments totalling some £460,000 each year. In return for depasturing their animals for laid down minimum periods, Commoners receive an annual headage payment, which in 2007 was £56.00 each for cattle, ponies and donkeys. The Scheme defines limits on the numbers of livestock that Commoners are allowed to enter. The grazing plan developed in conjunction with this Scheme states that the number of animals (ponies, donkeys and cattle) is not to fall below 3,500 or exceed 7,000 (Verderers of the New Forest 2005). Yet, as indicated on Figure 74, numbers have exceeded this total for each of the years 2005–2007. In 2007, for example, the total was 7,363. Although such totals do not necessarily provide an accurate indication of the livestock actually depastured on the Forest, this does highlight a potential difficulty in regulating livestock numbers.

Based on the analysis presented by Tubbs (2001, p.161), it would appear that grazing and browsing pressure in the New Forest is currently at a very high level, with livestock numbers among the highest on record. In the past, deer densities would have been much higher than at present; for example, around 8000 fallow and red deer were recorded in the Crown lands in 1670 (Putman 1986). Deer densities within the Crown lands are currently maintained at around 2000 animals through a programme of culling (Forestry Commission 2007). Over the past two centuries, there has therefore been a shift from deer to livestock (ponies and cattle) in terms of the main contribution to grazing and browsing pressure. Taking account of the higher forage requirement of ponies than of either cattle or deer, grazing and browsing pressure in the New Forest may currently be higher than at any time in the past. If history is to be used to guide current management, as suggested by the SAC Management Plan (Wright and Westerhoff 2001), then there may now be a need to consider reducing livestock numbers. However, what is actually required is an identification of an appropriate stocking density, adjustable in response to monitoring information, beyond which any financial support (such as headage payments) would cease (Tubbs 2001, p.374). Identification of this stocking density should be based on a thorough ecological understanding of the New Forest ecosystem, and the role that large herbivores play within that system. Further research is required to provide this understanding.

Scrub clearance

As noted in Table 58, scrub clearance has been implicated as a cause of species loss in the New Forest, particularly for invertebrate groups such as saproxylic invertebrates and Lepidoptera (although it should be noted that some species, for example some bryophytes and dragonflies, have also been threatened by development of scrub). As noted by Putman (1986), the Commoners have repeatedly pressed for management aimed at increasing the available grazing in the New Forest, which includes clearance of scrub from grasslands. According to Putman (1986), this *runs counter to conservation interests within the Forest, threatening structural diversity [and]… the integrity of whole communities*. As noted in Chapter 13, scrub plays an important role in the dynamics of woodland colonisation, and if the New Forest is to be managed according to the 'Vera model' (as suggested in the SAC Management Plan), then such colonisation should be allowed to occur, at least in some areas.

Tubbs (2001) considers this issue in some detail, noting that Section 11 of the New Forest Act 1949 requires that the Forestry Commission shall ensure that 'the grazings shall be kept sufficiently clear of coarse herbage, scrub and self-sown trees', reflecting a perception that the unenclosed Forest should be managed primarily for the benefit of Commoners and their stock. As noted by Tubbs (2001), this is potentially in conflict with nature conservation, to which the Commission is committed under the New Forest Act of 1964, through the Wildlife and Countryside Acts of 1981 and 1985, and through international designations. Tubbs (2001) strongly deplores the 'quite irrational flailing of old gorse thickets' and removal of blackthorn thickets, leading to an erosion in the 'character and naturalness of the Forest in the name of management, most of it of little measurable benefit'. Most importantly, Tubbs (2001) points out that no assessment of the ecological costs and benefits of such management is carried out, and neither does the Forestry Commission monitor its impacts. As a result, 'habitats are often damaged or destroyed without benefit to the Commoners from increased forage'; in fact, such interventions can even reduce the availability of food plants to stock (Tubbs 2001, p.355).

Tubbs' emphasis on the importance of monitoring the effects of management is entirely consistent with recent calls for an evidence-based approach to conservation management (Pullin and Knight 2001, Sutherland 2000, Sutherland *et al.* 2004). Such calls reflect growing concern that much conservation management is not currently based on any rigorous evidence regarding its effectiveness, as can be provided by a robust monitoring programme. The concerns raised by Tubbs (2001), and the undoubted habitat value of scrub (for example as a food source for nectar-feeding insects), highlight the need for such monitoring, supported by research into the ecological costs and benefits of such management.

How do current management plans address the issue of scrub clearance? The SAC Management Plan highlights the habitat value of scrub, and identifies the need *to maintain a good quality scrub component on Open Forest habitats within the limits set by Condition Assessment, and to maintain woodland edge / Open Forest transitions such that sharp boundaries between pasture woodland and open habitats are minimised* (Wright and Westerhoff 2001). The current Management Plan for the Crown lands similarly recognises the potential habitat value of scrub, and its importance in the ecological dynamics of natural woodland expansion, stating that *it would be unwise and impractical to remove more birch and scrub than is necessary from the Open Forest* (Forestry Commission 2008). The Plan identifies as a key action implementation of scrub clearance according to the generic prescriptions identified in the SAC Management Plan. As noted above, this should be supported by appropriate monitoring and research, to ensure that such interventions are targeted on appropriate areas, and deliver clear benefits. Given that evidence for such benefits is currently lacking, there is arguably a need for a much more sensitive approach to scrub clearance than has occurred in the past. In particular, there is a need to address the concern raised by Tubbs (2001, p.355), that 'too much has been done simply to demonstrate activity'.

Recreation

Tubbs (2001) similarly gives detailed consideration to growing pressure for recreation in the Forest, noting the recent growth in adjacent urban populations and the associated increase in the number of visitors. Specific issues that Tubbs (2001) identifies include the erosion 'fans' around car parks, the management and expansion of camp sites, damage caused by horse riding, and disturbance to wildlife caused by walkers, dogs, horse riders and cyclists. As noted by Tubbs (2001), much of the evidence of such disturbance is circumstantial, reflecting the difficulties of identifying disturbance as a cause in the decline or loss of a species. The possible role of disturbance as a cause of declines in breeding waders has attracted particular concern (Chapter 1).

Recreation in the New Forest was recently examined by the PROGRESS project, which was an EU-funded initiative that ran from 2003 to 2007 and undertook a range of visitor surveys and other studies to identify appropriate actions for managing recreation (Gallagher *et al.* 2007). The project commissioned a survey (undertaken by Tourism South East), which estimated that the New Forest National Park receives some 13.5 million day visitors per year (Tourism South East 2005). This suggests that visitor numbers have increased enormously in recent decades; in 1969, the number of day visits was estimated at 3.25 million (Tubbs 2001).

It is clear that demands for recreation on this scale represent a significant management challenge, and the issue is given detailed consideration in current management plans. For example key actions identified in the plan for the Crown lands (Forestry Commission 2008), which were informed by the PROGRESS project, include:

- Maintenance of a permanent Ranger and Keeper team supplemented by seasonal staff and volunteers to provide a visible presence on the Crown lands, to actively manage access and recreation.
- Seasonal closure of four car parks to monitor change in visitor movements and impact on ground-nesting birds.
- Improvement of access to and the aesthetics of certain Inclosures to encourage more people to use the generally more robust Inclosures for informal recreation.
- Installation of temporary information points and interpretation boards at carefully selected locations.
- Closure of certain laybys to reduce ease of access to sensitive habitats on the Open Forest.
- Installation and maintenance of 'dragons teeth', roadside ditches and banks to try to minimise damage to road site verges and prevent inappropriate roadside parking.

The New Forest National Park Authority has recently developed a draft Recreation Management Strategy, which is designed to set out the strategic direction for the management of outdoor recreation over the next 20 years (New Forest National Park Authority 2008b). At time of writing (2009), the Strategy is undergoing further consultation and revision; once finalised, the next step will be to develop an action plan for its implementation. The draft Strategy is in many ways a visionary document, with some radical proposals that have inevitably generated substantial controversy, including the possibility of dog-free car parks, seasonal closure of minor roads, traffic management and zoning, road user pricing, car-free zones and landscaping for noise and visual screening. Proposed criteria for regulating equestrian development have proved particularly controversial. The National Park Authority should be commended for stimulating debate, regardless of the eventual outcome of this planning process. A visionary, strategic approach to management is surely something that the New Forest requires (Tubbs 2001). The Strategy's commitment to research and monitoring, to strengthen the evidence base for future management, should also be strongly commended.

It is surely appropriate that recreation management should continue to form a central element of any management plan for the New Forest. However, any restrictions on visitor movements or activities are inevitably going to generate controversy. Any evidence suggesting that recreational pressure is the cause of environmental degradation, or negative impacts on biodiversity, is therefore likely to be scrutinised very closely. Although there are clearly areas of concern in terms of recreation impacts on biodiversity, such as possible disturbance to ground-nesting birds (Chapter 1), there is also a great deal of uncertainty regarding what the precise impacts actually are. Such uncertainty can only be addressed by an increased emphasis on research and monitoring in future.

A vision for future management

A number of the contributors to this book highlighted the need for a landscape-scale approach to conservation management. The future status of biodiversity in the New Forest will be strongly influenced not only by management of the Forest itself, but by patterns of surrounding land use. The importance of a landscape-scale approach to conservation management is now widely recognised, based on developments in landscape ecology and metapopulation ecology. Evidence suggests that the maintenance of many species depends on the spatial characteristics of habitat, such as the size and connectivity of habitat patches, and their influence on ecological processes such as dispersal and colonisation (Lindenmayer and Franklin 2002). In the current era of rapid environmental change, the maintenance of species within a landscape is likely to depend strongly on providing an appropriate landscape pattern to support such processes.

The landscape ecology of the New Forest has received relatively little attention to date, and clearly there is tremendous scope for research in this area. Ideally, management of the New Forest would be informed by a thorough understanding of the spatial dynamics of different vegetation types, and how such dynamics influence populations of the various species associated with them. Understanding the spatial movement and behaviour of large herbivores in relation to vegetation pattern is clearly key to understanding such dynamics, building on the pioneering work of Putman and colleagues (Putman 1986, Chapter 14). The use of landscapes by people is another important area where further knowledge is required, in order for recreation to be managed effectively.

The development of a landscape-based approach to the management of the New Forest was recently considered in a report produced by the Land Management subcommittee of the New Forest Association (Reeves et al. 2006), which is an independent, campaigning charity dedicated to protecting the New Forest, and is thought to be one of the oldest conservation organisations in the world. The report was stimulated by the creation of the New Forest National Park, which as noted in Chapter 18, considers the unique New Forest landscape as among its 'special qualities' that merit protection.

As noted in the report, much of the New Forest landscape is now dominated by commercial forestry, specifically through the previous establishment of forest plantations. This report suggests that future management should involve the natural restoration of selected areas through the controlled retreat of commercial forestry where it has come to dominate the landscape, to produce a sustainable pastoral landscape in which forestry continues to play a part, but no longer dominates. This would be achieved by restoring a number of the Inclosures to the Open Forest, and by stocking retained Inclosures with broadleaved trees, to provide a reservoir from which species less tolerant of heavier grazing could exploit and colonise surrounding areas (Reeves *et al.* 2006). The remaining area would be thrown open to grazing animals, with the conifers in such areas being felled at a commercially viable age, and broadleaved trees being left largely to their own devices. In time, it is suggested, these woodlands would take on the characteristics of the open pasture woodlands, and be colonised by those species associated with them. This would help address the fact that pasture woodlands are currently fragmented, which reduces the potential for dispersal and colonisation of the species associated with them. The result would be a matrix of wooded and unwooded areas, perhaps similar to that recorded in the New Forest in the late 18th century (Reeves *et al.* 2006). Most importantly, the spatial dynamics of such habitats would be allowed to develop naturally, in response to patterns of herbivory, and as influenced by the underlying geology, topography and climate. In other words, natural processes would be allowed to predominate, leading to the restoration of habitat features on a landscape scale, which would be far more sustainable than the current situation (Reeves *et al.* 2006).

Reeves *et al.* (2006) suggest that this approach would benefit the wildlife of the Forest, as well as providing a high quality recreational experience for visitors. It would also benefit the commoning community by opening up a large area of currently unavailable land for grazing. It would provide a unique opportunity for long-term scientific study to understand landscape scale ecological change. Furthermore, it would be economically advantageous, as the felling of the conifer stands would continue to provide financial revenue, while the costs of maintaining fencing and undertaking new planting would be reduced. The requirement for grazing the newly opened areas would be absorbed by the current commoning system, to its benefit.

Does this visionary idea provide a suitable basis for managing the New Forest in future? Would it really help meet the needs of local communities and visitors, as well as helping to maintain the biodiversity of the area? Might it even provide greater resilience to the environmental change that could be just around the corner? As noted by Tubbs (2001, p.374), it is this kind of radical thinking that is needed, to ensure that the special character and value of the New Forest is maintained into the future.

Acknowledgements

Thanks to Elena Cantarello for assistance with the analysis of habitat condition.

References

Balmford, A., Mace G. M. and Ginsberg, J. R. (1998). The challenges to conservation in a changing world: putting processes on the map. In: Mace, G. M., Balmford, A. and Ginsberg, J. R. (eds.) *Conservation in a changing world. Conservation biology series 1*, pp. 1–28. Cambridge University Press, Cambridge, UK.

Chatters, C. and Read, M. (2006). *New Forest National Park*. Halsgrove, Tiverton, Devon.

Gallagher, K., Graham, M. and Colas, S. (2007) *PROGRESS project handbook*. Forestry Commission, Lyndhurst. http://www.progress-eu.info/uk.htm

Forestry Commission (2007). *New Forest District deer management plan 2005–2015*. Forestry Commission, Lyndhurst.

Forestry Commission (2008). *The Crown Lands Management Plan 2008–2013*. The Forestry Commission, Lyndhurst, Hampshire. http://www.forestry.gov.uk/forestry/INFD-7A3F82

Lindenmayer, D. and Franklin, J. (2002). *Conserving forest biodiversity. A comprehensive multiscaled approach*. Island Press, Washington, D.C.

New Forest National Park Authority (2008a). *New Forest National Park Plan. Consultation draft. August 2008*. New Forest National Park Authority, Lymington, Hampshire.

New Forest National Park Authority (2008b). *Draft recreation management strategy for the New Forest National Park*. New Forest National Park Authority, Lymington, Hampshire.

Pullin, A. S. and Knight, T.M. (2001). Effectiveness in conservation practice: pointers from medicine and public health. *Conservation Biology*, 15, 50–54.

Putman, R. J. (1986). *Grazing in temperate ecosystems. Large herbivores and the ecology of the New Forest*. Croom Helm, London and Sydney.

Reeves, R. P., Cox, J., Frost, P., Tubbs, J. M., Sanderson, N. A. and Humbert D. (2006). *The New Forest Design Plan: recovering lost landscapes*. New Forest Association, Lyndhurst.

Sutherland, W. J. (2000). *The conservation handbook: techniques in research, management and policy*. Wiley Blackwell, Oxford.

Sutherland, W. J., Pullin, A. S., Dolman, P. M. and Knight. T. M. (2004). The need for evidence-based conservation. *Trends in Ecology and Evolution*, 19 (6), 305–308.

Tourism South East (2005) Visitor survey of the New Forest National Park 2004–2005. http://www.forestry.gov.uk/forestry/INFD-6TLKNY

Tubbs, C. R. (1991). Grazing the lowland heaths. *British Wildlife*, 2, 276–289.

Tubbs, C. R. (2001). *The New Forest. History, ecology and conservation*. New Forest Ninth Centenary Trust, Lyndhurst, Hampshire.

Verderers of the New Forest (2005). Verderers' Countryside Stewardship Scheme Grazing Management Plan. *Verderers of the New Forest Lyndhurst, Hampshire*.

Wright, R. N. and Westerhoff, D. V. (2001). *New Forest SAC Management Plan*. English Nature, Lyndhurst.

Appendix

Reasons for designation of the New Forest Special Area of Conservation (SAC). (Adapted from http://www.jncc.gov.uk/ProtectedSites/SACselection/).

Annex I habitats that are a primary reason for designation

3110 Oligotrophic waters containing very few minerals of sandy plains (*Littorelletalia uniflorae*)
Hatchet Pond is important as a southern example of this lake type where species more common in the uplands of the UK co-exist with southern species.

3130 Oligotrophic to mesotrophic standing waters with vegetation of the *Littorelletea uniflorae* and/or of the *Isoëto-Nanojuncetea*
In the New Forest this vegetation occurs on the edge of large temporary ponds, shallow ephemeral pools and poached damp hollows in grassland, which support a number of specialist species, such as coral-necklace *Illecebrum verticillatum* and yellow centaury *Cicendia filiformis*.

4010 Northern Atlantic wet heaths with *Erica tetralix*
The New Forest contains the most extensive stands of lowland northern Atlantic wet heaths in southern England.

4030 European dry heaths
The New Forest is the largest area of lowland heathland in the UK.

6410 *Molinia* meadows on calcareous, peaty or clayey-silt-laden soils (*Molinion caeruleae*)
These species-rich grasslands occur in situations of heavy grazing in areas known locally as 'lawns', often in a fine-scale mosaic with wet heath, mire and grassland communities. The New Forest *Molinia* meadows are unusual in the UK in terms of their species composition, management and landscape position.

7150 Depressions on peat substrates of the *Rhynchosporion*
The New Forest holds the largest area in England of this community, in complex habitat mosaics associated primarily with extensive valley bogs.

9120 Atlantic acidophilous beech forests with *Ilex* and sometimes also *Taxus* in the shrublayer (*Quercion robori-petraeae* or *Ilici-Fagenion*)
The New Forest is the largest area of mature, semi-natural beech *Fagus sylvatica* woodland in Britain.

9130 *Asperulo-Fagetum* beech forests
The New Forest is the largest area of mature, semi-natural beech *Fagus sylvatica* woodland in Britain. The mosaic with other types of woodland and heath has allowed unique and varied assemblages of epiphytic lichens and saproxylic invertebrates to be sustained.

9190 Old acidophilous oak woods with *Quercus robur* on sandy plains
The New Forest is the most extensive area of active wood-pasture with old oak (*Quercus* spp.) and beech (*Fagus sylvatica*) in north-west Europe, and has outstanding invertebrate and lichen populations.

91D0 Bog woodland * Priority feature
Within the New Forest, birch – willow (*Betula – Salix*) stands occur over valley bog vegetation, with fringing alder (*Alnus*) – *Sphagnum* stands where there is some water movement. These stands appear to have persisted for long periods in stable association with the underlying *Sphagnum* bog-moss communities.

91E0 Alluvial forests with *Alnus glutinosa* and *Fraxinus excelsior* (*Alno-Padion, Alnion incanae, Salicion albae*) * Priority feature
The New Forest contains many streams and some small rivers that are less affected by drainage and canalisation than those in any other comparable area in the lowlands of England. Associated with many of the streams are strips of alder woodland, associated with a rich flora.

Annex I habitats present as a qualifying feature, but not a primary reason for designation

7140 Transition mires and quaking bogs

7230 Alkaline fens

Annex II species that are a primary reason for designation of this site

1044 Southern damselfly *Coenagrion mercuriale*
The New Forest in central southern England is an outstanding locality for southern damselfly, and represents one of the four major population centres in the UK.

1083 Stag beetle *Lucanus cervus*
The New Forest is a major stronghold for the species in the UK.

Annex II species present as a qualifying feature, but not a primary reason for site designation

1166 Great crested newt *Triturus cristatus*

Afterword

Clive Chatters

These comments are provided as a personal view, stimulated by the conference on which this book is based, and in particular, by some of the issues raised during the closing discussion session of the meeting that I chaired. Adrian Newton opened the conference with brief definitions of the Forest, from Colin Tubbs and from myself, together with an expression of a celebration of the Forest's extraordinary biodiversity. Within that celebration was a shadow, a question, as to whether that biodiversity was changing, and if so whether this change was for the better. The conference included many speakers and presentations. As always at conferences it is the conversations outside the formal sessions that have greatly added to mutual understanding of issues. Based on such discussions, as well as the material presented during the conference, I will endeavour to draw conclusions and to speculate on ways forward.

Ecological considerations

Whilst everyone seems to be delighted that the Forest has this extensive wealth of biodiversity we have heard many speakers focus on just one part of the New Forest, the Open Forest, and within that group of ownerships many speakers have focused on the subset of the Crown lands as managed by the Forestry Commission. The Open Forest is a remarkable place, indeed the defining landscape of the National Park, however it is a component part of a much larger and more complex series of landscapes, seascapes and habitats. We have yet to start to understand the collective ecological character and functioning of the whole Forest.

Most biodiversity is unseen and unknown. In the New Forest we are fortunate in the range of species that have been studied. We have a history of biological recording going back to the early 17th century, with great strides made with the coming of the railway in the mid 19th century and a particularly productive period in the mid/late 20th century. There are still enormous gaps in information and with a place as complex as the Forest, and this will probably always be the case. The Forest regularly appears to be amongst the richest localities of whatever group of species comes under investigation. The ecosystem is relatively intact and the range of niches highly diverse. It is interesting that the importance of the Forest does not appear to derive from it being intrinsically "special" as a source of endemism, but because of the large-scale survival of what was formerly much more widespread.

Some of our speakers have touched on the important role of large herbivores in maintaining the particular character of the Open Forest. In the historic period, large herbivores have been a mixture of domestic livestock alongside native and non native deer. The domestic livestock are a manifestation of the ancient practice of commoning; in turn commoning is dependant on a coherent community and supportive economy. If that chain breaks at any point, the biodiversity of the Forest will fundamentally change. What has only been touched on at this conference is the relationship between biodiversity and the economy, and the legal and social fabric of the Forest. There are social scientists, economists and others investigating these issues. There is already some connectivity between these lines of research and the biological sciences, with considerable scope for greater understanding.

We have had some interesting but inconclusive forays into the debate on the nature of naturalness. One person's minimal intervention is another person's traditional management. We must remember that the Forest is very much a cultural working landscape. Everywhere has an anthropogenic element to some degree. To the tutored eye, the Open Forest is far from a wilderness, it is decidedly near natural but it is a landscape that reflects its culture, community and economy.

Within the Open Forest, we felt comfortable with the quality and condition of biodiversity associated with two interrelated ecological processes. The first of these is associated with grazed woodlands with abundant old-growth stands, with their highly diverse structure. The structure ranges in scale from micro-habitats within individual trees to landscape-scale diversity of shade, glades and margins. The other processes with which we found comfort were associated with a broad range of well-illuminated low fertility habitats, stressed by continuous grazing by large herbivores. These habitats are frequently of low biomass but high biodiversity. A degree of upheaval within extensive periods of continuity appears important to provide the full range of habitats upon which Open Forest species are dependant. The scale of the Open Forest is important in providing sufficient opportunities over time for species to persist in an ever-changing environment. The stresses upon the Forest mean that it is in a suboptimal but adequate condition for many species; the constraining influence of stress derived from large herbivores suppresses competitive exclusion and supports a high biodiversity.

Concerns about declines in biodiversity have focused on two areas. The first are species vulnerable to disturbance at certain parts of their life-cycles. Disturbance is arising from the understandable attractiveness of the Forest for informal recreation combining with the growth of the urban areas on the Forest's edge. The second concern relates to species dependant on herbaceous vegetation with a higher biomass than that currently present in the Open

Forest. An important line for future work is exploring how the management of the enclosed landscapes within the matrix of the Open Forest and beyond can contribute to addressing these concerns. It is interesting that only at the very end of the conference was there any mention of the current dramatic changes in the sediment shore habitats of the Forest, with consequent losses of and changes to biodiversity.

There were a number of important elements of the Forest that we heard either nothing about, or just a little, in passing. The Forest's coastline is one of the less urbanised parts of the Solent system. This is regarded as of international importance for its habitats and species. The important species are both sedentary and migratory, and are a small part of a very much larger series of related wetlands, on scales ranging from the sub-regional to the northern hemisphere and beyond. The habitats are highly dynamic, and in the face of relative sea level rise, are likely to undergo fundamental change in the foreseeable future. The marine environment of the Forest's coastline is similarly recognised to be of international importance and, to a great degree, is still undescribed.

The majority of the enclosed landscapes of the Forest have received little attention, despite containing very extensive habitats comparable and complementary to those of the Open Forest. The biodiversity of the enclosed lands is part of the same pastoral social and economic system upon which the management of the Open Forest is dependant. The biodiversity of the enclosed landscapes is poorly understood. What little we know suggests it is undergoing dramatic changes, involving simplification of its biodiversity, with changes in land management driven by agricultural and leisure use intensification, or, in contrast, by neglect. The social, cultural and economic relationship of the enclosed landscapes to the management of the Open Forest is now better understood. The biological interactions between these two types of land tenure remain poorly understood.

Some speakers have touched on how the Forest may respond to the challenges of climate change. What we reached agreement on is that the Forest is a relatively large ecosystem that is biologically dynamic, with management processes that maintain the creation of niches for colonisation and thus opportunity to respond to change. Such ecosystems are likely to be more robust than smaller sites. The Forest is still a fragment, albeit a large one, and currently lacks adequate connectivity with other wildlife rich habitats. The potential for connectivity is being diminished through the processes of urban growth within and around the Forest. Will it be possible both to expand the Forest and to reconnect it to the Dorset Heaths and other important fragments, ultimately to enable species to migrate to stay within their climate space? Will a measure of success for Forest conservation be in providing the wherewithal for the biodiversity we care about to be able to migrate out of the Forest, and a new biodiversity to establish itself in its stead? The future Forest will be different from the present, but to what degree we cannot reasonably predict. Despite the pace of change, we have yet to find a consensus as to what we need to do to rise to these challenges, and how we refocus our finite resources to make a difference on the ground.

Conservation considerations

Our conference has touched on the debate as to how conservationists relate to the Forest. The Open Forest is unlike any other place in lowland Britain, as the land tenure and management is a large-scale modern manifestation of a pre-enclosure movement landscape. The exceptional biodiversity of the Open Forest is to a large degree an accidental by-product of that legal and social system. The Forest is unlike a nature reserve. Nature reserves are managed by sequences of considered interventions. The wildlife in the Open Forest is just that, it is wild, it is the biological expression of the Forest's history, culture and economy.

If biologists and conservationists wish to participate in management decisions on the Forest, they need to understand how those decisions are made. We need to respect the long-standing rights and sensitivities of those whose lives and livelihoods are bound up in that landscape. To illustrate this, the science of lichenology (Chapter 9) has been very influential in guiding the management of the ancient woodlands. A sound science base has been articulated in a way that identifies strategic priorities. The science guided tentative experiments, which in turn supported a larger scale series of works. The nature of these works were welcomed not only by those who own and manage the land, but also by other interest groups ranging from those appreciating the landscape to other biologists.

However, I strongly advise against single interests expecting the Forest to be changed to accommodate their personal enthusiasms. The Forest does not work that way.

There have been successful conservation interventions. We have been shown the restoration of Open Forest biodiversity from 19th and 20th century timber plantations. Similarly, wetlands within the plantations have been restored (Chapter 17). In some cases, what has happened is the restoration of the ecological and hydrological processes disrupted by past decisions. I believe that the measure of a successful restoration is that the ecological functioning of the landscape is restored, and no further interventions are required. Monitoring of all interventions is needed and the findings disseminated (Chapter 20).

What additional data on biodiversity do we need? Existing data reflect personal enthusiasms and I'm sure that this will also underpin future work. Most data are gathered by volunteers for the many reasons that individuals engage with wildlife. The work of naturalists over the centuries unpins our knowledge of the Forest's biodiversity. Of priority to managers is baseline data, particularly relating to places where interventions are being considered. It is surprising what baseline data do not exist, for example there is no definitive map of the extent of the Open Forest.

There are many opportunities within both Inclosed and enclosed landscapes to maintain and enhance, to understand and enjoy, what makes the biodiversity of the Forest special. To date this aspect of the Forest's biodiversity has received less attention than the Open Forest, yet it is an exceptional resource in its own right.

Where next?

One of the issues that arose, even before the Conference opened, was an appreciation that a lot is currently going on. Research into the biodiversity of the Forest is being undertaken by a number of communities and individuals. Communication between individuals and even within communities is imperfect. In some respects this is understandable, particularly amongst those where the control of data gives access to budgets and career enhancement. On many occasions during the last two days it has been very apparent how little connection the academic world has with a substantial body of research and knowledge that exists in the Forest outside academia. I hope that all knowledge can be mutually respected. Data are there to be shared. The Hampshire Biodiversity Information Centre liaises with its equivalent in Wiltshire to store and manage biodiversity data for the Forest. Please invest in it and use it. In addition the Forest has a dedicated library, the Christopher Tower Library, in Lyndhurst. The library can accommodate any literature or manuscripts associated with the Forest. The library has an important and growing collection of both published and grey literature. Please use it.

If people are considering research, please remember there is an existing great depth of knowledge and experience in the Forest. Do draw on that experience and knowledge in helping identify research priorities and project design.

With the establishment of the National Park, there are now opportunities for everyone to contribute to the National Park's Management Plan and the Biodiversity Action Plan. These plans will, I hope, deal with the strategic issues both inside and outside the Park boundaries that impact upon biodiversity. It will be really helpful for those engaging with these plans to take a strategic view themselves: how does their particular field of interest relate to the future of the Forest? Please do take up the opportunities to inform this debate.

Over the last two days there have been many references to the work of the late Colin Tubbs on the Forest. He was a colleague and a friend to many and he remains a great inspiration in our work. Colin's *New Naturalist* book (Tubbs 2001) on the New Forest remains the standard reference. The opening lines of the editor's preface succinctly sums up our thoughts of the last two days: 'There is nowhere in the world quite like the New Forest'.

Reference

Tubbs, C. R. (2001). *The New Forest. History, ecology and conservation*. New Forest Ninth Centenary Trust, Lyndhurst.

Index